The MCAT Chemistry Book

Ajikumar Aryangat

Additional educational titles from Nova Press (available at novapress.net):

- ➤ **GRE Prep Course** (624 pages, includes software)

  GRE Math Bible (528 pages)

- ➤ **GMAT Prep Course** (624 pages, includes software)

  GMAT Math Prep Course (528 pages)

  GMAT Data Sufficiency Prep Course (422 pages)

- ➤ **Master The LSAT** (560 pages, includes software, and 2 official LSAT exams)

  Ace The LSAT Logic Games (504pages)

  Law School Basics: A Preview of Law School and Legal Reasoning (224 pages)

- ➤ **The MCAT Physics Book** (444 pages)

  The MCAT Biology Book (412 pages)

- ➤ **SAT Prep Course** (640 pages, includes software)

  SAT Math Bible (480 pages)

- ➤ **ACT Math Prep Course** (402 pages)

- ➤ **Speaking and Writing Strategies for the TOEFL® iBT:** (394 pages, includes audio CD)

- ➤ **Vocabulary 4000:** The 4000 Words Essential for an Educated Vocabulary (160 pages)

ISBN-10: 1–889057–37–1
ISBN-13: 1–889057–37–8

MCAT is a registered service mark of the Association of American Medical Colleges.

11659 Mayfield Avenue
Los Angeles, CA 90049

Phone: 1-800-949-6175
E-mail: info@novapress.net
Website: www.novapress.net

To my parents, Vasu and Nalini Aryangat, for their guidance and encouragement for the pursuit of educational excellence.

CONTENTS

Part I General Chemistry

Part II Organic Chemistry

INTRODUCTION

The science portion of the Medical College Admission Test (MCAT) consists of questions which test the basic concepts in general chemistry, organic chemistry, physics, and biology. The concepts are tested with respect to application, problem solving, and analytical thinking. These skills, which are measured by the test, are considered essential in the study of medicine. Most of the questions asked are based on passages. There will be independent questions as well. On the MCAT, the general chemistry questions appear as a part of the physical sciences section, and the organic chemistry questions as a part of the biological sciences section.

The MCAT Chemistry Book provides all the key concepts in general chemistry and organic chemistry that are required for the MCAT. The topic reviews in this book have been written with respect to their relevance to the MCAT.

The MCAT tests your ability to understand new concepts based on undergraduate science courses. Sometimes the passages contain topics and data that you have not seen before. Nevertheless, you do not need advanced courses in chemistry to be successful in the MCAT. All you need is to understand the basic concepts in chemistry. You should be familiar with the common equations and constants that are used in the undergraduate level of studies. For example, simple formulas such as the density-mass equation, or the gas equations may not be given to you in the passages or independent questions. Such simple equations should be memorized. More importantly, you should know how to use the equations in both numerical and conceptual situations. Advanced equations will be provided to you in the passages, if necessary. A periodic table will be provided for both physical and biological science sections of the test.

When studying this book, you should not focus just on facts. You should grasp the reasoning behind the facts and think conceptually about the various ideas in chemistry. The following guidelines will help you maximize your efficiency in reviewing this book.

A Few Guidelines for the Efficient Study of this Book

1) Read the review sections actively.
2) Take side notes as you review the material.
3) Give special attention to the topics that you have forgotten from your undergraduate courses.
4) Plan ahead and give yourself sufficient time for reviewing and studying.
5) Avoid cramming.
6) Create a schedule of study that fits into your daily agenda.
7) Study the examples that are provided, thoroughly and analytically, to understand the concepts discussed.
8) After reviewing each chapter, answer practice questions.
9) After answering the questions, refer to the answers and explanations for the practice questions provided at the end of the book.

Good Luck!

PART I

GENERAL CHEMISTRY

1

Matter

A. INTRODUCTION

A firm grasp of the basic ideas of division of matter is important for the understanding of physical sciences. These basic ideas presented here are not only used in chemistry and physics, but in many diverse fields such as medicine, engineering, astronomy, geology, and so on. In this chapter, we will discuss ideas about atoms and molecules, and related aspects such as moles, Avogadro number, percentage composition, atomic mass, atomic weight, and subatomic particles.

B. ATOMS

Atoms are the basic units of elements and compounds. In normal chemical reactions, atoms retain their identity. In this section, we will present a quick review of some of the basic terms and concepts such as elements, compounds, and mixtures.

Elements

An **element** is defined as matter which is made of only one type of atom. Elements are the basic building blocks of more complex matter. Some examples of elements include hydrogen (H), helium (He), potassium (K), carbon (C), and mercury (Hg).

Compounds

A **compound** is matter formed by the combination of two or more elements in fixed ratios. Let's consider an example. Hydrogen peroxide (H_2O_2) is a compound composed of two elements, hydrogen and oxygen, in a fixed ratio.

Mixtures

A combination of different elements, or a combination of elements and compounds, or a combination of different compounds is called a **mixture**. For example, an aqueous solution of potassium hydroxide ($KOH + H_2O$). In this example, the two components are potassium hydroxide and water.

Though these definitions illustrate basic ideas, you need to understand them fully; otherwise it will be almost impossible to decipher higher concepts that are based on these simple ideas. The MCAT tests your understanding of basic concepts by incorporating simple ideas into passages. So in order to succeed on the test, you need to thoroughly understand the basics.

C. DALTON'S ATOMIC THEORY

In 1803, John Dalton proposed the atomic theory of matter. The main postulates of his atomic theory can be summarized as follows:

1) Matter is composed of indivisible particles – atoms.
2) An element is composed of only one kind of atom. These atoms in a particular element have the same properties such as mass, size, or even shape.
3) A compound is composed of two or more elements combined in fixed ratios or proportions.
4) In a chemical reaction, the atoms in the reactants recombine, resulting in products which represent the combination of atoms present in the reactants. In the process, atoms are neither created, nor destroyed. So a chemical reaction is essentially a rearrangement of atoms.

Ramifications of Dalton's Theory

The atomic theory put forward by Dalton is consistent with the law of conservation of mass. As the fourth postulate says, chemical reaction is just a rearrangement of atoms, and thus the total mass remains constant during a chemical reaction.

The postulates also account for the law of definite proportions. Compounds are made of elements in fixed or definite proportions. Since the atoms have fixed mass, compounds should have elements in a fixed ratio with respect to mass. Finally, these postulates predict what is known as the law of multiple proportions. According to this law, if two elements form two or more different compounds, the ratio of the mass of one element of these compounds to a fixed mass of the other element is a simple whole number.

D. THE GENERAL STRUCTURE OF THE ATOM

During the early twentieth century, scientists discovered that atoms can be divided into more basic particles. Their findings made it clear that atoms contain a central portion called the **nucleus**. The nucleus contains protons and neutrons. **Protons** are positively charged, and **neutrons** are neutral. Whirling about the nucleus are particles called **electrons** which are negatively charged. The electrons are relatively small in mass. Take a look at Table 1-1 for a size comparison.

Table 1-1

PARTICLE	ABSOLUTE CHARGE (Coulombs)	RELATIVE CHARGE	MASS (kg)
Neutron	0	0	1.675×10^{-27}
Proton	$+1.6 \times 10^{-19}$	$+1$	1.673×10^{-27}
Electron	-1.6×10^{-19}	-1	9.11×10^{-31}

E. ELECTRONS

As mentioned above, the late nineteenth century scientists conducted several experiments, and found that atoms are divisible. They conducted experiments with gas discharge tubes.

Figure 1-1 Gas discharge tube

A gas discharge tube is shown in Figure 1-1. The gas discharge tube is an evacuated glass tube and has two electrodes, a cathode (negative electrode) and an anode (positive electrode). The electrodes are connected to a high voltage source. Inside the tube, an electric discharge occurs between the electrodes. The discharge or 'rays' originate from the cathode and move toward the anode, and hence are called **cathode rays**. Using luminescent techniques, the cathode rays are made visible and it was found that these rays are deflected away from negatively charged plates. The scientist J. J. Thompson concluded that the cathode ray consists of negatively charged particles (electrons).

Charge of Electrons

R. A. Millikan conducted the famous oil drop experiments and came to several conclusions: The charge of an electron is -1.602×10^{-19} C. From the charge-to-mass ratio, the mass of an electron was also calculated.

$$\frac{\text{Charge}}{\text{Mass}} = -1.76 \times 10^8 \text{ Coulombs / gram}$$

$$\text{mass} = \frac{-1.6 \times 10^{-19}}{-1.76 \times 10^{8}} = 9.11 \times 10^{-28}\,\text{g} = 9.11 \times 10^{-31}\,\text{kg}$$

F. PROTONS

Protons are positively charged nuclear particles. The charge of a proton is (positive electronic charge) +1.6 × 10⁻¹⁹ C. The net positive charge of the nucleus is due to the presence of the protons. A proton is about 1800 times more massive than an electron.

G. NEUTRONS

Neutrons have mass comparable to that of protons, but neutrons are devoid of any electric charge. We will talk more about neutrons and their whereabouts when we study radioactivity.

Now a natural question is whether electrons, protons, and neutrons are the most fundamental particles. The answer is no. These fundamental particles are made of more fundamental particles called quarks. But, we don't have to go that far for the MCAT. Just be aware that such sub-fundamental particles exist, fundamental particles being electrons, protons, and neutrons.

H. ATOMIC NUMBER AND MASS NUMBER

The **atomic number** denotes the number of protons in an atom's nucleus. The **mass number** denotes the total number of protons and neutrons. Protons and neutrons are often called nucleons. By convention, the atomic number is usually written to the left of the elemental notation, and the mass number to the left above the elemental notation as represented by the example below. The element shown is aluminum.

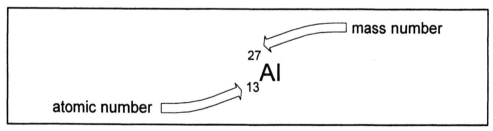

Some atoms have the same atomic number, but different mass numbers. This means different number of neutrons. Such atoms are called **isotopes**.

I. ATOMIC WEIGHT

The **atomic weight** of an element is the average weight of all the isotopic masses of the element, calculated on the basis of their relative abundance in nature. The atomic weights are set on a "carbon-12" scale. This is the standard weight scale that is used worldwide to express atomic weights. Exploring this further, we can say that 12 atomic mass units (amu) make up the mass of one atom of $^{12}_{6}C$ isotope. In other words, one amu is equal to 1/12 the mass of one carbon-12 atom. We can also say that the atomic weight of carbon-12 is 12 amu. Even though it is popular to use the term atomic weight, atomic mass is a more appropriate term since we are really talking about the mass rather than the weight.

J. MOLECULES

A **molecule** is a set or group of atoms which are chemically bonded. It can be represented by a molecular formula. A molecular formula represents the different kinds of atoms that are present in a molecule, along with the actual ratio of its atomic combination in forming that molecule.

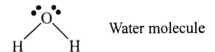
Water molecule

A molecule of H_2O (water) contains two hydrogen atoms bonded to one atom of oxygen.

NaOH   Sodium Hydroxide

A molecule of sodium hydroxide contains one sodium atom, one oxygen atom, and one hydrogen atom. The point is that molecular formula represents the molecules and the actual ratio of the atoms present in them.

Molecular Weight

Molecular weight represents the sum of the atomic weights of all the atoms in that molecule. Molecular weight is also known as formula weight.

Example 1-1

Calculate the molecular weight of sulfuric acid (H_2SO_4).

2 hydrogens	$2 \times 1 = 2$
1 sulfur	$1 \times 32 = 32$
4 oxygens	$4 \times 16 = \underline{64}$
	98 g/mol

Example 1- 2

Calculate the molecular weight of carbon dioxide (CO_2).

1 carbon	$1 \times 12 = 12$
2 oxygens	$2 \times 16 = \underline{32}$
	44 g/mol

Empirical Formula

Empirical formula of a molecule represents the simplest ratio of the atoms present in the molecule. For example, acetylene has the molecular formula C_2H_2. The empirical formula of acetylene is CH. In essence, empirical formula gives the simplest ratio of atoms in a molecule.

Problem 1-1

Write the empirical formula of the following molecules.

1. H_2O_2
2) C_2H_6
3) H_2O

Answers:

1) HO
2) CH_3
3) H_2O

Notice that sometimes the empirical formula is the same as the molecular formula as in the case of water (H_2O).

K. THE CONCEPT OF MOLE

The quantity of a given substance that contains as many units or molecules as the number of atoms in 12 grams of carbon-12 is called a **mole**. For example, one mole of glucose contains the same number of glucose molecules as in 12 grams of carbon-12. The mass of one mole of a substance is called its **molar mass**. The number of atoms in 12 grams of carbon-12 is represented by the **Avogadro number (6.023×10^{23})**. So one mole of any substance contains Avogadro number of units in them.

To understand this concept thoroughly, try different possible scenarios where the Avogadro number can be used. Here are some. One mole of hydrogen atoms contains Avogadro number of hydrogen atoms. One mole of hydrogen molecules contains Avogadro number of hydrogen molecules. A mole of water contains 6.023×10^{23} water molecules. These are all different ways of expressing the same concept.

The molar mass of a substance is equal to the molecular weight of that substance. The molecular weight (formula weight) of water is 18 amu. Since this is the molar mass, we can express it as 18 grams/mol.

Example 1-3

Calculate the mass of one molecule of sodium hydroxide (NaOH).

Ans: We know that the formula weight of sodium hydroxide is 40 g/mol.

Sodium	23
Oxygen	16
Hydrogen	1
	40 g/mol

We also know that one mole of NaOH contains Avogadro number of molecules. So the mass of the NaOH molecule can be found by the following method:

Mass of one molecule of sodium hydroxide

$$= \frac{40g}{6.02 \times 10^{23}} = 6.64 \times 10^{-23} g$$

Example 1-4

Calculate the number of moles in 109.5 grams of hydrogen chloride.

Ans: Just like the last example, we have to find the molar mass of the molecule. The molar mass is 35.5 + 1 = 36.5 g/mol.

$$\text{Number of moles} = 109.5 \text{ g HCl} \times \frac{1 \text{ mol HCl}}{36.5 \text{ g HCl}} = 3 \text{ moles of HCl}$$

So, 109.5 grams of HCl correspond to 3 moles of HCl.

You should be able to do these types of conversions back and forth, from grams to moles and moles to grams.

Try the next problem to see whether you have mastered the idea.

Problem 1-2

Calculate the number of grams in 8 moles of sulfur dioxide.

Ans: If your answer is close to 512.8 g, you solved the problem correctly.

L. COMPOSITION BY PERCENTAGE

The MCAT often contains percentage composition problems. Percentage composition is the percentage contribution (by weight) of each element to the total mass. Let's explore this idea by looking at some examples.

Example 1-5

Calcium carbonate ($CaCO_3$), commonly known as limestone is used in the preparation of a variety of compounds. Calculate the percentage composition of each element in calcium carbonate.

Solution:

# of atoms per molecule	molar weight of the atoms	total mass of the element per mol
1 Calcium	1×40.1 g	40.1 g
1 Carbon	1×12.0 g	12.0 g
3 Oxygen	3×16.0 g	48.0 g
		100.1 g

The percentage composition of each element can be found as follows:

$$\% \text{ of calcium } = \frac{40.1}{100.1} \times 100 = 40.1\% \text{ calcium}$$

$$\% \text{ of carbon } = \frac{12}{100.1} \times 100 = 12\% \text{ carbon}$$

$$\% \text{ of oxygen } = \frac{48}{100.1} \times 100 = 47.9\% \text{ oxygen}$$

Predicting Formulas from Percentage Compositions

You should be able to predict the formula of a compound on the basis of a given data of percentage compositions. Study the next example to understand how it is done.

Example 1-6

A carbon compound contains 27.27% carbon and 72.73% oxygen by mass. Predict the simplest ratio or formula of the compound.

Solution:

The best way to approach this problem is to consider that we have 100 grams of this compound. Logically it should contain 27.27 grams of carbon and 72.73

grams of oxygen. With that in mind, we can calculate the number of moles of each element or atom. After that we can obtain the simple ratio.

Step 1

$$\text{\# of moles of carbon atoms} = \frac{27.27}{12} = 2.2725 \text{ moles of carbon atoms}$$

$$\text{\# of moles of oxygen atoms} = \frac{72.73}{16} = 4.546 \text{ moles of oxygen atoms}$$

Step 2

Divide every number of moles with the smallest number of moles that you got in Step 1. Here the smaller one is 2.2725. So divide the number of moles of carbon atoms and the number of moles of oxygen atoms by 2.2725. That will give you the simplest ratio between them.

$$\text{Carbon:} \quad \frac{2.2725}{2.2725} = 1$$

$$\text{Oxygen:} \quad \frac{4.546}{2.2725} \approx 2$$

Since the ratio of carbon to oxygen is 1:2, the compound is CO_2.

Example 1-7

Calculate the mass of sulfur in 150 grams of H_2SO_4.

Solution:

The easiest way to calculate this is to find the percentage composition of sulfur. Then, use that percentage to find the mass of sulfur in the given amount of substance.

Step 1

$$\% \text{ of sulfur} = \frac{32.1}{98} \times 100, \text{ roughly } 33\%$$

Step 2

The mass of sulfur present in 150 grams of sulfuric acid is

$$150 \times \frac{33\%}{100} = 49.5 \text{ g}$$

M. DENSITY

Density is defined as the mass per unit volume.

$$\text{Density} = \frac{\text{mass}}{\text{volume}}$$

This property can be used to identify a compound or an element, since the density of a pure substance is a constant. Since density relates mass and volume, it can be used to find the volume occupied by a given mass, or if the volume is known, we can find the mass.

Density of water is 1.0 g/ml.

Let's explore some calculations involving density. You'll see that these calculations have tremendous laboratory significance.

Example 1-8

The density of carbon tetrachloride is about 1.6 g/ml at 20°C. Calculate the volume occupied by 320 g of CCl_4.

Solution:

$$\text{Density} = \frac{\text{mass}}{\text{volume}}$$

$$\text{Volume} = \frac{\text{mass}}{\text{density}} = \frac{320 \text{ g}}{1.6 \text{ g / ml}} = 200 \text{ ml}$$

So, 320 grams of carbon tetrachloride will occupy a volume of 200 ml.

Example 1-9

A 20 ml sample of mercury has a mass of 271 g. Calculate the density of mercury.

Solution:

$$\text{Density} = \frac{\text{mass}}{\text{volume}} = \frac{271 \text{ g}}{20 \text{ ml}} = 13.55 \text{ g / ml}$$

This question tests your knowledge of a basic equation. Though the equation is simple, you should be able to manipulate this equation so that you can connect this piece of information with other facts and formulas that are given in your test question or passage.

CHAPTER 1 PRACTICE QUESTIONS

1. A student preparing a solution for an experiment measured the weight of the sample solute to be used. If she is supposed to use 2 moles of calcium hydroxide, she must use:

    A. 57.1 grams.
    B. 74.1 grams.
    C. 114.2 grams.
    D. 148.2 grams.

2. Which of the following best represents the total number of atoms present in a sample of oxygen gas weighing 56 g?

    A. 6.0×10^{23} ions
    B. 10.5×10^{23} ions
    C. 12.0×10^{23} ions
    D. 21×10^{23} ions

3. Experiments conducted with gas discharge tubes during the late 19th century resulted in many important conclusions in atomic chemistry. Among those, one of the most important was the discovery of rays known as cathode rays. Cathode rays when passed near negative plates will most likely:

    A. bend toward the negative plate.
    B. bend away from the negative plate.
    C. will not bend, because they are uncharged.
    D. will not bend, because they are high energy radiations.

4. Which of the following is true regarding a typical atom?

    A. Neutrons and electrons have the same mass.
    B. The mass of neutrons is much less than that of electrons.
    C. Neutrons and protons together make the nucleus electrically neutral.
    D. Protons are more massive than electrons.

5. The empirical formula of butane is:

    A. CH_3
    B. C_2H_5
    C. C_4H_{10}
    D. CH_2

6. The mass of one mol of a substance is numerically equal to:

    A. mass number.
    B. Avogadro number.
    C. molecular weight.
    D. 22.4.

7. If m represents the number of moles of a substance, M represents the molar mass of the substance, and d represents the density of the substance, which of the following expressions equals to the volume of the sample substance?

A. $\dfrac{mM}{d}$

B. $\dfrac{m}{dM}$

C. $\dfrac{d}{mM}$

D. $\dfrac{m}{d}$

8. The mass of oxygen in 96 grams of sulfur dioxide is closest to:

A. 16 g.
B. 24 g.
C. 32 g.
D. 47 g.

9. Choose the best value that corresponds to the percentage composition of chlorine in carbon tetrachloride?

A. 92%
B. 90%
C. 86%
D. None of the above

10. A student researcher analyzing the identity of the by-product of a reaction found that the compound contained 63.6% nitrogen and 36.4% oxygen. What is the most likely formula of this compound?

A. NO
B. NO_2
C. N_2O
D. N_2O_3

Questions 11-14 are based on the following passage.

Passage 1

The following reactions were conducted in a lab for studies related to reaction kinetics. Consider the reactions shown below:

Reaction 1

$$CH_4 \;+\; 2O_2 \longrightarrow CO_2 \;+\; 2H_2O$$

$$2C_2H_6 \;+\; 7O_2 \longrightarrow 4CO_2 \;+\; 6H_2O$$

Reaction 2

11. Reaction 2 is best described by which of the following?

A. A metathesis reaction
B. A combustion reaction
C. An endothermic reaction
D. A decomposition reaction

12. In Reaction 2, if 54 g of water was formed, how much ethane and oxygen must have reacted?

   A. 30 g of ethane and 224 g of oxygen
   B. 60 g of ethane and 224 g of oxygen
   C. 30 g of ethane and 112 g of oxygen
   D. 60 g of ethane and 112 g of oxygen

13. Which of the following is the actual formula of dextrose, if the empirical proportion is 1:2:1, where the proportion number 2 is that of hydrogen. Dextrose has a molecular weight of 180 g/mol? (Dextrose molecule is composed of carbon, hydrogen, and oxygen)

   A. CHO
   B. $C_6H_{12}O_6$
   C. $C_{12}H_6O_3$
   D. CH_2O

14. Which of the following equals the number of hydrogen atoms in 40 grams of methane?

   A. 1.5×10^{24}
   B. 2.4×10^{24}
   C. 6.0×10^{24}
   D. 6.023×10^{23}

2

Chemical Reactions

A. INTRODUCTION

Chemical reaction is a process at the molecular or ionic level by which one or more types of substances are transformed into one or more new types of substances by different modes of combination. In this chapter, we will explore the different types of chemical reactions including oxidation-reduction reactions. We will also learn how to balance equations.

B. CHEMICAL REACTIONS

A chemical reaction can be represented by a chemical equation. In a chemical equation representing an irreversible reaction, the substances that react (reactants) are written on the left side, while the resulting substances (products) are written on the right side of an arrow.

$$2\,H_2 \quad + \quad O_2 \quad \longrightarrow \quad 2\,H_2O$$

In the reaction shown above, two molecules of hydrogen react with one molecule of oxygen, forming two molecules of water. Balancing of equations will be covered a little later in this chapter.

C. TYPES OF CHEMICAL REACTIONS

There are five types of chemical reactions.

1) Combination reaction
2) Combustion reaction
3) Decomposition reaction
4) Displacement reaction or single-replacement reaction
5) Metathesis reaction or double-replacement reaction

Combination Reaction

A reaction involving the formation of a compound from two or more substances is called a **combination reaction**.

Some representative combination reactions

$$2Na\,(s) \quad + \quad Cl_2\,(g) \quad \longrightarrow \quad 2\,NaCl\,(s)$$

$$SO_2\,(g) \quad + \quad H_2O\,(l) \quad \longrightarrow \quad H_2SO_3\,(aq)$$

Combustion Reaction

A **combustion reaction** involves the reaction of substances with oxygen, and it is usually accompanied by the release of large amounts of heat. Combustion reactions are thus highly exothermic.

Some representative combustion reactions

$$C\,(s) \quad + \quad O_2\,(g) \quad \longrightarrow \quad CO_2\,(g)$$

$$2\,H_2S\,(g) \quad + \quad 3\,O_2\,(g) \quad \longrightarrow \quad 2\,SO_2\,(g) \quad + \quad 2\,H_2O\,(g)$$

Decomposition Reaction

A **decomposition reaction** is a process in which one compound decomposes or splits to form two or more simpler compounds and/or elements.

A representative decomposition reaction

$$CaCO_3\,(s) \quad \longrightarrow \quad CaO\,(s) \quad + \quad CO_2\,(g)$$

Displacement Reaction (single-replacement reaction)

In a **single-replacement reaction**, an element reacts with a compound, and results in the displacement of an element or group from the compound. An example of a single-replacement reaction is shown.

A single-replacement reaction

$$Zn \ (s) \ + \ CuCl_2 \ (aq) \longrightarrow ZnCl_2 \ (aq) \ + \ Cu \ (s)$$

In this reaction, Zn substitues for Cu.

Metathesis Reaction (double-replacement reaction)

A **metathesis (double-replacement) reaction** involves the exchange of two groups or two ions among the reactants. Remember that in a single-replacement reaction, there is only one group or ion being switched. A metathesis reaction can often result in an insoluble product from soluble reactants, and the insoluble compound formed is called a precipitate.

A metathesis reaction

$$AgNO_3 \ (aq) \ + \ NaCl \ (aq) \longrightarrow AgCl \ (s) \ + \ NaNO_3 \ (aq)$$

Note that this reaction involves the formation of a precipitate of AgCl.

With respect to the types of reactions, your objective should be to understand the basis behind the categorization.

D. BALANCING SIMPLE EQUATIONS

A chemical equation is said to be balanced if all the atoms present in the reactants appear in the same numbers among the products. Here is an example.

Example 2-1

Balance the following equation.

$$Fe \ + \ O_2 \longrightarrow Fe_2O_3$$

Solution:

Start by balancing the oxygen atoms. There are two oxygen atoms on the reactant side and three oxygen atoms on the product side. To balance this, put 3 as the coefficient of oxygen on the reactant side. When we write '3 O_2,' that means we have 6 oxygen atoms on the reactant side. To make the same number of oxygen atoms on the product side, let's put 2 as the coefficient of Fe_2O_3. Now the oxygen atoms seem to be balanced.

Let's take a look at Fe. Since the coefficient of Fe_2O_3 is 2, we have 4 atoms of Fe on the product side. We can balance this by writing 4 as the coefficient of Fe on the reactant side. So the balanced equation is as follows:

$$4\,Fe + 3\,O_2 \longrightarrow 2\,Fe_2O_3$$

Problem 2-1

Balance the following equations:

(a) $Cu + AgNO_3 \longrightarrow Ag + Cu(NO_3)_2$

(b) $Fe_2O_3 + CO \longrightarrow Fe + CO_2$

(c) $H_2SO_4 + NaOH \longrightarrow Na_2SO_4 + H_2O$

(d) $Ba(OH)_2 + HCl \longrightarrow BaCl_2 + H_2O$

Answers:

(a) $Cu + 2\,AgNO_3 \longrightarrow 2\,Ag + Cu(NO_3)_2$

(b) $Fe_2O_3 + 3\,CO \longrightarrow 2\,Fe + 3\,CO_2$

(c) $H_2SO_4 + 2\,NaOH \longrightarrow Na_2SO_4 + 2\,H_2O$

(d) $Ba(OH)_2 + 2\,HCl \longrightarrow BaCl_2 + 2\,H_2O$

E. OXIDATION NUMBER

Electrons are exchanged during oxidation-reduction reactions. The behavior of atoms or ions in terms of the number of electrons transferred is expressed as the oxidation state (oxidation number). We can define oxidation number as the charge of an atom or ion, based on a set of standard rules. If the given species is an ion containing a single atom, then its oxidation state is its charge itself. Let's analyze this by looking at a few examples.

In NaCl, the oxidation state of sodium is +1 and the oxidation state of chlorine is −1. Generally, the elements at the top right corner of the periodic table are assigned negative oxidation numbers. Some of the elements on the right side of the periodic table can have positive or negative oxidation numbers depending upon the atom to which the given element is bonded to. The elements in the middle and the left portions of the periodic table have almost exclusively positive oxidation numbers.

Table 1-1

General guidelines for assigning oxidation numbers

1. The elemental natural state oxidation number of any atom is zero. For example, the oxidation number of oxygen atom in O_2 is zero.
2. The sum of the oxidation numbers of the atoms in a compound should be zero.
3. The sum of the oxidation numbers of the atoms in an ionic species (a species with a net charge) should equal the net charge of the ionic species.
4. The oxidation number of a given ion containing a single atom is its charge itself.

Oxidation numbers of some common elements

1. The common oxidation number of Group IA metals is +1. E.g., lithium, sodium, potassium.
2. The common oxidation number of Group IIA metals is +2. E.g., beryllium, magnesium, calcium.
3. The common oxidation number of Group IIIA is +3. E.g., aluminum, boron.
4. The common oxidation number of Group IVA is +4. +2 is also seen in some compounds such as CO.
5. The common oxidation numbers of Group V A are +5 and −3.
6. The common oxidation number of Group VIA is −2.
7. The common oxidation number of Group VIIA is −1.
8. The common oxidation number of H is +1. In some metal hydrides, hydrogen shows an oxidation number of −1.

The above list of common oxidation numbers is not comprehensive. Nevertheless, it gives you a basic and essential picture about assigning oxidation numbers in common compounds and ionic species. Most elements can have multiple oxidation states, depending on the element or ionic species they are bonded to. You have to always follow the general guidelines in Table 1-1, and check whether the items listed are satisfied.

Now that we have learned the theory of assigning oxidation numbers, let's do an example to see how it works.

Example 2-2

What is the oxidation number of sulfur in sulfuric acid?

Solution:

Sulfuric acid is H_2SO_4. The oxidation number of hydrogen is +1. But we have two hydrogens which add up to a charge of +2. Since the total charge of this molecule should be zero, we can say that the charge of sulfate ion is –2. We also know that the oxidation number of oxygen is –2. But there are four oxygens in a sulfate ion. So the charge adds to –8. Now let's solve this algebraically.

ON^{Sulfur} - Oxidation number of sulfur
ON^{Oxygen} - Oxidation number of oxygen

$ON^{Sulfur} + 4\,(ON^{Oxygen}) = -2$
$ON^{Sulfur} + 4\,(-2) = -2$
$ON^{Sulfur} = +6$

So the oxidation number of sulfur in sulfuric acid is +6.

Problem 2-2

Calculate the oxidation state of the element indicated in each of the following problems.

(a) What is the oxidation state of hydrogen in MgH_2?
(b) What is the oxidation state of chlorine in ClO_3^-?
(c) What is the oxidation state of oxygen in Na_2O_2?
(d) What is the oxidation state of nitrogen in NH_3?
(e) What is the oxidation state of oxygen in O_2?
(f) What is the oxidation state of bromine in $HBrO_2$?
(g) What is the oxidation state of manganese in $KMnO_4$?

Answers:

(a) –1
(b) +5
(c) –1
(d) –3
(e) 0
(f) +3
(g) +7

F. OXIDATION-REDUCTION REACTIONS

Oxidation-reduction (redox) reactions involve the transfer of electrons from one compound or species to another. In this section, we will discuss oxidation-reduction reactions and learn how to balance them.

Oxidation is the process by which an atom or species loses its electrons. In **reduction**, an atom or species gains electrons. Let's first consider oxidation and reduction separately.

Mnemonic:
LEO** the lion says **GER
*Losing **E**lectrons **O**xidation*
<u>G</u>aining <u>E</u>lectrons <u>R</u>eduction

Consider the conversion of iron from its neutral elemental state to its ionic form.

$$Fe \longrightarrow Fe^{2+} + 2\,e^{-}$$

Notice that in the process iron lost electrons. The process is oxidation.

Consider another example. An example involving the conversion of bromine to its ionic form.

$$Br_2 + 2\,e^{-} \longrightarrow 2\,Br^{-}$$

Notice that in the process bromine gained electrons. The process is reduction.

Now let's go one step forward. Consider the next reaction.

$$2\,Fe + 3\,Br_2 \longrightarrow 2\,FeBr_3$$

This reaction is a typical example of an oxidation-reduction reaction. The oxidation number of iron on the reactant side is 0. The oxidation number of bromine on the reactant side is also 0. What are the oxidation numbers of iron and bromine in $FeBr_3$? Well, we know that bromine has an oxidation number of -1. So the oxidation number of iron in $FeBr_3$ is $+3$. Thus iron is oxidized and bromine is reduced. The species that gets oxidized is called the **reducing agent**. The species that gets reduced is called the **oxidizing agent**. In this reaction, evidently iron acts as the reducing agent, and bromine acts as the oxidizing agent.

> *Oxidation results in an increase in the oxidation number. In the process of oxidation, electrons are lost.*
>
> *Reduction results in a decrease in the oxidation number. In the process, electrons are gained.*

Balancing Oxidation-Reduction Reactions

Balancing of an oxidation-reduction reaction is a little more complex than balancing a simple reaction. The main rule that you have to follow when balancing oxidation-reduction reactions is that the absolute value of the increase in oxidation number of all the atoms that are oxidized should equal the absolute value of the decrease in oxidation number of all the atoms that are reduced. Balancing oxidation-reduction reaction is sometimes time-consuming and quite often frustrating. We will look at two methods of balancing oxidation-reduction reactions.

Method A

1. Write the unbalanced equation.
2. Find the oxidation numbers of the atoms that undergo change in oxidation states and write on top of each atom the corresponding oxidation number.
3. By this process, we will be able to see which atoms are getting oxidized and reduced.
4. Compare and indicate the change in oxidation numbers from the reactant side and the product side, and write down the change in the oxidation numbers.
5. Make the necessary changes by writing coefficients that will equalize the changes in the oxidation numbers. In other words, the net decrease in the oxidation numbers should equal the net increase in the oxidation numbers. Add water if necessary.
6. Do a final check on whether all the atoms and charges balance out.

Method B

1. Write the unbalanced equation.
2. Separate the two half-reactions, write them out, and balance any of the atoms. From this point onward, we balance the reactions separately. Do the obvious or the simple balancing by inspection if possible.
3. Balance the oxygen atoms by adding water on the appropriate side of the half-reaction.
4. Balance the hydrogen atoms by adding H^+ on the appropriate side of the half-reaction.
5. Add sufficient number of electrons so that the charges are balanced.
6. Once the half-reactions are balanced, combine the half-reactions and cancel out any common terms that appear on both sides of the equation to get the refined and balanced oxidation-reduction equation.

Example 2-3

Balance the following oxidation-reduction reaction.

$$Zn \ + \ NO_3^- \longrightarrow Zn^{2+} \ + \ N_2O$$

| Method A |

1. $Zn \ + \ NO_3^- \longrightarrow Zn^{2+} \ + \ N_2O$

2. $\overset{0}{Zn} \ + \ \overset{+5}{NO_3^-} \longrightarrow \overset{+2}{Zn^{2+}} \ + \ \overset{+1}{N_2O}$

3. $\overset{0}{Zn} \ + \ 2 \ \overset{+5}{NO_3^-} \longrightarrow \overset{+2}{Zn^{2+}} \ + \ \overset{+1}{N_2O}$

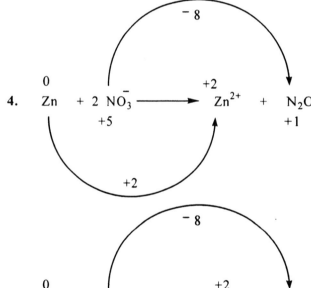

4. $\overset{0}{Zn} \ + \ 2 \ \underset{+5}{NO_3^-} \longrightarrow \overset{+2}{Zn^{2+}} \ + \ \underset{+1}{N_2O}$

    -8 $+2$

5. $\overset{0}{4 \ Zn} \ + \ 2 \ \underset{+5}{NO_3^-} \longrightarrow 4 \ \overset{+2}{Zn^{2+}} \ + \ \underset{+1}{N_2O}$

    -8 $+8$

6. | $10 \ H^+ \ + \ 4 \ Zn \ + \ 2 \ NO_3^- \longrightarrow 4 \ Zn^{2+} \ + \ N_2O \ + \ 5 \ H_2O$ |

$$\boxed{\textbf{Method B}}$$

$$Zn \;+\; NO_3^- \longrightarrow Zn^{2+} \;+\; N_2O$$

Half-reaction I

1. $Zn \longrightarrow Zn^{2+}$

2. $Zn \longrightarrow Zn^{2+} + 2\,e^-$

Half-reaction II

1. $NO_3^- \longrightarrow N_2O$

2. $2\,NO_3^- \longrightarrow N_2O$

3. $2\,NO_3^- \longrightarrow N_2O + 5\,H_2O$

4. $10\,H^+ + 2\,NO_3^- \longrightarrow N_2O + 5\,H_2O$

5. $8\,e + 10\,H^+ + 2\,NO_3^- \longrightarrow N_2O + 5\,H_2O$

Before we combine the equations, the electrons need to be balanced out. So multiplying the balanced half-reaction # (**I**) by 4, we get

$$4\,Zn \longrightarrow 4\,Zn^{2+} + 8\,e^-$$

Combining the two half reactions

$$4\,Zn \longrightarrow 4\,Zn^{2+} + \cancel{8\,e^-}$$

$$\cancel{8\,e^-} + 10\,H^+ + 2\,NO_3^- \longrightarrow N_2O + 5\,H_2O$$

$$\overline{10\,H^+ + 4\,Zn + 2\,NO_3^- \longrightarrow 4\,Zn^{2+} + N_2O + 5\,H_2O}$$

G. CALCULATIONS INVOLVING CHEMICAL REACTIONS

In this section, we will look at some chemical equations and find what we can do with the information represented in a chemical equation. The equation shown below represents the reaction of methane and oxygen to form carbon dioxide and water.

$$CH_4 \quad + \quad 2\,O_2 \quad \longrightarrow \quad CO_2 \quad + \quad 2\,H_2O$$

From this balanced equation we can infer many things. Let's consider a few.

1) One molecule of methane reacts with 2 molecules of oxygen to form 1 molecule of carbon dioxide and 2 molecules of water.
2) We can also say that 1 mole of methane reacts with 2 moles of oxygen to form 1 mole of carbon dioxide and 2 moles of water.
3) Since one mole contains Avogadro number of molecules, we can say that 6.023×10^{23} molecules of methane reacts with 1.2046×10^{24} ($= 2 \times 6.023 \times 10^{23}$) molecules of oxygen to form 6.023×10^{23} molecules of carbon dioxide and 1.2046×10^{24} molecules of water.
4) We can confidently say that 16 g of methane reacts with 64 g of oxygen to form 44 g of carbon dioxide and 36 g of water.

Example 2-4

Calculate the number of moles of water produced when 5.25 moles of methane undergo the reaction depicted below. (Assume there is plenty of oxygen for the reaction)

$$CH_4 \quad + \quad 2\,O_2 \quad \longrightarrow \quad CO_2 \quad + \quad 2\,H_2O$$

Solution:

From the equation, it is clear that for every mole of methane, 2 moles of water are formed. So without any elaborate calculations, you should be able to come up with the correct answer. It is very much like a ratio problem. Since there are 5.25 moles of methane, 10.5 moles of water will be formed.

Number of moles of water formed = 5.25 × 2 = 10.5 moles

Example 2-5

110 g of CO_2 were formed as a result of the reaction shown below. How many grams of oxygen must have reacted to form that much carbon dioxide?

$$CH_4 \quad + \quad 2\,O_2 \quad \longrightarrow \quad CO_2 \quad + \quad 2\,H_2O$$

Solution:

According to the equation, 2 moles of oxygen result in 1 mole of carbon dioxide. For example, if 2 moles of carbon dioxide were formed, 4 moles of oxygen must have reacted. Here, the amount of carbon dioxide formed is given in terms of grams. So the first step is to convert the grams to moles.

$$\text{Moles of carbon dioxide} = \frac{110 \text{ g}}{44 \text{ g / mol}} = 2.5 \text{ moles}$$

Hence, <u>5 moles of oxygen</u> must have reacted to form 2.5 moles of carbon dioxide. But the question asks for this quantity in grams. So the final step is to convert moles to grams.

$$\text{The amount of required oxygen} = 5 \text{ moles} \times \frac{32 \text{ g}}{1 \text{ mol}} = 160 \text{ g}$$

H. THE CONCEPT OF LIMITING REAGENT

So far we have been considering reactions in which all the reactants exist in adequate quantities. In this section, we will consider what happens when the amount of one of the reactants available is less than the amount required to complete the reaction. When such a condition exists, we call that reactant or reagent the limiting reagent.

We will further explore this scenario through the following examples.

Example 2-6

A reaction mixture contains 60.75 g magnesium and 146 g hydrogen chloride. Predict the limiting reagent if the reaction occurs as shown below.

$$Mg \quad + \quad 2\,HCl \quad \longrightarrow \quad H_2 \quad + \quad MgCl_2$$

Solution:

First, we have to convert the grams of the substances to moles. Then make the comparison to see which one is the limiting reagent. By now, you should be comfortable with the conversion of moles to grams and vice versa. The number of moles of magnesium present is 2.5 moles. According to the equation, 1 mole of magnesium reacts with 2 moles of hydrogen chloride. For magnesium to completely react, there should be at least 5 moles of hydrogen chloride present. If you calculate the number of moles of hydrogen chloride present, you will get 4 moles. This amount of hydrogen chloride is not enough to completely react with the amount of magnesium present. So the limiting reagent is hydrogen chloride.

I. PERCENT YIELD

If we know the chemical equation and the amounts of reactants, we can calculate the theoretical yield of that reaction. But in reality, the yield depends on many other factors also. Most of the time in synthesis reactions, even in your own lab experiments, you probably noticed that the actual yield is lower than the theoretical yield. The percent yield denotes the amount of actual yield in terms of the theoretical yield. The formula to find the percent yield is given below:

$$\text{Percent yield} = \frac{\text{actual yield of the product}}{\text{theoretical yield of the product}} \times 100\%$$

Example 2-7

$$NaNO_2 + HCl \longrightarrow HNO_2 + NaCl$$

A student conducted the above reaction in a lab as a part of her research assignment. She used 138 g of sodium nitrite, with excess of hydrogen chloride. What is the percent yield of HNO_2, if the actual yield of HNO_2 was 61.1 g?

Solution:

First, you should find the number of moles of $NaNO_2$. Since she used 138 g, the number of moles of $NaNO_2$ is 2 (Mol.wt of $NaNO_2$ is 69 g/mol). Since the ratio of formation of HNO_2 is 1:1 with respect to $NaNO_2$, theoretically 2 moles of HNO_2 should be formed. Two moles of HNO_2 correspond to 94 g. But actually, only 61.1 g of HNO_2 was formed. Now it is just a matter of plug and chug in the percent yield formula.

The percentage yield of HNO_2 = $\dfrac{61.1 \text{ grams}}{94 \text{ grams}}$ $\times$ 100% = 65%

In this experiment, the actual yield was not high (i.e., only 65% of the theoretically predicted yield) as expected.

Example 2-8

Match the following reactions with the appropriate type of reaction

1. $2KClO_3 \longrightarrow 2KCl + 3O_2$ **A.** Combination reaction

2. $2KCl + Cl_2 \longrightarrow 2KCl$ **B.** Double-replacement reaction

3. $HNO_3 + NaOH \longrightarrow NaNO_3 + H_2O$ **C.** Decomposition reaction

Solution:

$2KClO_3 \longrightarrow 2KCl + 3O_2$ **C.** Decomposition reaction

$2KCl + Cl_2 \longrightarrow 2KCl$ **A.** Combination reaction

$HNO_3 + NaOH \longrightarrow NaNO_3 + H_2O$ **B.** Double-replacement reaction

CHAPTER 2   PRACTICE QUESTIONS

$$2HI \; + \; PbCl_2 \longrightarrow PbI_2 \; + \; 2HCl$$

1. The reaction shown here can be best classified as a:

    A. combustion reaction.
    B. combination reaction.
    C. single-replacement reaction.
    D. double-replacement reaction.

2. All the following reactant-combinations are neutralization reactions, EXCEPT:

    A. $HNO_2 \; + \; NaOH$

    B. $KOH \; + \; HCl$

    C. $Al^+ \; + \; 3OH$

    D. $H_3PO_4 \; + \; NaOH$

3. An unbalanced equation is shown below. What is the coefficient of aluminum hydroxide in the final balanced equation?

    $$H_2SO_4 \; + \; Al(OH)_3 \longrightarrow H_2O \; + \; Al_2(SO_4)_3$$

    A. 1
    B. 2
    C. 3
    D. 7

4. How many grams of sodium chloride are required to synthesize 73 grams of hydrogen chloride, if the reaction involves sodium chloride and sulfuric acid?

    $$NaCl \; + \; H_2SO_4 \longrightarrow Na_2SO_4 + HCl$$

    A. 58.5 grams
    B. 117 grams
    C. 175.5 grams
    D. 234 grams

5. In some reactions, you will often encounter ions in aqueous solutions which are not actually involved in the reaction. Such ions are best termed:

    A. cations.
    B. anions.
    C. salt-bridge ions.
    D. spectator ions.

6. Some substances can act as a base or an acid. Such substances are called:

    A. aliphatic substances.
    B. amphibasic substances.
    C. lyophilic substances.
    D. amphoteric substances.

7. Predict the coefficient of iron in the balanced equation for a reaction in which iron reacts with oxygen to form Fe_2O_3.

    A. 1
    B. 2
    C. 3
    D. 4

8. The number of molecules are the same in which of the following pairs?

   A. 32 grams of O_2 and 32 grams of SO_2
   B. 49 grams of NO_2 and 40 grams of NaOH
   C. 20 grams of HF and 36 grams of H_2O
   D. 60 grams of C_2H_6 and 156 grams of C_6H_6

Questions 9-15 are based on the following passage.

Passage 1

Information regarding the amounts of substances that actually react to form the products are of extreme help. Analyzing reactions and having the balanced equations help chemists to determine the correct and optimum proportions of reactants to be used. There are various other factors besides the amount of reactants, which determine the efficiency of reactions.

Experiment 1

$$2\,Al + Fe_2O_3 \longrightarrow 2\,Fe + Al_2O_3$$

Student 1 used 40.5 g of aluminum and 80 g of Fe_2O_3 for Reaction I. A second student conducted the same reaction with a different amount for one of the reactants. The second student used 40.5 g of aluminum, and 90 grams of Fe_2O_3. A third student also conducted the same reaction with 54 g of aluminum and the same amount of Fe_2O_3 used by the first student.

Experiment 2

Reaction II involved the production of Al_2O_3 from aluminum hydroxide This was done by heating aluminum hydroxide.

$$2\,Al(OH)_3\,(s) \longrightarrow Al_2O_3\,(s) + \text{product x}$$

Experiment 3

$$Fe_2O_3\,(s) + 3\,CO\,(g) \xrightarrow[\text{heat}]{} 2\,Fe\,(s) + 3\,CO_2\,(g)$$

9. What is the most likely identity of product x?

   A. aluminum
   B. water
   C. hydrogen
   D. oxygen

10. In Experiment 3, which of the following is the limiting reagent?

    A. Fe_2O_3 because there is only 1 mole of it
    B. CO because of its gas phase
    C. Fe because of its insufficiency
    D. Cannot be determined without more data

11. Based on the given information, which of the following are true regarding Experiment 1?

    I.   The second student had the highest yield for aluminum oxide.
    II. The third student had a higher yield for aluminum oxide than the first student.
    III. The first and the third students had the same yield for aluminum oxide.

    A. I only
    B. I and II only
    C. I and III only
    D. II and III only

12. Which of the following changes will further increase the overall yield for the reactions conducted in the Experiment 1?

    A. Increasing the amount of aluminum used by Student 1
    B. Increasing the amount of aluminum used by Student 2
    C. Increasing the amount of Fe_2O_3 used by Student 2
    D. None of the above

13. Roughly 80 g of Fe_2O_3 was present in Experiment 3, and upon completion of the reaction, it was measured that 22 g of CO_2 was formed. If this is true, how much CO must have reacted before reaching completion of the reaction?

    A. 14 grams
    B. 28 grams
    C. 56 grams
    D. 84 grams

14. In the previous question, which of the reactants acts as the limiting reagent?

    A. Fe_2O_3
    B. CO
    C. CO_2
    D. Cannot be determined

15. If 0.1 mol of CO was reacted with excess of Fe_2O_3, how many molecules of carbon dioxide will be produced?

    A. 6.0×10^{23} molecules
    B. 6.0×10^{22} molecules
    C. 3.0×10^{23} molecules
    D. 18.0×10^{23} molecules

3

Electronic Structure

A. INTRODUCTION

In this chapter, we will discuss the electronic arrangement of atoms. We will also talk about quantum numbers, orbitals, various rules pertaining to electron-filling, and electronic configuration.

B. ATOMIC STRUCTURE

The first ideas about electronic arrangement in atoms were primarily figured out from atomic emission spectra. In various experiments, atoms were made to be thermally or electrically excited, and this resulted in different kinds of bands or lines on photographic plates. Our understanding of atomic structure is based on these types of experiments. All elements have their characteristic line spectra with which they can be analyzed and identified.

Electromagnetic Waves

Before we discuss the atomic structure, we will touch on the topic of electromagnetic radiation to have a better analytical understanding of the key ideas. All electromagnetic radiations travel with a constant speed of 3×10^8 **m/s**. The electromagnetic spectrum ranges from radiowaves to gamma rays.

The Wave Nature

Light has wave nature. It has electric and magnetic fields which are perpendicular to each other, and can travel through space. No medium is required. Because of its wave character, we can define light in terms of frequency and wave length. The distance between two adjacent crests or troughs, or any two adjacent identical points on a wave is called **wave length** (λ). **Frequency** (f) is the number of wavelengths passing through a point in unit time. Wavelength and frequency are related by the relation given below. Frequency is usually expressed in 1/second (s^{-1}), which is otherwise known as *hertz* (Hz).

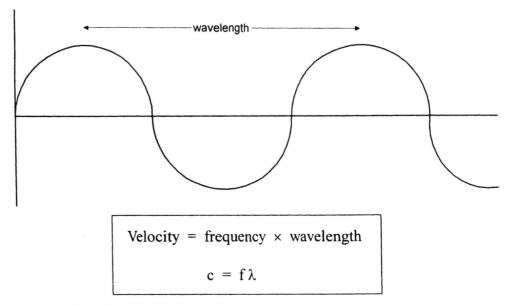

$$\text{Velocity} = \text{frequency} \times \text{wavelength}$$

$$c = f \lambda$$

The Particle Nature and Quantum Theory

Light has particle nature. These particles or forms (packages) of energy are called quanta. A more modern term for such as particle of light is photon. The energy of a photon can be expressed in terms of the following formula.

$$\text{Energy} = h\, f,$$

where h is the Planck's constant, and f is the frequency.

$$\text{Planck's constant} = 6.63 \times 10^{-34}\ \text{J.s}$$

According to **Heisenberg's Uncertainty Principle**, we cannot determine both the momentum and the position of subatomic particles simultaneously. This is because we are using other particles (electromagnetic particles–like photons) of comparable energy to detect these subatomic particles, and by the time these other particles find the subatomic particles (say electrons), they are also disturbing the pathway of these electrons. In essence, the study of something extremely small and fast (about the magnitude of electrons) cannot be done without interference of its natural course or position.

Photoelectric Effect

The photoelectric effect can be defined as the ejection of electrons from a metal surface when light rays strike on it. The ejected electrons are often called "photoelectrons." The ejection of electrons occurs only if the incident light has a certain minimum or *threshold frequency*. The required threshold frequency is a characteristic specific to each metal. Experimentally, it has been found that the photoelectrons emitted with maximum energy do not have the full energy equivalent supplied by the incident photon. This is because energy is required to break loose the electrons from the surface of the metal. The energy required for this is called the "work function," which is characteristic of each metal. The photoelectrons can be accelerated to a positively charged plate, creating a flow of charges along a wire–photocurrent. The current can be measured by an ammeter connected to the wire.

The maximum kinetic energy (K_{max}) of a photoelectron is given by the following equation:

$$K_{max} = \tfrac{1}{2}\, m v_{max}^{\,2} = hf - \varphi$$

In this equation, m is the mass of an electron, $v$max is the maximum velocity of the electrons, h is the Planck's constant, f is the frequency of the incident light, φ (pronounced *phi*) is the "work function" of the metal. The entity hf represents the energy of the incident photon.

Key Observations on Photoelectric Effect

1) The photoelectric effect exemplifies the particle nature of light.
2) Based on conservation of energy, no photoelectron can have energy more than that of an incident photon.
3) The energy of the photoelectrons is always less than that of the incident photons, because some energy (work function) is required to break the electrons loose.
4) The maximum energy of the photoelectrons is independent of the intensity of the incident light.
5) Electrons are not ejected no matter how high the intensity of the incident light is, unless the incident light has the energy corresponding to the threshold frequency characteristic of a particular metal.

Atomic Emission Spectra

When we pass white light through a prism, dispersion of the light occurs resulting in *continuous spectrum* of wavelengths. Another type of spectrum results when heated gas emits light. This results in a *line spectrum*. Line spectrum contains only certain specific wavelengths of light. The wavelengths in the <u>visible spectrum</u> of hydrogen is given by the following formula:

$$\frac{1}{\lambda} = \frac{R}{hc}\left(\frac{1}{4} - \frac{1}{n^2}\right)$$

where λ is the wavelength of the light, R (Rydberg constant) = 2.18×10^{-18} J, h (Planck's constant) = 6.63×10^{-34} J.s, c (speed of light) = 3.0×10^8 m/s, and n is some whole number that is greater than 2 which corresponds to the orbit-number from which the electron is making the transition. For example, if the transition of an electron is from orbit-number 4 to 2, the n value is 4.

Bohr's Model of Hydrogen Atom

Niel Bohr's explanation of the hydrogen spectrum was a major breakthrough toward the understanding of atomic structure. The following are the postulates:

1) In each hydrogen atom, the electron revolves around the nucleus in one of the several stable orbits.
2) Each orbit has a definite radius and thus has a definite energy associated with it.
3) An electron in an orbit closest to the nucleus has the lowest energy, and if the electron is in the lowest orbit the atom is said to be in its *ground state*.
4) The electron in an atom may absorb discrete amounts of energy and move to another orbit with higher energy, and this state is called the *excited state*.
5) An electron in an excited atom can go back to a lower energy level and this process will result in the release of excess energy as light.
6) The amount of energy released or absorbed is equal to the difference between the energies of the initial and final orbits.

Based on Bohr's theory, light energy is emitted when an electron in a higher energy level ($E_{initial}$) jumps to a lower energy level(E_{final}). Based on the law of conservation of energy, the sum of energies of the emitted photon (hf) and the electron's final energy(E_{final}) should be equal to the electron's initial energy($E_{initial}$). This can be represented mathematically as follows:

$$hf + E_{final} = E_{initial}$$

Transitions of the electron in the hydrogen atom result in different spectral lines.

The energy of the emitted photon $hf = R\left(\dfrac{1}{n_{final}^{2}} - \dfrac{1}{n_{initial}^{2}}\right)$,

where n_{final} and $n_{initial}$ are the principal quantum numbers of final and initial energy levels, and R is the Rydberg constant(2.18×10^{-18} J). The figure given below shows the transitions that can result in the Lyman (ultraviolet region), Balmer (visible region), and Paschen series (infrared region) for $n$final values 1, 2, and 3 respectively.

A photon is emitted when an electron in an atom jumps from a higher to a lower energy level. The energy of the emitted photon is equal to the difference in energy between the two energy levels.

C. QUANTUM NUMBERS

All electrons present in an atom have specific addresses or attributes by which each electron can be referred to. The four quantum numbers are the ones with which we can describe each and every electron that is present in an atom. One of the quantum numbers describes the shape or the most probable area around the nucleus where we can find the particular electrons of interest. This wave function of an electron is called an **orbital**.

Principal quantum number (n). The principal quantum number denotes the energy level of electrons. The larger the principal quantum number is, the larger the energy. The smaller the principal quantum number is, the lower the energy. The shells are often named K, L, M, N, . . ., which correspond to the principal quantum numbers 1, 2, 3, 4, . . ., respectively.

Letter	*K*	*L*	*M*	*N* . . .
n	1	2	3	4 . . .

The orbital size depends on n. This means that the larger the n value, the larger the orbital. Orbitals with the same n belong to the same shell.

Angular momentum quantum number (l). Angular momentum quantum number (azimuthal quantum number) denotes the shape of the orbital. The values range from 0 to $n - 1$, where n stands for the principal quantum number. If an electron has a principal quantum number of 4, the values of angular momentum quantum numbers are 0, 1, 2, and 3. The angular momentum quantum numbers correspond to different subshells. An angular momentum quantum number 0 corresponds to s subshell, 1 to p subshell, 2 to d subshell, 3 to f subshell, and so on. For instance, $3d$ denotes a subshell with quantum numbers $n = 3$ and $l = 2$.

Orbital	*s*	*p*	*d*	*f* . . .
l	0	1	2	3 . . .

s orbital

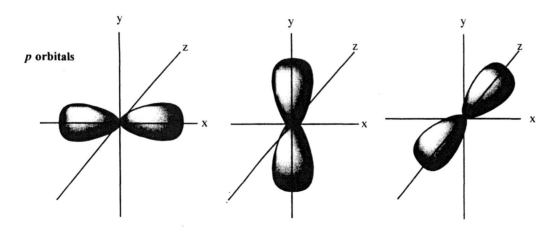

p **orbitals**

2 p_x orbital   2 p_y orbital   2 p_z orbital

Magnetic quantum number (m_l). Magnetic quantum numbers define the different spatial orientations of the orbitals. The values range from $-l$ to $+l$. For example, let's say the value of l is 1. So the magnetic quantum numbers will be -1, 0, and $+1$. The l value corresponds to p sublevel and the three magnetic quantum numbers correspond to the three atomic orbitals in the p subshell.

Spin quantum number (m_s). Spin quantum number has to do with the spin orientations of an electron. The two possible spins are denoted by the spin quantum numbers $+\frac{1}{2}$ and $-\frac{1}{2}$.

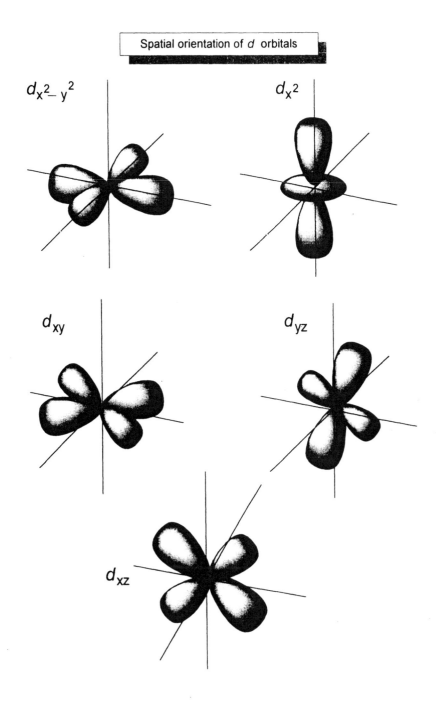

Spatial orientation of d orbitals

$d_{x^2-y^2}$

d_{x^2}

d_{xy}

d_{yz}

d_{xz}

D. ELECTRONIC CONFIGURATION

We talked about quantum numbers and atomic orbitals. In this section, we will focus our attention mainly on writing the electronic configuration of atoms and the rules associated with it. First, let's talk about the ground state electronic configuration. The ground state configuration means the electronic configuration at the lowest energy state.

There are certain rules that should be applied to the filling of orbitals. In order to do that properly, we need to know the Aufbau principle. According to the Aufbau principle, the filling order of electrons obeys a general pattern in which the electrons try to occupy the orbitals in such a way as to minimize the total energy; that is, they occupy the lowest energy orbitals first and then step-by-step go to the next available higher energy levels successively. Of course, there are some exceptions to these generalizations. Some students find it hard to remember the order of filling. The diagram given below may help you. So take a close look. Filling order can be depicted as follows:

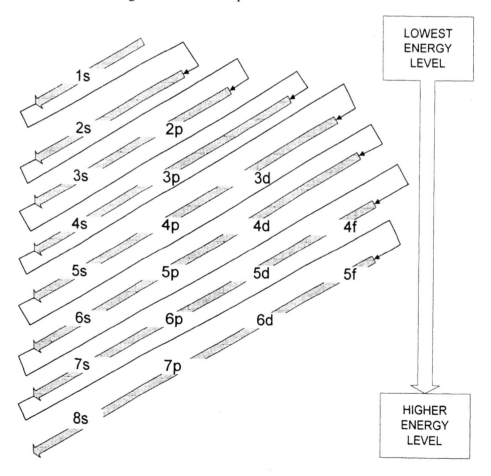

This is an easy way to remember the general order of electron-filling in the subshells. The order of filling is 1*s*, 2*s*, 2*p*, 3*s*, 3*p*, 4*s*, 4*p*, 5*s*, . . ., and so on.

An *s* orbital is spherical in shape. All *p* orbitals have dumbbell shape with two lobes aligned along an axis (see page 47). All *d* orbitals have slightly complex shapes (see page 48) and are beyond the scope of our discussion. Each orbital can accomodate a maximum of two electrons. Hence, an *s* subshell, (only one orbital) can accomodate a maximum of two electrons. Similarly, *p* (three orbitals), *d* (five orbitals), and *f* (seven orbitals) subshells can have maximum of six, ten, and fourteen electrons, respectively.

Table 3-1   Some possible combinations of quantum numbers for atomic orbitals

Principal quantum number (*n*)	Angular momentum quantum number (*l*)	Magnetic quantum number (m_l)	Subshells	Number of orbitals	Maximum number of electrons
1	0	0	1*s*	1	2
2	0	0	2*s*	1	2
2	1	-1,0,+1	2*p*	3	6
3	0	0	3*s*	1	2
3	1	-1,0,+1	3*p*	3	6
3	2	-2,-1,0,+1,+2	3*d*	5	10
4	0	0	4*s*	1	2
4	1	-1,0,+1	4*p*	3	6
4	2	-2,-1,0,+1,+2	4*d*	5	10
4	3	-3,-2,-1,0,+1,+2,+3	4*f*	7	14

Example 3-1

Write the electronic configuration of lithium.

Solution: From the periodic table, we can get the atomic number of lithium. The lithium atom has 3 electrons. As we know, 1*s* subshell is the first one to be filled. The *s* orbital can hold a maximum of 2 electrons. We have one electron remaining. It will occupy the 2*s* subshell which is the next energy level. So the third electron will occupy the 2*s* subshell. Hence, the configuration of lithium is $1s^2 2s^1$.

Example 3-2

Write the electronic configuration of oxygen in its ground state form.

Solution: The oxygen atom contains 8 electrons. The first 2 electrons will go to the 1*s* level. The next 2 electrons will occupy the 2*s* level. We have 4 electrons remaining. What is the next subshell according to the filling order? It is $2p$. The p subshell can hold a maximum of 6 electrons in its orbitals. So the remaining 4 electrons will occupy the $2p$ level. Hence, the configuration of oxygen is $1s^2\,2s^2\,2p^4$.

Hund's Rule

We have learned the order of filling the subshells. Now let's take a closer look at the filling of electrons in an orbital level. Each orbital can be occupied by a maximum of 2 electrons, and these electrons will have opposite spins as dictated by the spin quantum number. Hund's rule describes the way the electrons fill up the orbitals. According to the Hund's rule, each electron starts filling up each orbital of a given subshell. After all the orbitals in a given subshell have been filled singly (half-filled), then the electrons start pairing. Let's look at some examples.

Example 3-3

Write the electronic configuration of sulfur and also show the filling of electrons with orbital notation.

Solution: Sulfur atom has 16 electrons. The electronic configuration is written as $1s^2\,2s^2\,2p^6\,3s^2\,3p^4$. To see the significance of the Hund's rule, look at the $3p$ subshell. In the $3p$ subshell, we have 3 orbitals.

Note that the electrons first occupy singly in the orbitals. Altogether there are 4 electrons in the $3p$ subshell. Instead of filling the orbitals in pairs, the first 3 electrons start filling the three orbitals singly, and then the remaining electron occupies the orbital with the other electron as paired electrons. (See the orbital notation of $3p$ subshell shown above.) If this were not the case, you would have seen two electron-paired orbitals followed by an empty orbital.

Another idea we want to touch on concerns paramagnetic and diamagnetic substances. Substances that have unpaired electrons are called paramagnetic. Substances that have only paired electrons are called diamagnetic.

CHAPTER 3 PRACTICE QUESTIONS

1. Which of the following shows the correct order of filling of subshells?

    A. $3s$, $3p$, $4s$, $3d$, $4p$
    B. $3s$, $3p$, $3d$, $4s$, $4p$
    C. $3s$, $3d$, $3p$, $4s$, $4p$
    D. $3s$, $3d$, $3p$, $4p$, $4s$

2. Which of the following represents the outer most shell configuration of an inert gas?

    A. $4s^2\,4p^2$
    B. $4s^2\,4p^3$
    C. $4s^1\,4p^6$
    D. $4s^2\,4p^6$

3. The electronic configuration shown below is that of the element:

    $$[Kr]\ 5s^2\ 4d^{10}\ 5p^2$$

    A. Sb.
    B. Rb.
    C. In.
    D. Sn.

4. The maximum number of electrons that can occupy the energy levels is calculated using a formula, where n represents the number corresponding to the energy level. The formula is:

    A. n^2
    B. $2n^2$
    C. $2n + 1$
    D. $4n + 2$

5. Consider this statement: No two electrons of an atom can have the same sets of four quantum numbers. This is known as the:

    A. Heisenberg's Uncertainty Principle.
    B. Hund's Rule.
    C. Pauli Exclusion Principle.
    D. Aufbau Principle.

6. Which of the following is true with respect to subshells?

    A. The $4p$ subshell has higher energy than the $5s$ subshell.
    B. The $3p$ subshell can have a maximum of 3 electrons.
    C. The $5d$ subshell has higher energy than the $6s$ subshell.
    D. The $4f$ subshell has higher energy than the $5d$ subshell.

7. Which of the following is NOT isoelectronic with any of the noble gases?

    A. Ca^{2+}
    B. Br^-
    C. S^{2-}
    D. Mg^+

8. Which of the following is NOT a possible set of quantum number values for the nitrogen atom, in the order of principal quantum number, azimuthal quantum number, magnetic quantum number, and spin quantum number?

    A. $1, 0, 0, -\frac{1}{2}$
    B. $2, 1, +1, +\frac{1}{2}$
    C. $2, 0, 0, -\frac{1}{2}$
    D. $2, 1, +2, +\frac{1}{2}$

9. The electronic configuration [Ar] $3d^{10}\,4s^2$ $4p^2$ is that of:

    A. Ge.
    B. Zn.
    C. Se.
    D. Ar.

10. The electronic configuration of a given element has a $4d$ subshell. This CANNOT be the electronic configuration of:

    A. Os.
    B. Cu.
    C. Ag.
    D. Ra.

PERIODIC TABLE OF THE ELEMENTS

Main-Group Elements

Main-Group Elements

s BLOCK

p BLOCK

Transition Metals

d BLOCK

f BLOCK

Inner-Transition Metals

	IA																		VIIIA
		IIA		IIIB	IVB	VB	VIB	VIIB	VIIB			IB	IIB	IIIA	IVA	VA	VIA	VIIA	
1	1 H 1.0																			2 He 4.0
2	3 Li 6.9	4 Be 9.0													5 B 10.8	6 C 12.0	7 N 14.0	8 O 16.0	9 F 19.0	10 Ne 20.2
3	11 Na 23.0	12 Mg 24.3													13 Al 27.0	14 Si 28.1	15 P 31.0	16 S 32.1	17 Cl 35.5	18 Ar 39.9
4	19 K 39.1	20 Ca 40.1		21 Sc 45.0	22 Ti 47.9	23 V 50.9	24 Cr 52.0	25 Mn 54.9	26 Fe 55.8	27 Co 58.9	28 Ni 58.7	29 Cu 63.5	30 Zn 65.4	31 Ga 69.7	32 Ge 72.6	33 As 74.9	34 Se 79.0	35 Br 79.9	36 Kr 83.8
5	37 Rb 85.5	38 Sr 87.6		39 Y 88.9	40 Zr 91.2	41 Nb 92.9	42 Mo 95.9	43 Tc (98)	44 Ru 101.1	45 Rh 102.9	46 Pd 106.4	47 Ag 107.9	48 Cd 112.4	49 In 114.8	50 Sn 118.7	51 Sb 121.8	52 Te 127.6	53 I 126.9	54 Xe 131.3
6	55 Cs 132.9	56 Ba 137.3		57 La* 138.9	72 Hf 178.5	73 Ta 180.9	74 W 183.9	75 Re 186.2	76 Os 190.2	77 Ir 192.2	78 Pt 195.1	79 Au 197.0	80 Hg 200.6	81 Tl 204.4	82 Pb 207.2	83 Bi 209.0	84 Po (209)	85 At (210)	86 Rn (222)
7	87 Fr (223)	88 Ra 226.0		89 Ac** 227.0	104 Unq (261)	105 Unp (262)	106 Unh (263)	107 Uns (262)	108 Uno (265)	109 Une (267)									

*	58 Ce 140.1	59 Pr 140.9	60 Nd 144.2	61 Pm 145	62 Sm 150.4	63 Eu 152.0	64 Gd 157.3	65 Tb 158.9	66 Dy 162.5	67 Ho 164.9	68 Er 167.3	69 Tm 168.9	70 Yb 173.0	71 Lu 175.0
**	90 Th 232.0	91 Pa (231)	92 U (238.0)	93 Np (237)	94 Pu (244)	95 Am (243)	96 Cm (247)	97 Bk (247)	98 Cf (251)	99 Es (252)	100 Fm (257)	101 Md (258)	102 No (259)	103 Lr (260)

METAL

NONMETAL

METALLOID

PERIOD

4

Periodic Table

A. INTRODUCTION

The periodic table is a systematic representation of elements in a particular order. From the periodic table, we can gather a tremendous amount of information about the characteristics of an element. In this chapter, we will look at the trends and other important aspects of the periodic table.

> *The properties of elements are periodic functions of their atomic numbers.*

B. THE PERIODIC TABLE

The vertical columns of elements represented in the periodic table are called **groups**, and the horizontal rows are called **periods**. There are seven periods in the periodic table. The groups are usually designated by roman numerals followed by the letter A or B as shown in the periodic table.

The groups IA through VIIA are called the representative elements. These elements have either *s* or *p* orbital valence electrons. The last group in the periodic table is the noble gas group otherwise known as the zero group. The groups ranging from IB through VIII are called transition metals, and finally the metals from lanthanum through hafnium and metals from actinium onward are called the inner transition metals.

We will discuss some of these groups.

Group IA

The Group IA contains hydrogen, lithium, sodium, potassium, rubidium, cesium, and francium. The Group IA elements are also known as **alkali metals**, with the exception of hydrogen which is not a metal. Alkali metals are very reactive.

All of them react with water to form alkaline solutions.

$$2 \, Na \, (s) \quad + \quad 2 \, H_2O \quad \longrightarrow \quad H_2 \, (g) \quad + \quad 2 \, NaOH \, (aq)$$

The reactivity of alkali metals to water increases from top to bottom of the periodic table. For example, potassium reacts much more rapidly than lithium. They can also form oxides (For example, lithium can form oxides such as Li_2O.) and a variety of other compounds, since they are highly reactive. Alkali metals are good electrical and thermal conductors. All of them have one valence electron in their outer most shell, which is in the s orbital in the ground state. The Group IA elements usually exhibit an oxidation state of $+1$. They have a valence shell configuration of ns^1.

Group IIA

The Group IIA elements are called alkaline earth metals. The alkaline earth metals consist of beryllium, magnesium, calcium, strontium, barium, and radium. Their oxides are basic. They have a valence shell configuration of ns^2, and exhibit an oxidation state of $+2$. These elements are not as reactive as alkali metals.

Metallic character decreases from left to right along a period, and increases from top to bottom of a group.

Group IIIA

The Group IIIA elements consist of boron, aluminum, gallium, indium, and thallium. They have a valence shell configuration of ns^2np^1. They usually have oxidation states of $+1$ and $+3$.

Group IVA

The Group IVA is the carbon family. Carbon is the most versatile element, and thus it has its own separate subject. Yes, you guessed right – organic chemistry. Carbon can exist in many different forms by itself such as graphite and diamond. These forms of carbon are very contrasting in the sense that graphite is relatively soft whereas diamond is very hard. The Group IVA elements have a valence shell configuration of ns^2np^2.

The carbon family consists of carbon, silicon, germanium, tin, and lead. All these form oxides which look like CO_2 (e.g., SiO_2, PbO_2). They also form monoxides. As medical enthusiasts, you probably have heard of carbon monoxide, and its harmful effects. CO is a colorless and odorless gas, and it has even higher affinity for hemoglobin than oxygen in the red blood cells.

Group VA

The Group VA is the nitrogen family. The group consists of nitrogen, phosphorus, arsenic, antimony, and bismuth. Nitrogen is a diatomic, colorless, and odorless gas, and is not a very reactive element. The Group VA elements have a valence shell configuration of ns^2np^3.

Group VIA

The Group VIA elements are oxygen, sulfur, selenium, tellurium, and polonium. They have a valence shell configuration of ns^2np^4. Oxygen (O_2) is a diatomic gas, and it also exists in an allotropic form called ozone (O_3). Sulfur forms acidic oxides (e.g., SO_2, SO_3).

Group VIIA

The Group VIIA is more commonly known as the halogen family of elements. They are fluorine, chlorine, bromine, iodine, and astatine. They have an outer configuration of ns^2np^5. Halogens are highly reactive nonmetals, and form diatomic molecules. Halogens form hydrogen halides which are very acidic. These hydrogen halides can dissolve in water to form aqueous acids (e.g., HCl).

Fluorine	-	yellow gas
Chlorine	-	greenish-yellow gas
Bromine	-	reddish brown liquid
Iodine	-	dark colored solid

Group VIIIA

The elements of the Group VIIIA, otherwise known as noble gases are extremely unreactive. They are found as non-combined forms in nature. Because of this, they are called inert gases. They have an outer configuration of ns^2np^6.

C. PERIODIC TRENDS – ONE BY ONE

In this section, we will discuss the periodic properties and trends. It is very important from the MCAT point of view to understand the trends of the periodic table.

Atomic Size

As mentioned earlier, the periodic table is very versatile. The periodic table can give you the relative atomic sizes of atoms, and elemental ions. The two trends regarding the atomic radii are given below.

1. *From left to right along a period, the atomic radius decreases, as the atomic number increases.*
2. *Along a group from top to bottom, the atomic radius increases.*

One reason for such a trend is attributed to the principal quantum number. As the principal quantum number increases, the size of the orbital increases. Another reason for this trend is attributed to the nuclear shielding by the electron cloud that is between the nucleus and the outermost shells, thereby decreasing the influence of the effective nuclear charge.

Problem 4-1

Arrange the following elements in terms of increasing atomic radius:

Mg, K, Cl, Ba

A) Cl, Mg, K, Cs
B) Cl, K, Mg, Cs
C) Cs, K, Mg, Cl
D) Mg, K, Cl, Ba

The answer is choice A. Mg and Cl are in the same period (Period 3). But Cl is in Group VIIA and Mg is in Group IIA. So Mg is larger than Cl. The next is K which is in period 4, and thus bigger than both Mg and Cl. Finally, Cs which is in period 6 has the largest atomic radius. So in the increasing order of atomic size is: Cl<Mg<K<Cs.

Ionic Radius

Often you will get questions on arranging ions and atoms according to their sizes. Some of the trends that you should keep in mind regarding ionic radii are listed below:

1. *Negatively charged ions have bigger ionic radii than the corresponding neutral atoms.*
2. *Positively charged ions have smaller ionic radii than the corresponding neutral atoms.*

Ionization Energy (IE)

Ionization energy is the minimum amount of energy required to remove an electron from an atom. The amount of energy required to remove the first electron is called the first ionization energy (IE_1). The second ionization energy (IE_2) refers to the amount of energy required to remove the second electron. The second ionization energy is always greater than the first ionization energy, since it is more difficult to remove a second electron from an already positive ion, compared to the removal from an electrically neutral atom. The third ionization energy is greater than the second ionization energy, and so on.

First IE < Second IE < Third IE < Fourth IE < Fifth IE < Sixth IE < . . .

The general trend of ionization energy is summarized as follows:

1. *Generally, along a period from left to right, the ionization energy increases with increasing atomic number.*
2. *The ionization energy decreases from top to bottom along a group as the atomic size increases.*

Electron Affinity

Electron affinity is the change in amount (energy either released or absorbed) of energy for the process of adding an electron to an atom (neutral) in its gaseous state, resulting in an ion of −1 charge. The general trend of electron affinity is given below:

The electron affinity increases or in other words, the negativeness of the electron affinity increases from left to right along a period.

Electronegativity

The relative tendency of an atom to attract the bonding electrons to itself is called **electronegativity**. The popularly used electronegativity scale is based on a system called Pauling's scale, according to which fluorine (the most electronegative element) has an electronegativity value of 4.0. Nonmetals are the most electronegative elements. The general trend of the electronegativity is as follows:

1. *Generally, the electronegativity increases from left to right along a period.*
2. *The electronegativity decreases down a group from top to bottom.*

CHAPTER 4 PRACTICE QUESTIONS

1. Sulfur belongs to the classification of elements called the:

    A. inner transition elements.
    B. representative elements.
    C. transition elements.
    D. alkali metals.

2. Which of the following is an alkaline earth metal?

    A. Na
    B. Mn
    C. Sr
    D. Fe

3. Which of the following elements has the lowest electronegativity?

    A. Rb
    B. F
    C. S
    D. Ba

4. Which of the following belongs to the f block in the periodic table?

    A. Sc
    B. U
    C. Si
    D. Pd

5. Which of the following is NOT diatomic?

    A. Oxygen
    B. Nitrogen
    C. Neon
    D. Chlorine

6. Choose the atom that has the biggest atomic radius.

    A. Al
    B. Cl
    C. Ge
    D. Rb

7. Which of the following represents the correct arrangement of atoms according to their atomic radii?

    A. F < B < Ca < Sr
    B. B < F < Sr < Ca
    C. Sr < Ca < B < F
    D. F < B < Ca < Sr

8. Choose the true statement regarding the periodic trends.

    A. Along a period from left to right, atomic radius increases.
    B. Along a period from left to right, ionization energy decreases.
    C. Electronegativity of elements increases from right to left along a period.
    D. None of the above.

9. Which of the following is the most acidic?

    A. HF
    B. HBr
    C. HCl
    D. HI

10. The outer electronic configuration $ns^2\ np^2$ belongs to which of the following groups?

    A. II A
    B. IV A
    C. IV B
    D. II B

5

Chemical Bonding

A. INTRODUCTION

MCAT students are expected to know the electronic structures of atoms and apply this knowledge to the formation of bonds and other related aspects. This chapter is devoted to the review of chemical bonding and related aspects such as ionic character and polarity.

What are Chemical Bonds?

Chemical bonds are strong attractive forces that enable atoms or groups of atoms to hold together. The two major categories of chemical bonds are ionic and covalent bonds. In this chapter, we will discuss ionic bonds, covalent bonds, and other atomic and molecular interactions.

B. IONIC BOND

The major force behind the formation of an **ionic bond** is the electrostatic attractive force that exists between negative and positive ions. It is formed by the transfer of one or more electrons from one atom to another. The atom that donates the electrons becomes positive (cation), and the counterpart atom that receives those electrons becomes negative (anion). The attractive force between two oppositely charged ions or species holds the atoms together in an ionic bond.

In an ionic compound, any ion can attract not only the pairing ion or group, but it can also attract neighboring oppositely charged ions, resulting in strong ionic solids.

Now let us take a look at an example to understand this better. The sodium fluoride (NaF) molecule is a result of ionic bond formation between sodium and fluoride ions. Together with this, you should also try to understand Lewis dot structures. Lewis structure will be discussed in detail later in this chapter.

Lewis Electron-Dot Formulas: *Lewis electron-dot formulas are diagrammatic representations of the atoms involved and their valence electrons. The valence electrons are usually represented as dots around the elemental symbol.*

Formation of the Ionic Bond in NaF

THE ELECTRONIC CONFIGURATION OF SODIUM AND FLUORINE

$$Na \quad - \quad 1s^2 2s^2 2p^6 3s^1$$

$$F \quad - \quad 1s^2 2s^2 2p^5$$

In the formation of the ionic bond, the sodium atom loses the electron from its $3s$ subshell, thereby becoming Na^+.

$$Na \longrightarrow Na^+ + e^-$$

On the other hand, the fluorine atom takes the electron that is being lost from the sodium atom to form a (F^-) fluoride ion.

$$F + e^- \longrightarrow F^-$$

These resulting ions are oppositely charged and therefore have electrostatic attractive forces between them, resulting in the formation of the ionic bond.

The attractive energy in an ionic bond can be expressed in terms of Coulombic energy, according to Coulomb's law. Imagine this by considering that the ions are spherical and are separated by particular distances. The attractive energy can be expressed as follows:

$$Energy,\ E \quad = \quad \frac{k\, q_1 q_2}{r}$$

Here, k ($= 9 \times 10^9$ J.m/C^2) is a constant, q_1 and q_2 are the charges, and r is the distance between the nuclei of the two ionic entities involved in the bonding.

C. COVALENT BOND

A **covalent bond** is formed as a result of the sharing of a pair of electrons between atoms. Covalent bonds result when the difference in electronegativities between the bonding atoms is very small. Though the intramolecular bonds of covalent compounds are significant, the intermolecular forces are relatively weak. Because of this, covalent compounds have relatively lower boiling and melting points when compared to ionic compounds.

Covalent Bond Formation

Figure 5-1

In this section, we will look at the covalent bond formation in the hydrogen molecule (H_2). The hydrogen molecule is diatomic. The hydrogen atom has an electronic configuration of $1s^1$. The formation can be expressed in terms of Lewis formula as follows:

$$H\bullet \ + \ \bullet H \longrightarrow H \colon H \qquad or \qquad H\!\!-\!\!-\!\!H$$

After the bond is formed, the electrons are shared by both hydrogen atoms, as expected in a covalent bond. This $1s$ overlap makes the configuration of hydrogen atom the same as that of helium ($1s^2$). Another aspect that you should understand is that the total potential energy (see Figure 5-1) of the hydrogen molecule is lower than that of the hydrogen atoms in their separate forms. The potential energy diagram of hydrogen molecule formation should make this clear.

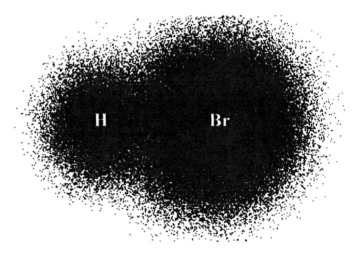

Figure 5-2

The distribution of bonded electrons in the HBr molecule is shown above (Figure 5-2). In this bond formation, hydrogen shares its electron with bromine, whereas bromine gives the one electron that is needed for hydrogen to complete its shell. Bromine atom has 7 electrons in its outermost shell, and it requires 1 more to complete its octet. Octet is the state in which an atom has 8 electrons in its outermost shell. Now, since hydrogen has 2 electrons, and bromine has eight electrons in its valence shell, they are both satisfied in terms of their stability, the stability being facilitated by the formation of the covalent bond.

D. COORDINATE COVALENT BOND

In **coordinate covalent bonds**, the same aspect of the sharing of electrons exists, just as in simple covalent bonds, but the difference is that both shared electrons are supplied by the same atom.

Coordinate covalent bond is formed when the two electrons that are shared in the formation of the bond are donated by one group or atom involved in the bond.

An example of coordinate covalent bond is seen in the formation of ammonium ion (NH_4^+).

$$H^+ \quad + \quad \overset{\overset{\textstyle H}{\bullet\bullet}}{\underset{\underset{\textstyle H}{\bullet\bullet}}{:N:}} H \quad \longrightarrow \quad \left[\overset{\overset{\textstyle H}{\bullet\bullet}}{\underset{\underset{\textstyle H}{\bullet\bullet}}{H:N:}} H\right]^+$$

Proton   Ammonia   Ammonium ion

Ammonium ion can also be represented as

$$\left[\begin{array}{c} H \\ | \\ H—N—H \\ | \\ H \end{array}\right]^+$$

E. POLAR AND NONPOLAR COVALENT BONDS

When two atoms combine, just like in the formation of a hydrogen molecule, the atoms are one and the same and they have the same electronegativity. But, if the two atoms that are combined via covalent bond are different, then there is unequal sharing of electrons due to the electronegativity difference between those atoms. Such a bond is called a **polar covalent bond**. The former case (H_2 molecule) is an example of a nonpolar covalent compound. In the HBr molecule, the bonding electrons will be more attracted to the more electronegative of the two atoms, namely bromine. So the bonding electrons are likely to spend more time closer to the more electronegative atom or group. Hence, this bond is polar.

$$\overset{\delta^+ \quad\quad \delta^-}{H\text{——}Br}$$

The delta$^+$ (δ^+) indicates the partial positive charge of the hydrogen atom, and delta$^-$(δ^-) indicates the partial negative charge of the bromine atom. Small and equal charges being separated by a small distance constitute a dipole. The polarity is quantitatively represented in terms of dipole moment, which is the charge times the distance between the charges. Now that you know dipole moment, let's learn how to represent this.

$$\overset{\delta^+ \quad\quad \delta^-}{H\text{——}Br}$$ Here the net dipole moment is as indicated by the arrow.

$$\vdash\!\longrightarrow$$

When there are more than two dipoles, the net effect is the vector sum of all individual dipoles in the molecule. For example, in carbon dioxide (CO_2) the net dipole moment is as shown below.

Since the dipoles are equal and opposite, the vectors of the dipoles cancel out.

F. THE LEWIS ELECTRON-DOT FORMULAS

Lewis Electron-Dot Formulas: Lewis electron-dot formulas are diagrammatic representations of the atoms involved and their valence electrons. The valence electrons are usually represented as dots around the elemental symbol. It is a two-dimensional way of representing the structural formula, showing the bonding electrons and the lone electrons that are in the valence shells.

Writing Lewis Formulas

The objective of this section is to become comfortable with writing Lewis structural formulas. We can only predict the Lewis structures of simple molecules. Other complex structures require complicated analysis and predictions based on experimental data.

1. First, determine the main structural make up of the molecule, such as guessing which atom will be the central atom of the molecule. The central atom of the molecule is usually the atom with the lowest electronegativity.
2. Next, determine the total number of valence (outermost) electrons.
3. Draw the basic skeletal structure of the molecule or ion.
4. Next, determine the distribution of those valence electrons so as to complete the octet of the atoms that are around or bonded to the central atom.
5. The remaining electrons are to be distributed in pairs around the central atom.
6. Sometimes you might find that the central atom is not reaching the octet level even at this point. The most likely reason is that there might be a need of a double bond or a triple bond.

Let's go through an example. Before looking at the solution of the example shown below, determine the Lewis structure on your own.

Example 5-1

Write the Lewis dot formula of carbonate ion $(CO_3)^{2-}$.

Solution:

Since carbon is the least electronegative, it is the most likely atom to be in the center. With this information, we can draw the carbonate ion as indicated below.

$$\left[\begin{array}{ccc} & O & \\ O & C & O \end{array} \right]^{2-}$$

Next, calculate the number of valence electrons. Carbon has 4 electrons, whereas oxygen has 6 electrons each, and do not forget the net charge of –2, which accounts for two more electrons. This tallies to a total of 24 electrons. We can set up all these valence electrons around individual atoms in the structure drawn so far, as shown below:

$$:O:$$
$$:O : C : O:$$

Now that we have set all the valence electrons, we are done, right? No! Watch out for the carbon. The octet of carbon is not satisfied, and thus carbon will not be very stable with its valency at this point. Since there are no more electrons to spare, we have to move one of the pairs of electrons from an oxygen atom, which results in 1 double bond and 2 single bonds. The completed Lewis structure of the carbonate ion should look as follows:

G. RESONANCE

Resonance is an important concept in chemistry. Though we represent definite Lewis structures of molecules, in actuality the electrons are not localized. They are shared and delocalized by atoms in such a way as to be in the most stable electron distribution. This is called **resonance**.

Acetate ion

The actual form of these resonance structures is an average of all the possible resonance forms of the group or molecule.

H. FORMAL CHARGE

The concept of **formal charge** is based on the assumption that the electrons involved in the bonds are equally shared between the involved atoms. As you have already seen, this is not exactly the case. But for simplicity and from an analytical point of view, we assume that the electrons are equally distributed.

> *Formal charge of the atoms is the charge of those atoms in a formula, under the assumption that the electrons in the bonds are equally distributed between the atoms that contain the bond.*

$$\text{Formal charge} = \text{Group number of the atom of interest} - \text{Number of bonds} - \text{Number of unshared electrons}$$

There are different ways to find formal charges. One way is mentioned here. You can either choose to do it this way, or whichever way you are comfortable with.

Example 5-2

Find the formal charges of all the atoms in thionyl chloride (SOCl$_2$).

Solution:

The Lewis structure of thionyl chloride is written below:

$$:\overset{\bullet\bullet}{\underset{}{O}}:$$
$$:\overset{\bullet\bullet}{\underset{\bullet\bullet}{Cl}}:\overset{\bullet\bullet}{\underset{\bullet\bullet}{S}}:\overset{\bullet\bullet}{\underset{\bullet\bullet}{Cl}}:$$

Using the formal charge formula, it is just a matter of plugging in the numbers. Both oxygen and sulfur belong to Group VI. Chlorine belongs to Group VII. Sulfur has 3 bonds and 2 unshared electrons. Oxygen has 1 bond and 6 unshared electrons. Chlorine has 1 bond and 6 unshared electrons.

$$\begin{array}{c}\text{Formal} \\ \text{charge}\end{array} = \begin{array}{c}\text{Group number} \\ \text{of the atom of interest}\end{array} - \text{Number of bonds} - \begin{array}{c}\text{Number of} \\ \text{unshared electrons}\end{array}$$

The formal charge of sulfur = 6 − 3 − 2 = +1
The formal charge of oxygen = 6 − 1 − 6 = −1
The formal charge of chlorine = 7 − 1 − 6 = 0

Notice that the net charge of the molecule is zero, as expected, since it is a molecule and not an ion.

Problem 5-1

Which of the following represents the formal charge of sulfur in sulfuric acid (H$_2$SO$_4$)?

A) −1
B) +1
C) −2
D) +2

Solution:

If you draw the structure, you'll see that sulfur is the central atom, and has 2 single bonds to the 2 oxygen atoms, and 2 single bonds to the OH groups. The answer is +2.

I. BOND LENGTH AND BOND ENERGY

Bond length is the distance between the nuclei of the atoms that are bonded together. **Bond energy** is the amount of energy required to pull the atoms involved in the bond away from each other. Bond order is the number of bonds (covalent) that exist between the two bonded atoms. The bond length and bond order are inversely proportional. Hence, as the bond order increases, the bond length decreases and the bond energy increases.

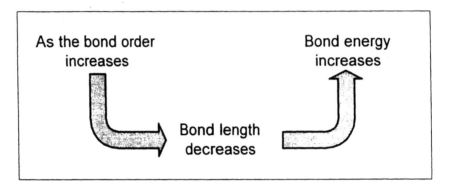

Problem 5-2

Which of the following will have the highest bond energy?

A) A carbon-carbon single bond
B) A carbon-carbon double bond
C) A carbon-carbon triple bond
D) A carbon-hydrogen bond

Solution:

The bond order of a triple bond is 3. Carbon-carbon single bond and carbon-hydrogen bond have bond orders of 1. This eliminates choices A and D. The bond order of carbon-carbon double bond is 2. The one with the highest bond order will have the highest bond energy. So the answer is choice C.

J. MOLECULAR GEOMETRY

In this section, we will study the valence shell electron pair repulsion theory and the basis for predicting the shapes of some structures.

Valence Shell Electron Pair Repulsion Theory

Valence shell electron pair repulsion theory (VSEPR) can be used to predict the shapes of molecules. According to this theory, the geometry of a molecule is such that the valence-electron pairs of the central atom are kept farthest apart to minimize the electron repulsions. Again, you have to view molecules in terms of Lewis structure so that the shape of the molecules can be predicted with the VSEPR theory.

Molecular geometry of a molecule is the directional orientation of the bonded pairs around the central atom, excluding the unshared electron pairs.

Let's look at the practical significance of this theory through some examples.

Example 5-3

Predict the molecular geometry of the CO_2 molecule.

Solution:

Carbon, obviously the central atom, has four electrons in its valence shell. In order to complete the octet, carbon requires four more electrons or two pairs of electrons. Oxygen atom has six electrons in its valence shell. In order to complete its octet, each oxygen atom requires two electrons or one pair of electrons. The Lewis structure of CO_2 should look like the figure shown below. Note that the valence electrons of the carbon atom are denoted by asterisks (*) and that of the oxygen are denoted by dots.

$$\ddot{\text{O}}\text{:}\ddagger\text{C}\ddagger\text{:}\ddot{\text{O}}\text{:}$$

The molecule keeps this linear shape, so that the electrons are placed far apart as predicted by the VSEPR theory. Also notice that the carbon-oxygen bonds are double bonds. Hence the CO_2 molecule is linear in shape.

Example 5-4

Predict the shape of the BeF_2 molecule.

Solution:

Beryllium has two electrons in its outer most shell. In this case, there is an exception to the octet rule, because in the formation of the molecule, only two pairs (four electrons) are present in the valence shell of beryllium. Each fluorine atom requires one electron to attain the complete octet. Take a look at the structure shown below. Again for clarity, beryllium electrons are denoted by asterisks and fluorine electrons are denoted by dots.

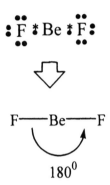

Example 5-5

Predict the shape of the water (H_2O) molecule.

Solution:

When dealing with bond formation with the possibility of existence of lone pairs, we have to take that into consideration. You will see that in this example. The oxygen atom has six valence electrons, and the hydrogen atom has one valence electron. So in the structural formation, there are two lone pairs in the central oxygen atom. How do you think this will change the shape of the molecule? Well, because of the lone pairs, the molecule will be bent, rather than linear. The structure is shown below.

Angular, or bent shape of the water molecule

Problem 5-3

Predict the geometry of the following molecules.

A) $BeCl_2$
B) NH_3
C) $SiCl_4$

D) BF_3

E) CH_4

Answers:

A) linear

B) trigonal pyramidal

C) tetrahedral

D) trigonal planar

E) tetrahedral

Table 5-1
SOME COMMON GEOMETRIES AND THEIR CHARACTERISTICS

BONDING ELECTRON PAIRS	LONE PAIRS	GEOMETRY
2	NONE	LINEAR
3	NONE	TRIGONAL PLANAR
2	1	BENT
4	NONE	TETRAHEDRAL
3	1	TRIGONAL PYRAMIDAL
5	NONE	TRIGONAL BIPYRAMIDAL
4	1	SEESAW SHAPED
3	2	T-SHAPED
6	NONE	OCTAHEDRAL

CHAPTER 5 PRACTICE QUESTIONS

1. Which of the following best represents the Lewis structure of SO_3^{-2}?

    A.

    B.

    C.

    D.

2. Which of the following has a net dipole moment of zero?

    A. H_2O
    B. HCl
    C. CO
    D. CH_4

3. The bond between nitrogen and oxygen in NO_2 is most likely:

    A. an ionic bond.
    B. a covalent bond.
    C. a hydrogen bond.
    D. a dipole-dipole interaction.

4. Ammonia (NH_3) can bond with boron trifluoride (BF_3). For the bond formation, the electrons are most likely supplied by:

    A. nitrogen.
    B. boron.
    C. both boron and nitrogen because the bond formed is covalent.
    D. hydrogen.

5. Which of the following has the highest dipole moment?

    A. HF
    B. CCl_4
    C. HBr
    D. CO_2

6. The molecular geometry of BCl_3 is:

    A. linear.
    B. trigonal planar.
    C. tetrahedral.
    D. trigonal bipyramidal.

7. CCl_4 molecule is:

    A. trigonal planar.
    B. linear.
    C. octahedral.
    D. tetrahedral.

8. Which of the following best describes the geometry of nitrate (NO_3^-)?

    A. Trigonal planar
    B. Trigonal bipyramidal
    C. Tetrahedral
    D. Angular

9. What is the molecular geometry of SF_6?

    A. Hexagonal
    B. Tetrahedral
    C. Octahedral
    D. Trigonal planar

10. CH_4 and SiF_4 are examples of tetrahedral geometry. Which of the following are true regarding these two molecules?

    I.   The carbon-hydrogen bonds are dipoles
    II. The silicon-fluorine bonds are dipoles
    III. Methane is nonpolar
    IV. SiF_4 has zero dipole moment

    A. I & II only
    B. II only
    C. II & III only
    D. I, II, III & IV

11. Which of the following types of bonds has the least electronegativity difference between the bonding atoms?

    A. Ionic bond
    B. Polar covalent bond
    C. Nonpolar covalent bond
    D. Cannot be predicted without the actual electronegativity data.

12. Which of the following choices represents the vectors of bond dipoles of the indicated (indicated by the arrows) bonds of the compounds A & B, respectively?

Compound A

Compound B

13. Choose the answer which best denotes the electronic orientation (electronic geometry) of the water molecule.

    A. Angular
    B. Bent
    C. Trigonal planar
    D. Tetrahedral

6

Gases

A. INTRODUCTION

In this chapter, we will review the essential aspects of gases, and the terms that are commonly associated with them. This chapter will also discuss the various laws such as Charles' law, Boyle's law, and ideal gas law. Finally, the kinetic law of gases will be explored.

B. GASES – AN OVERVIEW

Gases are unique when compared to liquids and solids. Gases can be compressed into smaller volumes, and they can be mixed extensively. They have relatively very low densities. Ideally, a gas exerts pressure on all sides of the container it occupies in a uniform manner. These are some of the properties of gases. Let's explore these ideas in detail.

Standard Temperature and Pressure

It is very important to understand the general aspects of gas pressure, its measurements, and calibrations. **Pressure** is force exerted over unit area. The unit of pressure is pascal (Pa) which is equivalent to $kg/(m.s^2)$. In chemistry, we usually use a mercury-based barometer to measure the pressure. The unit is millimeter of mercury (mmHg). This is the same as the unit torr. Another unit commonly used to denote pressure is atmosphere (atm). You should be able to convert these units back and forth as required.

$$1 \text{ atm} = 760 \text{ mmHg } = 760 \text{ torr}$$

$$1 \text{ atm} = 1.01 \times 10^5 \text{ Pa}$$

Gases can be compressed or expanded by adjusting the temperature and other conditions that prevail. In order to standardize the quantities of gases measured and conveyed, arbitrary reference conditions called standard temperature and pressure (STP) have been chosen and internationally accepted. The specific values of temperature and pressure at STP are $0°$ C (273 K) and 1 atm (760 mmHg).

STANDARD TEMPERATURE AND PRESSURE (STP)			
Temperature	-	$0°$ C or	273 K
Pressure	-	1 atm or	760 mmHg

You should know what STP is, because in many questions and passages, the actual temperature and pressure situations will not be explicit. Rather, they will say, for example, that the reaction was undertaken at standard temperature and pressure. This means, you have to automatically know that they are talking about the temperatures corresponding to STP reference conditions, which you already know.

Molar Volume

Ideally, one mole of gas at STP occupies a volume of 22.4 L. This is known as **molar volume**. We should bear in mind the fact that this is under standard conditions. Do the example below on your own, before you look at the solution.

Example 6-1

Calculate the number of moles of oxygen at STP present in a volume of 78.75 L.

Solution:

One mole of gas occupies a volume of 22.4 L. To get the number of moles, you have to divide 78.75 L by 22.4 L/mol.

$$\text{Number of moles of oxygen } = 78.75 \text{ L} \times \frac{1 \text{ mol of O}_2}{22.4 \text{ L}} = 3.5 \text{ moles}$$

C. GAS LAWS

Gases behave ideally under reasonably high temperatures and low pressures. The gas laws are helpful in quantitatively relating pressure, volume, temperature, and molar units.

Boyle's Law

According to Boyle's law, the volume of a fixed amount of gas is inversely proportional to the pressure, provided that the temperature is kept constant. A simple and good example with biological significance is the way we take air into our lungs. The way we breathe can be summarized as follows. As the respiratory centers signal, during inspiration the diaphragm contracts resulting in an increase in the thoracic volume, which in turn translates into an increase in the lung volume. This increase in lung volume results in a decrease in pressure. This decrease in pressure inside the lung results in the rushing of air into the lung from the outside – inspiration. The exact opposite conditions result in expiration. The point is that at constant temperature, the volume of a gaseous sample is inversely proportional to its pressure.

$$\text{Volume} \quad \propto \quad \frac{1}{\text{Pressure}}$$

This can be represented mathematically as shown below:

$$\text{BOYLE'S LAW} \qquad V \quad \propto \quad \frac{1}{P} \qquad \text{or} \qquad PV \ = \ k \ \text{(Constant)}$$

Example 6-2

200 ml of a gas is present in a cylinder at a pressure of 760 torr. If the gas is compressed by using a piston to a pressure of 950 torr, calculate the final volume occupied by the gas. (Assume the temperature to be constant)

Solution:

This problem specifically tests your knowledge of Boyle's law. We know that PV is a constant, provided that the temperature is kept constant. Since the temperature is constant, we can readily apply Boyle's law. We can equate the initial and final stages of the system. P_1 and V_1 represent the initial pressure and volume respectively. P_2 and V_2 represent, the final pressure and volume respectively.

$$P_1 V_1 = P_2 V_2$$

Now it is just a matter of solving for V_2 *(final volume)*.

$$V_2 = V_1 \left(\frac{P_1}{P_2} \right) = 200 \text{ ml} \left(\frac{760 \text{ torr}}{950 \text{ torr}} \right) = 160 \text{ ml}$$

Charles' Law

In 1787, Jacques Charles showed that gas expands to occupy a larger volume as the temperature increases. Volume can be plotted against the temperature as shown below:

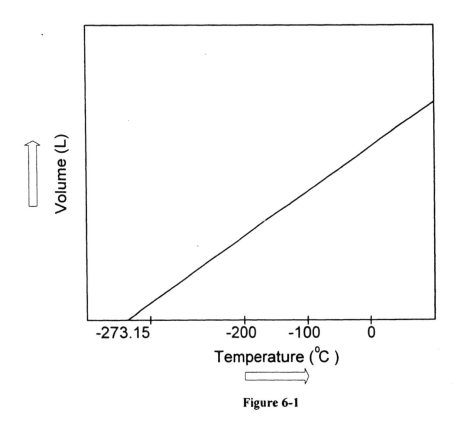

Figure 6-1

When the temperature is increased, the volume increases. Charles found that the volume of a gas is directly proportional to its absolute temperature, provided that the pressure is kept constant. So the volume and temperature have a linear relationship as represented by the graph. Charles's law can be mathematically expressed as follows:

CHARLES' LAW

Volume $\propto$ Temperature

$$V \propto T$$

$$V = kT \qquad \text{or} \qquad \frac{V}{T} = k \text{ (constant)},$$

where k represents the proportionality constant.

The volume-temperature graph shows that at zero volume, the corresponding temperature value is $-273.15°$ C. This means that at $-273.15°$ C, the volume occupied by the gas is zero. This temperature is unique, and scientists so far have not been able to devise a way to lower the temperature to $-273.15°$ C.

Combined Gas Law

The gas laws (Charles' and Boyle's law) can be combined to form the combined gas law. The resulting law can be represented mathematically as shown below:

COMBINED GAS LAW $\qquad \dfrac{P_1 V_1}{T_1} = \dfrac{P_2 V_2}{T_2} = k \text{ (constant)}$

This relationship can be used to do a variety of calculations involving gases, since it relates pressure, volume, and temperature.

The Ideal Gas Law

This is an extension of the combined gas law. In the combined gas law, we saw the relationship between pressure, volume, and temperature. The ideal gas law can be expressed mathematically as follows:

THE IDEAL GAS LAW $\qquad PV = nRT$

P - pressure
V - volume
n - number of moles
R - molar gas constant
T - temperature

Here, R (molar gas constant) has values 0.082 L.atm/(K.mol), or 8.31 J/(K.mol), and of course the difference in values is due to the fact that the gas constant is expressed here in two different units.

D. KINETIC THEORY OF GASES

The kinetic theory of gases can be explored in terms of the following assumptions. The theory tries to answer the questions regarding the various properties of gases. It also gives the relationship between the kinetic energy of the molecules and the absolute temperature. The important points in kinetic theory of gases are listed below:

Ideal gas molecules travel randomly in straight lines at different speeds.

1. A gas consists of small particles (sizes are considered relatively negligible) known as molecules, which are separated widely apart and thus the gas container is mostly empty.
2. The molecules are in a state of continuous random motion, and colliding against each other and also against the sides of the container, and furthermore the collisions are elastic.
3. These collisions result in the pressure of the gas.
4. The molecules are expected to travel in straight lines at different speeds in all directions.
5. The forces (attractive or repulsive) between the molecules are negligible.
6. The average kinetic energy of the molecules is proportional to the temperature.

Some Aspects Related to Kinetic Theory

The main aspect of kinetic theory is that the molecules in a gas are in a state of continuous random motion. The speed of molecules depends on the temperature, and can have a range of values. Maxwell's distribution curve is perfect to analyze this fact. In the Maxwell's distribution curve, the relative number of molecules are plotted against the molecular speed on the x-axis. Take a look at the curve in Figure 6-2.

Note that the speed corresponding to the maximum number of molecules is called the **most probable speed**. This is always smaller than the **average speed**, which is in turn smaller than the **root-mean-square speed** (rms speed).

The formula for root-mean-square speed is given below:

$$\text{Root-mean-square speed} = \sqrt{\frac{3\,RT}{M}}$$

Here, R is the gas constant, T is the absolute temperature, and M is the molar mass of the gas.

MAXWELL'S DISTRIBUTION CURVE

Figure 6-2

E. PARTIAL PRESSURE AND MOLE FRACTION

Let's consider a container which has different gases in it. According to the Dalton's law of partial pressures, the partial pressures of the gases present in a gaseous mixture can be added to get the net total pressure of the mixture. But, what is partial pressure? Partial pressure is the pressure exerted by a particular gas in a mixture of gases. Now that you know what partial pressure is, take a look at the boxed information which summarizes the whole idea of Dalton's law of partial pressures.

Dalton's Law of Partial Pressures

$$P_{total} = P_A + P_B + P_C + P_D + \ldots \text{ (at constant volume \& temperature)}$$

P_{total} – *Total pressure*

P_A, P_B, P_C, P_D, ... *represent the partial pressures of gases A, B, C, D, and so on.*

Another concept you have to understand is mole fraction. The **mole fraction** of a gas is the fraction or ratio of moles of that particular gas against the total number of moles of gases present in the mixture. Mole fraction is defined as follows:

$$\text{Mole fraction} = \frac{\text{Number of moles of gas A}}{\text{Total number of moles of gases in the mixture}} = \frac{n_A}{n_{Total}}$$

Example 6-3

A 1 liter flask contains 0.4 mol of helium and 1.2 moles of hydrogen gas. Find the mole fractions and partial pressures of both gases, if the total pressure of the mixture is 790 mmHg.

Solution:

The total number of moles of gases present in the container is $0.4 + 1.2 = 1.6$ moles

$$\text{The mole fraction of helium} = \frac{0.4}{1.6} = 0.25$$

$$\text{The mole fraction of hydrogen} = \frac{1.2}{1.6} = 0.75$$

Notice that the sum of the mole fractions is always one. If it is not, you probably made an error somewhere in your calculation. Here,

$$0.25 + 0.75 = 1.0$$

Next, we have to find the partial pressures of the gases. We know that the partial pressures of the gases should add up to get the total pressure of the gases. Now that we know the total pressure and the mole fractions, we can calculate the partial pressures of helium and hydrogen.

Partial pressure of gas A = mole fraction of gas A × total pressure

Partial pressure of helium = 0.25 × 790 mmHg = 197.5 mmHg

Partial pressure of hydrogen = 0.75 × 790 mmHg = 592.5 mmHg

F. GRAHAM'S LAW

Diffusion of gases can be described as the process by which a gas spreads to occupy the available and accessible space, thereby creating a uniform pressure throughout the space the gas occupies. A gas having a higher partial pressure will travel or diffuse toward regions of gases having a lower partial pressure, until an equilibrium is reached. To analyze the diffusion of gases, it is much simpler to think in terms of effusion. The difference between diffusion and effusion is that diffusion is the movement of gas through the entire volume of the container, whereas effusion is the movement of gas through a tiny hole of the container.

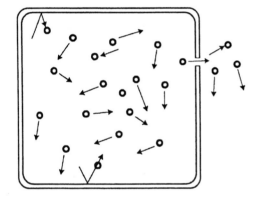

Figure 6-3
The figure depicts the effusion of gas molecules through a small hole in the container.

According to Graham's law of effusion, the effusion rate of a gas is inversely related to the square root of the molecular weight of the gas. This is true provided that we have the same pressure and temperature conditions. Graham's law can be expressed as shown below:

Graham's law of effusion
Effusion rate of gas molecules $\propto \dfrac{1}{\sqrt{\text{molecular weight}}}$

Graham's law can also be applied to diffusion.

Example 6-4

Calculate the ratio of effusion of the gases oxygen and hydrogen. Assume that the two gases are in the same container having a tiny hole in it.

Solution:

First, we have to consider the fact that according to Graham's law, the rate of effusion is inversely proportional to the square of molecular weight of the gas, which is effused. This can be represented as follows. Keep in mind that both gases are diatomic.

$$\frac{\text{Rate of effusion of } H_2}{\text{Rate of effusion of } O_2} = \sqrt{\frac{32}{2}} = \frac{4}{1} = 4$$

So the ratio of the rates of effusion of hydrogen and oxygen is 4 : 1.

We should think about the implications of this ratio. This means that the hydrogen molecules will effuse four times faster than the oxygen molecules.

CHAPTER 6 PRACTICE QUESTIONS

1. Consider the reaction between nitric oxide and oxygen to form nitrogen dioxide. If 4 liters of nitrogen dioxide were formed, how many liters of nitric oxide and oxygen must have reacted?

    A. 2 L of NO & 1 L of O_2
    B. 2 L of NO & 2 L of O_2
    C. 4 L of NO & 2 L of O_2
    D. 2 L of NO & 4 L of O_2

2. At a particular temperature and pressure, 1 mol of gas M occupies 45 liters. If the density of gas M at the same temperature and pressure is 1.8 g/L, the molecular weight of gas M is:

    A. 25 g/mol.
    B. 81 g/mol.
    C. 40.5 g/mol.
    D. 4 g/mol.

3. A certain gas behaves ideally at STP. If the density of the gas is 1.4 g/L, what is the most likely identity of this gas? (The gas is diatomic.)

    A. SO_2
    B. N_2
    C. O_2
    D. F_2

4. A hypothetical reaction R occurs only at elevated pressures. It was noted that the optimum pressure required for the reaction was 1330 mmHg. This value is roughly equal to: (1 atm = 101.3 kPa)

    A. 1.3×10^{-2} Pa.
    B. 1.8×10^5 Pa.
    C. 1.35×10^8 Pa.
    D. 1.8×10^2 Pa.

5. -27^0 C is the same as:

    A. 300 K.
    B. 246 K.
    C. 270 K.
    D. 127 K.

6. The volume occupied by 11.5 g of carbon dioxide at STP is approximately equal to:

    A. 5.9 L.
    B. 22.5 L.
    C. 86 L.
    D. 259 L.

Questions 7-13 are based on the following passage.

Passage 1

The behavior of gases can be predicted to a large extent on the basis of various laws. Gases are expressed mainly in terms of pressure, volume, and temperature. Many gases obey the ideal gas laws and those gases are called ideal gases. If we are not doing precision experiments, we can normally ignore the slight deviations that occur under normal conditions. Nevertheless, we cannot completely ignore the deviation factors.

According to Boyle's law, the pressure is inversely proportional to the volume at a constant temperature. Charles' law states that the volume is directly proportional to the temperature at a constant pressure. Combining these laws and Avogadro's law gives the combined gas law.

$$PV = nRT$$
(The ideal gas law)

Not all gases behave ideally. There are often deviations from the ideal behavior. At low temperatures, gases often behave differently apart from what is described by kinetic-molecular theory of gases. Considering these correction factors, the modified gas equation is:

$$\left(P + \frac{n^2 a}{V^2}\right)(V - nb) = nRT$$

The correction constants or Vander Waal constants, a and b, of gases are experimentally found. The Van der Waal constants of some gases are given in Table 1.

Table 1

Gas	a (L².atm/mol²)	b (L/mol)
Carbon monoxide	1.470	0.039
Hydrogen	0.245	0.026
Chlorine	6.340	0.054
Fluorine	1.170	0.029
Hydrogen sulfide	4.540	0.043
Nitrogen	1.380	0.039
Carbon dioxide	3.660	0.043
Argon	1.360	0.032
Propane	9.390	0.091

7. Under which of the following conditions will gases behave most ideally?

   A. Low temperature and high pressure
   B. High temperature and low pressure
   C. Low temperature and low pressure
   D. Gas behavior does not depend on temperature and pressure if the gas is an ideal gas, and such a gas will behave ideally regardless of the conditions

8. What is the unit of universal gas constant R?

   A. $\dfrac{mol.K}{L.atm}$

   B. $\dfrac{atm}{mol.K}$

   C. $\dfrac{L.atm}{mol.K}$

   D. $\dfrac{L.atm}{mol.}$

9. A group of general chemistry students were assigned to conduct gas experiments. The vessel that contained the gases had a small hole in it. The gases used in the experiments were SO_2 and O_2. What is the rate of leakage of SO_2 to O_2 through the hole?

   A. 0.7
   B. 4
   C. 2
   D. 1.4

10. If the Vander Waal constant a is found to be zero for gas A, what are true regarding this gas?

    I.   Gas A does not behave ideally.
    II. Gas A behaves ideally.
    III. Gas A is Xenon.

    A. I only
    B. II only
    C. II & III only
    D. III only

11. What is the most likely Van der Waal constant correction factor of bromine?

    A. 0.97 L^2.atm/mol^2
    B. 2.34 L^2.atm/mol^2
    C. 5.32 L^2.atm/mol^2
    D. 9.80 L^2.atm/mol^2

12. Equal volumes of gases will contain the same number of molecules at the same temperature and pressure. This prediction is directly based on:

    A. Charles law.
    B. Boyle's law.
    C. kinetic-molecular theory.
    D. Avogadro's law.

13. Based on kinetic-molecular theory, which of the following are true?

    I.   At a given temperature, all gases have the same average kinetic energy.
    II. At a given temperature, different gases have different average velocities.
    III. The average kinetic energy is proportional to the absolute temperature.

    A. I only
    B. II only
    C. I & III only
    D. I, II & III

7

Liquids, Solids, and Phase Transitions

A. INTRODUCTION

In this chapter, we will explore the other two important phases of matter; liquids and solids. From your own experience, you probably have noticed that it is easier to handle liquids and solids than to handle gases. Gases have negligible intermolecular interactions and attractive forces. But this is not the case with either liquids or solids. They both have much stronger intermolecular forces than gases. These forces make substances exist as liquids and solids. As we go along, we will explore the ideas such as hydrogen bonding, London dispersion forces, and dipole interactions.

In addition to just knowing these phases, you will have to know the different theories and their implications, and how to work with some of the formulas involved. We will review the different kinds of molecular interactions that dictate the phase characteristics of molecules. The phase diagram that is discussed in this chapter is also important from the MCAT point of view.

B. THE LIQUID STATE

Liquids are considered to be relatively incompressible. Unlike gas molecules, liquid molecules are tightly packed. Liquids have a fixed volume, whereas gases do not. Liquids do not have a definite shape. The properties of liquids can be attributed to the presence of various types of intermolecular forces.

C. INTERMOLECULAR FORCES

Intermolecular forces are weak attractive forces that contribute to many of the physical properties exhibited by liquids. From the MCAT point of view, you have to be familiar with the main three types of attractive forces:

1) Hydrogen bonding
2) Dipole-dipole interactions
3) London forces

Hydrogen Bonding

Hydrogen bonding is an intermolecular attractive force that exists between a hydrogen atom covalently bonded to an electronegative atom (fluorine, oxygen, nitrogen), and another electronegative atom (fluorine, chlorine, nitrogen) in the neighboring molecule. Hydrogen bonding in water is shown below:

HYDROGEN BONDS

Figure 7-1 Hydrogen bonding in water

As you can see in Figure 7-1, the hydrogen which is covalently bonded to the electronegative atom (in this case it is oxygen), can undergo hydrogen bonding with an electronegative atom (the oxygen of another water molecule) present in the neighboring molecule.

Dipole-Dipole Interactions

Polar molecules have negative and positive polarity. This is because of the difference in electronegativities of the bonded atoms in such molecules. This polarity results in the formation of attractive forces among molecules. Such interactions are called **dipole-dipole interactions**. Consequently, the positive end of one molecule is attracted to the negative end of another. Figure 7-2 illustrates the dipole-dipole interactions between hydrogen chloride molecules.

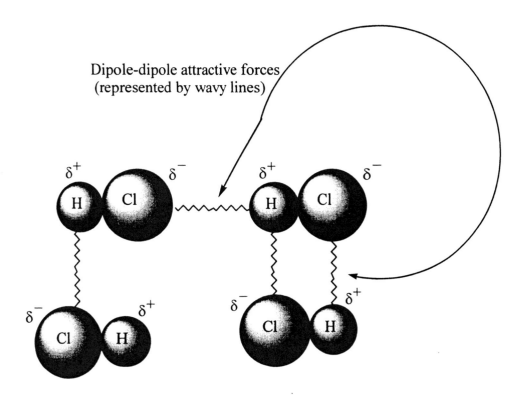

Figure 7-2 Dipole-dipole interaction between HCl molecules

London Forces

London forces are weak attractive forces that exist between instantaneous dipoles. What is an instantaneous dipole? In order to understand this, let us talk about atoms. Atoms have a central positively charged nucleus surrounded by electrons. These electrons are constantly moving and the electronic cloud may not be always perfectly distributed. In other words, the electrons at any given moment may be distributed more on one side and less on the other, creating an instantaneous dipole. The side which has more electrons at any moment will have a slight negative charge, whereas the side which is electron deficient will have a slight positive charge. The polarity that results from such charge separations in a molecule can induce polarity in other molecules when they are close enough to the instantaneous dipole molecule. For this reason, London forces are often called instantaneous dipole-induced dipole interactions. London forces are more pronounced in bigger molecules, because they are more polarizable.

Let us talk about the importance of these ideas. It is more likely that a polar molecule will exist as a liquid or solid than a nonpolar molecule. Why is it so? It is because of the intermolecular interactions that are possible among polar molecules.

D. THE SOLID STATE

A solid has a well-defined shape. Because of the tight packing of the molecules, solids can be considered almost incompressible. There are four types of solids:

1) Ionic solid
2) Metallic solid
3) Molecular solid
4) Network solid

Ionic Solid

An **ionic solid** consists of cations and anions which are held together by the electrostatic attraction between them. These attractive forces are very strong and thus ionic solids have high melting points. Sodium chloride (NaCl), and cesium chloride (CsCl) are examples of ionic solids.

Metallic Solid

A **metallic solid** consists of positive atomic cores surrounded by electrons. Almost all metals are solids at room temperature. The free electrons in metallic solids account for their superior electrical conductivity (e.g., iron, gold, silver).

Molecular Solid

A **molecular solid** consists of atoms or molecules held together by intermolecular attractive forces. In molecular solids, the attractive forces include hydrogen bonds and dipole-dipole forces (e.g., Ice [H_2O (s)]).

Network Solid

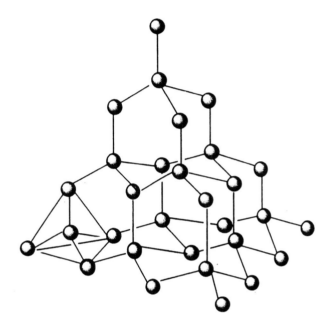

Figure 7-3 Structure of diamond

In a **network solid**, the atoms are held together by large networks of covalent bonds. A perfect example is diamond. Because of such an intricate network (see Figure 7-3) of covalent bonding through the entire crystal, the diamond crystal itself can be considered as one big molecule. Each and every carbon in a diamond is covalently linked to four other carbon atoms. For these reasons, network solids have very high melting points. Other examples of network solids include graphite and asbestos.

E. PHASE TRANSITIONS

Phase transition or change of state refers to the change of a substance's phase from one state to another. In this section, we will talk about the different phase changes, the associated terminology, and the key ideas related to all these.

Types of Phase Transitions

There are different types of phase transitions. From the MCAT point of view, you should have a good grasp of phase transitions. Let's look at the basic terminology.

The conversion of a solid to a liquid is called melting.

The temperature at which a substance changes from solid state to its liquid state is called its melting point.

The conversion of a liquid to a solid is called freezing.

The temperature at which a substance changes from liquid state to its solid state is called its freezing point.

The conversion of a liquid to a gas is called vaporization.

The temperature at which a substance changes from liquid state to its gas state is called its boiling point.

The conversion of a gas to a liquid is called condensation.

The direct conversion of a solid to a gas is called sublimation.

F. HEAT TRANSFER

In order to increase the temperature of a substance, we have to supply heat. The heat that should be supplied to increase the temperature varies from one substance to another. So scientists have come up with a way to define this – the specific heat. The **specific heat** (J/g.C°) of a substance is the amount of heat that should be added to one gram of that substance to raise its temperature by one degree Celsius. The **Heat capacity** of a given sample substance is the amount of heat that is required to increase the temperature by one degree Celsius. Heat capacity, specific heat, and temperature are related according to the following relations:

$$q = C\,(t_f - t_i) = C\,\Delta t,$$

where q is the heat required,
C is the heat capacity, and
Δt is the change in temperature.

$$q = m\,C_{sp}\,\Delta t,$$

where q is the heat required,
m is the mass of the substance in grams,
C_{sp} is the specific heat, and
Δt is the change in temperature.

Let's now talk about the temperature change when heat is added to a substance – the changes in temperature that occur during the change of a substance from its solid state to gaseous state or vice versa. It is easier to understand this from the Figure 7-4.

Let's say we are adding heat to a substance which is in its solid state. As the heat increases, the temperature increases until the melting point is attained. Then the temperature will not rise until the substance has melted. Keep in mind that the process of melting requires energy. As more heat is supplied, the temperature again starts increasing until the boiling point has been reached. Then again the temperature will not rise during the process of boiling or vaporization, because the energy that is supplied is used for the process of vaporization. After vaporization is completed, as more heat is supplied, the temperature again starts increasing.

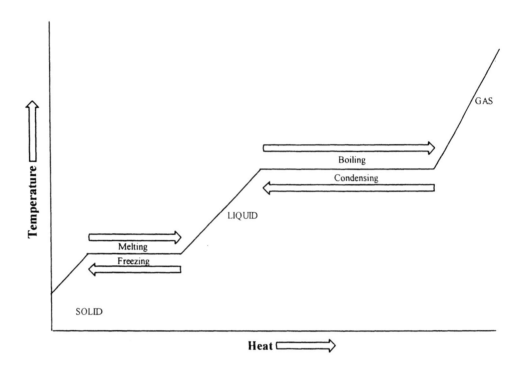

Figure 7-4

Some related terms:

Heat of fusion of a solid substance is the quantity of heat required to melt one gram of that substance at its melting point. The usual unit used is J/g.

Heat of vaporization of a liquid substance is the quantity of heat required to vaporize one gram of that substance at its boiling point. The unit used is J/g.

Heat of condensation of a substance is the quantity of heat that should be removed to condense one gram of that substance at its condensation point. The unit used is J/g.

Heat of crystallization of a substance is the quantity of heat that should be removed to crystallize one gram of that substance at its freezing point. The unit used is J/g.

G. PHASE DIAGRAMS

A **phase diagram** is a graphical representation of phase transitions under different pressures and temperatures. By analyzing the phase diagram of a substance, we can predict the state of that substance at a given temperature and pressure. For the MCAT, you should be familiar with the phase diagram and what exactly it represents, and also be able to predict some of the related trends from a given phase diagram.

In a phase diagram, there are three sections representing the solid, the liquid, and the gas phases. The phase diagram of a substance enables us to determine the phase of that substance at a given temperature and pressure. The phase diagram is actually plotted using experimentally determined values at different temperatures and pressures. Let's take a look at the phase diagram (Figure 7-5) of water.

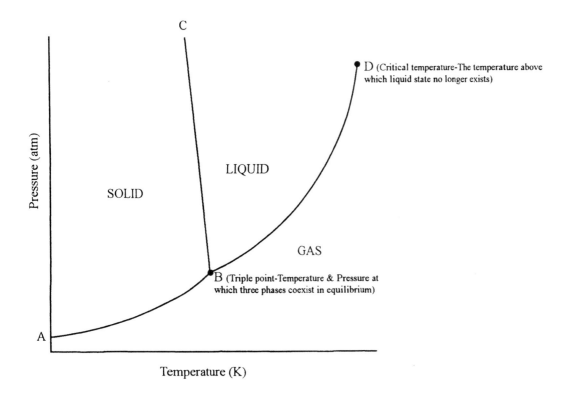

Figure 7-5 Phase diagram of water (diagram not drawn to scale)

As you can see in the phase diagram of water shown above, there are three regions in the graph representing solid, liquid, and gas phases. The segment BC divides the solid and the liquid phases of water. This segment represents the equilibrium region between the solid and the liquid phases. Because water is denser than ice, the segment BC is slightly slanting toward the left. For most phase diagrams (Figure 7-6), the segment BC will be slightly slanting toward the right (positive slope), since the liquid phase is usually less dense than the solid phase.

The segment BD divides the liquid and the gas phases in the graph. It also denotes the vapor pressures at different temperatures. The intersecting point of the curves represented by point B is called the **triple point**. This point represents the temperature and pressure at which the three phases of a substance are in equilibrium. How many triple points are likely to exist for a substance? The answer is one. There is only one pair of temperature-pressure combination for a substance at which the three states will be in equilibrium. Figure 7-6 shows a phase diagram representing the majority of other compounds that we see in nature.

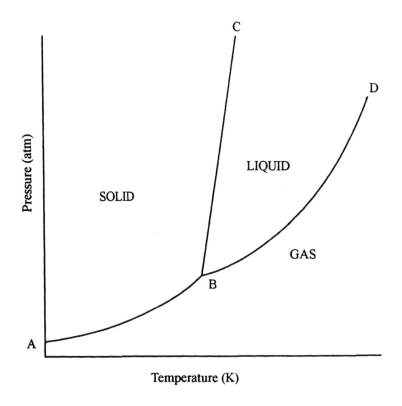

Figure 7-6 Phase diagram of most substances (diagram not drawn to scale)

(Notice the positive slope of segment BC, unlike that of water which has a negative slope)

Substances in their gas phase can usually be liquefied by increasing the pressure. But it reaches a point where this conversion is not possible. The temperature above which liquid phase cannot be achieved regardless of the applied pressure is called the **critical temperature**. The vapor pressure at the critical temperature is called the **critical pressure**.

H. COLLIGATIVE PROPERTIES

Colligative properties are properties that depend only on the number (concentration) of solute particles present in a solution. These properties do not depend on the identity of the solute. As an example let's talk about two aqueous solutions; one containing glucose and the other containing urea. As far as the colligative properties are concerned, the two solutions are not different as long as the number of glucose and urea particles are the same. In other words, if the concentration of the given samples of urea and glucose are the same, the colligative properties of both solutions will be the same.

The colligative properties that you have to be familiar with for the MCAT are:

1) vapor-pressure lowering
2) boiling-point elevation
3) freezing-point depression
4) osmotic pressure generating

> *A simple **solution** is a mixture of a solute and a solvent.*
>
> *SOLUTE + SOLVENT = SOLUTION*

Vapor-pressure Lowering

When a solvent contains impurities (solutes), there will be a reduction in its vapor pressure. This means the vapor pressure shown by a solvent when it is pure is lowered by the addition of solutes. The change in vapor pressure is proportional to the quantity of the dissolved solute. Raoult's law explains this relationship.

According to Raoult's law, the mole fraction of the solvent times the vapor pressure of the pure solvent is numerically equal to the vapor pressure of the solution. This is mathematically represented as shown below:

$$P_A = X_A \times P_A$$

Here, P_A is the vapor pressure of the solution (impure solvent),

X_A is the mole fraction of the solvent, and

P_A is the vapor pressure of the pure solvent.

Example 7-1

Calculate the mole fractions of sodium chloride and water in a solution containing 11.7 g of sodium chloride and 9 g of water.

Solution:

In this solution, we have 11.7 grams of NaCl and 9 grams of H_2O. First, you have to find the number of moles of NaCl and H_2O.

$$\text{Number of moles of NaCl} = \frac{11.7 \text{ g}}{58.5 \text{ g / mol}} = 0.2 \text{ mol}$$

$$\text{Number of moles of } H_2O = \frac{9 \text{ g}}{18 \text{ g / mol}} = 0.5 \text{ mol}$$

The total number of moles in the solution $= 0.2 + 0.5 = 0.7 \text{ mol}$

$$\text{Mol fraction of sodium chloride} = \frac{0.2 \text{ mol}}{0.7 \text{ mol}} \approx 0.3$$

$$\text{Mol fraction of water} = \frac{0.5 \text{ mol}}{0.7 \text{ mol}} \approx 0.7$$

Boiling-point Elevation

The **boiling point** of a liquid is defined as the temperature at which its vapor pressure equals the prevailing pressure. The prevailing pressure is normally the atmospheric pressure, provided that the container in which the liquid is present is kept open while boiling. When a nonvolatile solute is added to a pure solvent, the boiling point increases. The increase is proportional to the number of moles of the solute added to the solvent. The relationship is mathematically represented as shown below:

$$\Delta T_b = i\, K_b\, C_m$$

Here, ΔT_b is the boiling-point elevation,

i is the ionization factor,

K_b is the boiling-point elevation constant, and

C_m is the molal concentration of the solution.

Example 7-2

Calculate the boiling point of 0.2 m aqueous solution of glucose. (K_b of water is 0.512°C/m.)

Solution:

The formula for finding the boiling-point elevation is:

$$\Delta T_b = i\, K_b\, C_m$$

In this problem, we have all the necessary values to find the boiling-point elevation. Here, the ionization factor is 1, since glucose doesn't ionize. Let's substitute the values into the formula.

$$\Delta T_b = K_b\, C_m = 0.512°\,C/m \times 0.2\ m \approx 0.1°C$$

The boiling point of 0.2 m solution of glucose is 100 + 0.1 = 100.1°C

Freezing-point Depression

The solute concentration affects the freezing point of a solvent. The freezing point of a pure solvent is decreased when solutes are added to it. Just like the boiling-point elevation, freezing-point depression is proportional to the molal concentration. The relationship is shown:

$$\Delta T_f = i\, K_f\, C_m$$

Here, ΔT_f is the freezing-point depression,

i is the ionization factor,

K_f is the freezing-point depression constant, and

C_m is the molal concentration of the solution.

Example 7-3

Calculate the freezing point of 2 m aqueous solution of glucose. (K_f of water is 1.86°C/m)

Solution:

The formula for finding the freezing-point depression is:

$$\Delta T_f = i\, K_f\, C_m$$

In this problem, we have all the necessary values to find the freezing-point depression. The ionization factor is 1.

$$\Delta T_f = K_f\, C_m = 1.86°\, C/m \times 2\ m \approx 3.7°C$$

So the freezing point of 2 m solution of glucose is $0.0 - 3.7 = -3.7°C$

Osmotic Pressure

Osmotic pressure is also a colligative property. Before we talk about osmotic pressure let's turn our attention to the process of osmosis. Consider two solutions that are made out of the same solvent with different concentrations of solute separated by a semipermeable membrane. The solvent will flow through the semipermeable membrane from the solution of lower concentration to the solution of higher concentration. Thus, **osmosis** is defined as the flow of solvent through a semipermeable membrane resulting in the equilibrium of concentrations on both sides of the semipermeable membrane.

We will explore the process of osmosis with an experiment. A dilute solution of sodium chloride is taken in a funnel. The mouth of the funnel is covered by a semipermeable membrane. The funnel is then placed upside down into a beaker which is filled with pure distilled water. The set up is done according to the diagram shown (Figure 7-7):

Figure 7-7 Osmosis experiment

The arrow indicates the direction of flow of the solvent (H_2O).

Water will flow into the funnel through the semipermeable membrane, and the liquid level of the funnel will gradually increase. The **osmotic pressure** is the pressure required or applied to the solution to stop the flow of the solvent, or in other words, to stop the process of osmosis. The osmotic pressure and concentration are related by the following equation:

Osmotic pressure, π = MRT

Here, M is the molar concentration of the solute,
R is the gas constant, and
T is the absolute temperature.

CHAPTER 7 PRACTICE QUESTIONS

1. The phase change that involves the conversion of a gas to a solid is called:

   A. sublimation.
   B. condensation.
   C. freezing.
   D. deposition.

2. Which of the following processes accompanies a release of heat?

   A. Vaporization
   B. Condensation
   C. Sublimation
   D. Melting

3. Potassium fluoride is:

   A. a covalent solid.
   B. a metallic solid.
   C. a network solid.
   D. an ionic solid.

4. Which of the following is the strongest type of force that is present in an ionic bonding?

   A. London forces
   B. Covalent forces
   C. Electrostatic forces
   D. Hydrogen bonding forces

Questions 5-10 are based on the following passage.

Passage 1

A phase diagram illustrates the physical state of a substance with respect to the temperature and the pressure of the surroundings. The points plotted to draw the phase diagram are derived experimentally, and are usually plotted with temperature on the x-axis and pressure on the y-axis. A typical phase diagram is shown below in Figure-1.

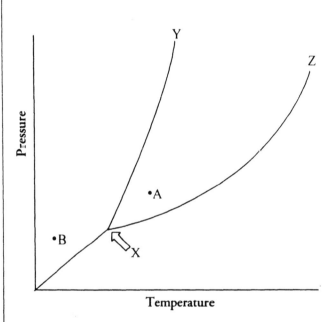

Figure 1

5. Which of the following represents the correct phase diagram of water?

A.

B.

C.

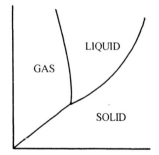

D.

6. The phase diagram given in the passage CANNOT be that of:

A. CO_2
B. H_2O
C. CO
D. O_2

7. From the phase diagram given in the passage, predict the likely phase change if the following changes happen. Consider point A as the current phase of substance M. What is the most likely effect on substance M, if the pressure was decreased without changing the temperature of the system?

A. Gas to liquid
B. Liquid to gas
C. Liquid to solid
D. Solid to liquid

8. The point marked 'X' in the phase diagram given in the passage is called:

A. the critical point.
B. the maximum point.
C. the triple point.
D. the critical pressure point.

9. The critical temperature of a substance is best defined as:

A. the temperature below which a gas cannot be liquefied.
B. the temperature above which a liquid cannot be vaporized.
C. the temperature above which a substance exists only as gas.
D. the temperature which is essential for a substance to obey ideal gas laws.

10. The segment XZ in the phase diagram given in the passage represents the equilibrium between:

A. gas and liquid.
B. liquid and solid.
C. solid and gas.
D. gas and plasma.

8

Chemistry of Solutions

A. INTRODUCTION

When we think of solutions, we normally think of a solution formed by dissolving a solid (e.g., sugar) in a liquid (e.g., water). In reality, any combination of the three states can be considered a solution. In fact, air is a solution which is a mixture of various gases. Carbonated water (soda) is a mixture of a gas (CO_2) dissolved in a liquid (H_2O). Even alloys such as gold-silver alloys are solutions containing two solids. A true solution is a solution which has only one solvent with one or more solutes. In this chapter, we will be limiting our discussion mostly to water based solutions because of their versatility and importance to life sciences. We will discuss various aspects such as solubility of compounds, and precipitation reactions.

B. THE CONCEPT OF SOLUBILITY

Solubility of a substance is defined as the amount of the substance that will dissolve in a particular solvent. Let's consider an example in which sucrose is added to water. When we add sucrose and stir, it dissolves in the water. Let's say we keep on adding more and more sucrose to the solution. Since more and more sucrose is dissolving, the solution is not saturated or it is called an unsaturated solution.

It reaches a point where additional amount of sucrose will not dissolve in that solution. At that point the solution is said to be saturated. We have yet another category in this tradition of categorizing solutions. In some cases, certain solutes become more soluble if the solution is heated. Such solutions are called supersaturated solutions. If we carefully and slowly cool down a supersaturated solution without disturbing its contents, normally we will still have a supersaturated solution. At this stage, even the slightest addition of the solute will result in crystallization.

The Reasons for Solubility

One basic rule that you have to keep in mind is **"like dissolves like."** This means that substances which have similar polarity dissolve one another. We know that water is a polar substance. Since oil is nonpolar, water and oil cannot mix. Solubility helps in maintaining the lowest energy possible when the solute and the solvent are mixed together.

Ionic Solutions

Ionic compounds have very peculiar solubility trends. Some are highly soluble, whereas some others have very little solubility. The solubility of ionic compounds can be explained in terms of the interactions between the ions and the water molecules. Let's take sodium chloride as an example. Sodium chloride has a solubility of 360 g per liter or 36 g per 100 ml at room temperature.

Since water is a polar molecule, when we add sodium chloride to water, the water molecules will orient themselves according to the surrounding ions. Here we have sodium (Na^+) and chloride (Cl^-) ions. So the slightly negative pole (the negative pole is due to the electronegativity of the oxygen atom) of the water molecules will align toward the sodium ions, and the other pole will orient toward the chloride ions. This attraction is otherwise called hydration. Besides hydration, there is another force called lattice energy of the crystal lattice. The greater the lattice energy of an ionic solid is, the lesser its solubility.

C. MOLARITY

When we are working with solutions, it is better to have a concentration measure in terms of the volume. **Molarity** is defined as the number of moles of the solute per liter of solution.

$$\text{Molarity} = \frac{\text{moles of solute}}{\text{liter of solution}} = \frac{\text{mol}}{\text{L}}$$

D. MOLALITY

The **molality** of a solution is defined as the number of moles of the solute per kilogram of solvent.

$$\text{Molality} = \frac{\text{moles of solute}}{\text{kilograms of solvent}}$$

Molarity is usually denoted by the letter M, and molality is denoted by the letter m.

Example 8-1

Calculate the molarity of a solution that contains 18.65 g of KCl in 3 liters of solution.

Solution:

We have 18.65 grams of KCl, and the total volume of the solution is 3 liters. First, find the number of moles of KCl present. The number of moles of KCl is 0.25 mol, which can be calculated from the formula weight and the grams of solute.

$$\text{Molarity} = \frac{\text{moles of solute}}{\text{liters of solution}}$$

$$= \frac{0.25 \text{ mol}}{3 \text{ L}} \approx 0.08 \text{ M}$$

E. NORMALITY

The normality (N) of a solution is the number of equivalents of solute per liter of solution. The *equivalent* is usually defined in terms of a chemical reaction. For acid-base reactions, an equivalent is the amount of substance that will react or form 1 mole of hydrogen (H^+) or hydroxide (OH^-) ions. For redox (oxidation-reduction) reactions, an equivalent is the amount of substance that will react or form 1 mole of electrons.

$$Normality = \frac{number\ of\ equivalents}{1\ liter\ of\ solution}$$

Normality is a multiple of molarity. The following equation relates normality and molarity.

$$N = n\,M$$

For acids, the number of H+ available from a formula unit of the acid gives the number of equivalents (n). For example, 1 M H_2SO_4 solution is a 2 N solution, because each molecule of H_2SO_4 can give two H^+. For bases, the number of OH^- available from a formula unit of the base gives the number of equivalents. For example, a 2 M $Ca(OH)_2$ solution is a 4 N solution.

F. THE SOLUBILITY PRODUCT CONSTANT

Let's say we are adding silver chloride (AgCl) into a liter of water. We can express the equilibrium as follows:

$$AgCl\ (s) \xrightleftharpoons{H_2O} Ag^+\ (aq) \ + \ Cl^-\ (aq)$$

The **solubility product (K_{sp})** is defined as the equilibrium constant for the solubility equilibrium of ionic compounds. The solubility product of AgCl is expressed as:

$$K_{sp} = \left[Ag^+ \right] \left[Cl^- \right]$$

The solubility product constant is equal to the product of the concentrations of the ions in a saturated solution, each concentration raised to a power equal to its coefficient (number of moles of <u>individual</u> ions formed per mole of the compound) in the balanced equation. Take a look at the solubility product equation of calcium fluoride (CaF_2).

$$CaF_2\ (s) \xrightleftharpoons{H_2O} Ca^{2+}\ (aq) \ + \ 2\ F^-\ (aq)$$

$$K_{sp} = \left[Ca^{2+} \right] \left[F^- \right]^2$$

It is imperative that you understand these ideas involving the solubility product constant. Let's look at another example. One mole of aluminum hydroxide [$Al(OH)_3$] gives one mole of aluminum ions and three moles of hydroxide ions in solution.

$$Al(OH)_3\ (s) \xrightleftharpoons{} Al^{3+}(aq) \ + \ 3\ OH^-(aq)$$

From the balanced equation, we can see that the coefficient of Al^{3+} is 1 and that of OH^- is 3. So, the solubility constant (K_{sp}) expression for $Al(OH)_3$ is given by:

$$K_{sp} = [Al^{3+}]\ [OH^-]^3$$

The solubility product depends on the temperature, and at a given temperature it is constant for a particular ionic compound. *Molar solubility* is defined as the number of moles of solute dissolved in one liter of its saturated solution. Using the molar solubility of a compound, the solubility product of that compound can be determined or vice versa.

Example 8-2

Calculate the molar solubility of silver chloride (AgCl). The solubility product (K_{sp}) of AgCl is 1.8×10^{-10}.

Solution:

$$AgCl \ (s) \ \xrightleftharpoons{\ H_2O\ } \ Ag^+ \ (aq) \ + \ Cl^- \ (aq)$$

$$K_{sp} = [Ag^+] \ [Cl-]$$

Let x be the molar solubility of AgCl. So we can write:

$$AgCl \ (s) \ \xrightleftharpoons{\ H_2O\ } \ Ag^+ \ (aq) \ + \ Cl^- \ (aq)$$

	Ag^+	Cl^-
Initial	0	0
Equilibrium	$x \ M$	$x \ M$

$$K_{sp} = [Ag^+] \ [Cl^-] = (x) \ (x) = (x)^2 = 1.8 \times 10^{-10}$$

So the molar solubility of AgCl, $x = \sqrt{1.8 \times 10^{-10}} = 1.34 \times 10^{-5} \ M$

Example 8-3

If 'x' represents the molar solubility of $Al(OH)_3$, find the expression for the solubility product of $Al(OH)_3$ in terms of x. What is the molar solubility of $Al(OH)_3$, if the solubility product constant is 2×10^{-33}?

Solution:

$$Al(OH)_3 \ (s) \ \xrightleftharpoons{} \ Al^{3+}(aq) \ + \ 3 \ OH^-(aq)$$

	Al^{3+}	OH^-
Intial Concentration	0	0
Equilibrium concentration	x	3 x

The solubility product expression is, $K_{sp} = [Al^{3+}] \ [OH^-]^3 = [x] \ [3x]^3 = 27x^4$

$$K_{sp} = 27x^4 = 2 \times 10^{-33}$$

$$x^4 = \frac{2 \times 10^{-33}}{27} = 7.4 \times 10^{-35}$$

The solubility, $x = \sqrt[4]{7.4 \times 10^{-35}} = \sqrt[4]{74 \times 10^{-36}} \approx 2.9 \times 10^{-9} \, mol / L$

You can approximate numbers to find the correct answer among the choices in the MCAT. In this example, to take the 4th root of 7.4×10^{-35}, first we can rewrite this as 74×10^{-36}. The 4th root of 81 is 3. Since 74 is less than 81, we can approximate the 4th root of 74 close to 2.8 or 2.9. If you had trouble realizing that, think of the 4th root of 16 which is 2. Again, the best approximation for the 4th root of 74 is a number below and close to 3. The 4th root of 10^{-36} is 10^{-9}. Such approximation-techniques can save time during the test.

Ion Product

Ion product is the product of the concentrations of the ions from the compound (solute) in a solution, each concentration raised to a power equal to its coefficient in the balanced equation. In other words, the expression for the ion product is the same as that of K_{sp}. In a saturated solution, the ion product is equal to K_{sp}. If the ion product is greater than K_{sp}, the solution is supersaturated and can undergo precipitation. If the ion product is less than K_{sp}, the solution is unsaturated. Thus, by comparing the ion product of a compound against its K_{sp}, we can predict whether or not precipitation is likely to occur.

Ion product $< K_{sp}$	Unsaturated solution	No precipitate is formed
Ion product $= K_{sp}$	Saturated solution	No precipitate is formed
Ion product $> K_{sp}$	Supersaturated solution	Precipitation can occur

G. COMMON-ION EFFECT

When a salt is added to a solution containing either the same cation or anion, there will be changes in the solubility because of what is commonly known as **common-ion effect**. This is so because the solubility of the salt added is affected by the common ions which are already present in the solution. Consider a solution of sodium fluoride (NaF). We are adding magnesium fluoride (MgF_2) to this solution. Notice that there is a common ion in sodium fluoride and magnesium fluoride, namely fluoride. You will see that the solubility of magnesium fluoride will be less than expected. To be more precise, the solubility of magnesium fluoride will be less than that of its solubility in pure water. Why is it so? Well the answer is simple; **common-ion effect**. The phenomenon can be best explained in terms of Le Chatelier's principle. Consider the dissociation of magnesium and sodium fluorides.

$$MgF_2 \ (s) \ \underset{H_2O}{\overset{H_2O}{\rightleftharpoons}} \ Mg^{2+} \ (aq) \ + \ 2F^- \ (aq) \qquad \text{equation 1}$$

$$NaF \ (s) \ \underset{}{\overset{H_2O}{\rightleftharpoons}} \ Na^+ \ (aq) \ + \ F^- \ (aq) \qquad \text{equation 2}$$

Magnesium fluoride is not a very soluble salt. It is a mildly soluble salt, whereas sodium fluoride is a highly soluble salt. Because of the higher solubility of sodium fluoride, there will be a lot of fluoride ions in the solution. This increased fluoride ion concentration in the solution will drive the equilibrium of Equation 1 to the left. Thus the solubility of magnesium fluoride will be highly diminished because of the fluoride ions already present in the solution.

Table 8-1 Some general trends regarding solubilities (in water) of common ionic compounds

SOLUBLE IONIC COMPOUNDS
All salts of alkali metals (e.g., sodium, potassium), and ammonium ion are soluble.
All nitrates, acetates, chlorates, and perchlorates are soluble.
All halides (chlorides, bromides, and iodides) are soluble. Exceptions include lead(II), mercury (I), and silver halides.
All sulfates are soluble. Exceptions include calcium, strontium, barium, and lead(II) sulfates.
INSOLUBLE IONIC COMPOUNDS
All carbonates and phosphates are insoluble except those of ammonium ion and alkali metals.
All hydroxides are insoluble except those of calcium, strontium, barium, and alkali metals.
All sulfides are insoluble except those of alkali metals and ammonium ion.

H. ELECTROLYTES

Pure distilled water is not a good conductor of electricity. If KCl is added to it, the resulting aqueous KCl solution becomes a good conductor of electricity. Such a substance that dissolves in water to give a solution that can conduct electricity is called an *electrolyte*. The free ions that are present in an electrolytic solution enable the flow of electric current. Most ionic substances are good electrolytes because they dissolve in water as ions. A substance that exists almost completely as ions in a solution is called a *strong electrolyte*. Hydrochloric acid is a strong electrolyte because when HCl is dissolved in water, it completely exists as H_3O^+ and Cl^- ions by reacting with water (H_2O).

$$HCl(g) + H_2O(l) \longrightarrow H_3O^+(aq) + Cl^-(aq)$$

Some substances (solutes) form aqueous solutions that weakly conduct electricity. Such substances are called *weak electrolytes*. This weak conduction of electricity is mainly because weak electrolytes only dissociate partially in solution. In other words, only a small fraction of the solute exists as ions, resulting in a solution that conducts electricity very weakly. Acetic acid (CH_3COOH) and ammonia (NH_3) are examples of weak electrolytes.

A substance that can dissolve in water but results in a poorly conducting solution is called a *nonelectrolyte*. Glucose ($C_6H_{12}O_6$) is a nonelectrolyte. A nonelectrolyte is not charged in solution because it dissolves as molecules in water rather than ions, and thus cannot conduct electricity.

Table 8-2

SOME COMMON POLYATOMIC IONS	
Acetate ($C_2H_3O_2^-$)	Nitrate (NO_3^-)
Ammonium (NH_4^+)	Nitrite (NO_2^-)
Bicarbonate (HCO_3^-)	Oxalate ($C_2O_4^-$)
Bisulfate (HSO_4^-)	Perchlorate (ClO_4^-)
Bisulfite (HSO_3^-)	Permanganate (MnO_4^-)
Carbonate (CO_3^{2-})	Peroxide (O_2^-)
Chlorite (ClO_2^-)	Phosphate (PO_4^{3-})
Chromate (CrO_4^{2-})	Sulfate (SO_3^-)
Cyanide (CN^-)	Sulfide (S^{2-})
Dichromate ($Cr_2O_7^{2-}$)	Sulfite (SO_3^-)
Dihydrogen phosphate ($H_2PO_4^-$)	Thiosulfate ($S_2O_3^{2-}$)
Hydroxide (OH^-)	Oxide (O_2^{2-})
Hypochlorite (ClO^-)	

CHAPTER 8   PRACTICE QUESTIONS

1. Equivalents of solute per liter of solution is:

   A. molality.
   B. molarity.
   C. normality.
   D. none of the above.

2. The concentration of a given solution of glucose ($C_6H_{12}O_6$) is 270 g per liter of solution. What is the molarity of this solution?

   A. 1.5 M
   B. 0.67 M
   C. 4.86 M
   D. 270 M

3. You are presented with a 2.5 M solution of hydrochloric acid. If the total volume of the solution is 1.25 L, how many grams of HCl is present in this solution?

   A. 36.5 g
   B. 91.25 g
   C. 111 g
   D. 114 g

4. You are asked to prepare 30 ml of a 2 M solution of HNO_3 from a stock solution of 10 M solution of HNO_3. How much of the stock solution is required to make this 30 ml of 2 M HNO_3 solution?

   A. 3 ml
   B. 6 ml
   C. 10 ml
   d. 30 ml

5. How many grams of NaCl are required to prepare 250 ml of 0.35 M NaCl solution?

   A. 0.0875 g
   B. 20.5 g
   C. 5.1 g
   D. 87.5 g

Questions 6-10 are based on the following passage.

Passage 1

   The concentration of solutions are generally expressed in terms of molarity, molality, normality, and weight percent. The formation of the solutions itself has many ramifications. The solubility of solutes differ considerably from one other. Some of the factors that can influence the solubility include temperature and pressure. Solubility depends on other factors as well. Given below in Figure-1 is a graph which depicts solubility differences of some solutes.

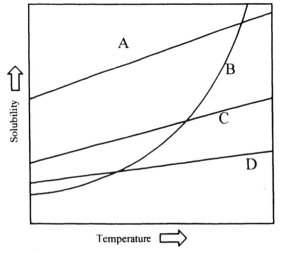

Figure-1

Quite often, the freezing and boiling point changes that are brought about by the dissolved solutes can be predicted reasonably. But this is not always the case.

The predictions and calculations are done for freezing point depression (ΔT_f) based on the following formula:

$$\Delta T_f = K_f\, m,$$

where m is the molality and K_f is the freezing point depression constant. ($Kf = 1.86\ °C/m$)

For boiling point elevation (ΔT_b), the calculations are based on the following formula:

$$\Delta T_b = K_b\, m,$$

where m is the molality and K_b is the boiling point elevation constant. ($Kb = 0.512\ °C/m$)

6. The graph in the passage shows the solubilities of some compounds (salts). Which of the following is most likely true regarding the Compounds A, B, C and D?

   A. The solubility process of Compound B is exothermic, and those of Compounds A, C and D are endothermic.
   B. The solubility process of Compound B is endothermic, and those of Compounds A, C and D are exothermic.
   C. The solubility processes of Compounds A, B, C and D are exothermic.
   D. The solubility processes of Compounds A, B, C and D are endothermic.

7. A solution was made by using 315 g of glucose in 750 g of water. What is the boiling point of this solution?

   A. 98.8^0 C
   B. 99.8^0 C
   C. 100.24^0 C
   D. 101.2^0 C

8. Two experiments were conducted for analyzing the solubility properties and their effects on colligative properties. In Experiment I, a 1.0 m solution of KBr was analyzed and in Experiment II, a 2.3 m solution of KBr was analyzed. The experimental values of freezing and boiling points were slightly different from the expected values based on the theoretical calculations discussed in the passage. Which of the following is most likely correct regarding the two experiments?

   A. The experimental values of the solution in Experiment I was more different from the theoretical calculations than the solution in Experiment II.
   B. The experimental values of the solution in Experiment II was more different from the theoretical calculations than the solution in Experiment I.
   C. Both experiments have the same extent of differences from the theoretical predictions.
   D. The discrepancy noted in the experiments is absolutely a result of instrumental error, because the differences in Experiments I & II cannot change colligative properties.

9. If the amount of glucose used in Question 7 is doubled, while the same 750 g of water was used, what must have happened to the boiling point of the solution?

    A. It doubled.
    B. It quadrupled.
    C. It decreased slightly.
    D. It increased slightly.

10. Which of the following statements is true regarding solutions?

    A. As the concentration of a solution increases, the vapor pressure increases.
    B. As the concentration of a solution decreases, the vapor pressure decreases.
    C. As the concentration of a solution increases, the vapor pressure decreases.
    D. None of the above

9

Acid-Base Equilibrium

A. INTRODUCTION

In this chapter, we will explore different aspects involving acids and bases. We will start with the definitions, followed by ionization reactions, including various key concepts involving strong acids, strong bases, weak acids, weak bases, and buffers. Finally, we will discuss some of the important titration reactions.

B. DEFINITIONS OF ACIDS AND BASES

The Arrhenius Definition

According to Arrhenius, an **acid** is a substance that increases H^+ ions in an aqueous solution. A **base** is a substance that increases OH^- ions in an aqueous solution. The Arhhenius definitions explain the reactions involving acids that contain acidic hydrogens, and bases that contain basic hydroxyl groups (e.g., metal hydroxides). But the definitions are not able to explain the behavior of acids and bases of other types, such as in nonaqueous solutions.

The Bronsted-Lowry Definition

During the early twentieth century, scientists J.N. Bronsted and T.M. Lowry put forth their theories. According to them, an **acid** is a proton donor, and a **base** is a proton acceptor.

Consider the ionization reaction of hydrogen iodide. Since hydrogen iodide is a strong acid, it completely dissociates. In this ionization reaction, note that the water molecule acts as the base.

$$HI\ (aq) \longrightarrow H^+\ (aq) + I^-\ (aq)$$

$$H^+\ (aq) + H_2O\ (l) \longrightarrow H_3O^+$$

$$\boxed{HI\ (aq) + H_2O\ (l) \longrightarrow H_3O^+ + I^-\ (aq)}$$ Overall reaction

⇧

THIS REACTION IS AN EXAMPLE THAT FITS THE BRONSTED- LOWRY DEFINITION

In this ionization reaction, obviously HI is the acid. HI transfers or donates its proton to water. Thus, water is the base in this reaction because it accepts the proton. The conjugate base of HI is I^-.

C. THE LEWIS THEORY

The scientist G.N. Lewis put forward a more elaborate theory regarding acids and bases. According to him, a **Lewis acid** is a species that can accept a pair of electrons from another species. He defined **Lewis base** as any species that can donate a pair of electrons to another species. For a thorough under- standing of this concept, let's look at a typical Lewis acid-base reaction. The reaction between ammonia (NH_3) and boron trichloride (BCl_3) is shown:

Lewis acid–electron pair acceptor

Lewis base–electron pair donor

Lewis acid   Lewis base

$$BCl_3 + NH_3 \longrightarrow Cl_3B \text{:} NH_3$$

In this reaction, the electron acceptor is boron trichloride (Lewis acid) and the electron donor is ammonia (Lewis base). The new bond that is formed between the acid and the base is a coordinate covalent bond.

D. IONIZATION OF WATER

Usually pure water is considered to be a nonelectrolyte. Nevertheless, it actually can conduct small amounts of electricity. This is because of the self- ionization of water. Since the species that act as the acid and the base are one and the same, we can describe it as follows:

A proton is grabbed from one water molecule, and is accepted by another water molecule. The resulting products are hydronium and hydroxide ions.

$$H_2O \ (l) \ + \ H_2O \ (l) \ \rightleftharpoons \ H_3O^+ \ (aq) \ + \ OH^- \ (aq)$$

The equilibrium expression (K_w) is written as:

$$K_w = [H_3O^+][OH^-] = 1.0 \times 10^{-14} \text{ at } 25° \text{ C}$$

K_w is more correctly called the ion-product constant for water, which is actually the equilibrium value of the ion product.

E. THE CONCEPT OF pH

In order to describe the acidity of a solution, scientists have devised the pH scale. The **pH** is defined as the negative log of the hydrogen-ion concentration.

$$\boxed{pH \ = \ -\log [H^+]}$$

Example 9 -1

What is the pH of a solution having a $1 \times 10^{-2} \ M$ hydrogen-ion concentration?

Solution:

The formula for pH is $pH \ = \ -\log [H^+]$. Substituting in this formula,

$$pH = -\log (1 \times 10^{-2}) = 2$$

The pH of this solution is 2.

We can also find pH if we know the hydroxide-ion concentration.

$$pOH = -\log [OH^-]$$

Since $pH + pOH = 14$, if we know the pOH, the pH can be easily calculated or vice versa.

Example 9-2

Find the pH of solution X, if it has a hydroxide-ion concentration of 1×10^{-8} M.

Solution:

Since the hydroxide-ion concentration is 1×10^{-8} M, the pOH is 8. Since we know that pH + pOH is 14,

$$pH = 14 - 8 = 6$$

The pH value of solution X is 6.

F. STRONG ACIDS AND BASES

Strong acids such as HNO_3, HCl, and HI dissociate almost completely. If we were asked to predict the direction of such a dissociation reaction, we should say that the direction of reaction favors the dissociation of the acid. The dissociation of HI is shown below:

$$HI\ (aq)\ +\ H_2O\ (l)\ \longrightarrow\ H_3O^+\ (aq)\ +\ I^-\ (aq)$$

Since there is complete dissociation for every mole of HI present, equal number of hydronium ions are formed. You may be wondering whether protons can be supplied by the water molecules that are present. Usually this supply is negligible (the self-ionization of water is extremely low) compared to the concentration of the strong acid present. But this may not be always the case. Think about an instance when the proton contribution of water is significant in an acidic solution such as that of hydrogen iodide. When you have a strong acid solution which is very dilute, water does contribute protons significantly compared to that of the strong acid present.

Now let's consider a strong base such as potassium hydroxide. Let's say the solution is 1×10^{-3} M. Since KOH is a strong base, it dissociates completely. So we can confidently say that the concentration of hydroxide-ion formed is also 1×10^{-3} M. Just like the strong acid, we can ignore the possibility of hydroxide-ion formation from water, since the self-ionization of water is negligible. Since the OH^- concentration is 1×10^{-3}, the pOH is 3. From this, we can say that the pH of this solution is close to 11, since pH + pOH = 14.

A pH value below 7 is acidic, a pH value above 7 is basic, and a pH value 7 is neutral.

Table 9-1

```
SOME EXAMPLES OF STRONG ACIDS

Sulfuric acid           H₂SO₄
Nitric acid             HNO₃
Hydrochloric acid       HCl
Hydrobromic acid        HBr
Hydroiodic acid         HI
Perchloric acid         HClO₄
Chloric acid            HClO₃


SOME EXAMPLES OF STRONG BASES

Lithium hydroxide       LiOH
Sodium hydroxide        NaOH
Potassium hydroxide     KOH
Cesium hydroxide        CsOH
Calcium hydroxide       Ca(OH)₂
Strontium hydroxide     Sr(OH)₂
Barium hydroxide        Ba(OH)₂
```

$$\overset{acid \quad base}{HCl + H_2O} \rightleftharpoons \overset{+}{H_3O} + \overset{-}{Cl}$$
$$\qquad\qquad\qquad \underset{acid \quad base}{}$$

*In this reaction, HCl (acid) reacts to form Cl⁻ (base). HCl and Cl⁻ can be inter-converted by the gain or loss of one proton. Such a pair is called a **conjugate acid-base pair**. Here, Cl⁻ is the conjugate base of HCl, and HCl is the conjugate acid of Cl⁻.*

G. WEAK ACIDS AND BASES

Weak acids and bases cannot dissociate completely. They undergo the same type of dissociation as that of strong acids and bases, but the extent of dissociation is very little compared to strong acid or strong base dissociations.

Acid-ionization Constant (K_a)

A typical way to represent the dissociation of a weak acid is shown below:

$$\underset{\text{weak acid}}{HA\ (aq)} \ + \ H_2O\ (l) \ \rightleftharpoons \ H_3O\ (aq) \ + \ A^-$$

In this reaction, the protons from the weak acid are transferred to the water molecules. The acid-ionization constant (K_a) of this reaction is shown below:

$$\text{Acid-ionization constant, } K_a \ = \ \frac{[H_3O^+][A^-]}{[HA]}$$

We encounter weak acids every day. An example is carbonated water that contains dissolved carbon dioxide, and is called carbonic acid. Fruits like lemons and oranges contain citric acid which is also a weak acid. The list goes on and on.

Percentage Ionization

Percentage ionization is the percentage expression of the degree of ionization. What is the degree of ionization of a weak acid? Degree of ionization is the fractional amount of the weak acid that gets ionized.

Example 9-3

Find the degree of ionization of 0.1 M solution of acetic acid (CH_3COOH). Also find the pH of the solution.
(The acid-ionization constant of acetic acid is 1.8×10^{-5})

Solution:

$$CH_3COOH\ (aq) \rightleftharpoons H^+(aq)\ +\ CH_3COO^-\ (aq)$$

We will logically dissect the events that lead to the dissociation. At first we do not have any H^+ and CH_3COO^- ions. Let's say we have a unit volume (a liter) of acetic acid and $x\ M$ (mol/L) of it was ionized. We can represent the equation as follows:

	$CH_3COOH\ (aq)$	$\rightleftharpoons$	$H^+(aq)$	$+$	$CH_3COO^-\ (aq)$
Initial	0.1 M		~ 0		~ 0
At equilibrium	$(0.1 - x)\ M$		$x\ M$		$x\ M$

With the concentrations at equilibrium we can substitute the concentrations in the acid-ionization constant expression.

$$\text{Acid-ionization constant, } K_a = \frac{[H^+][CH_3COO^-]}{[CH_3COOH]}$$

$$= \frac{(x)\ (x)}{(0.1 - x)}$$

$$= 1.8 \times 10^{-5}$$

Even though this has to be solved using a quadratic equation, we can skip that elaborate process by making some chemically acceptable assumptions. Since the acid-ionization constant is very small, we can assume the same with the value of x. So the expression changes as follows. For the MCAT, you won't be given problems that require extensive calculations. The problems will test mostly concepts, and when calculations are involved the numbers will usually be manageable ones.

$$\frac{(x)^2}{(0.1 - x)} \quad \text{becomes} \quad \frac{(x)^2}{0.1} = 1.8 \times 10^{-5}$$

Solving for x you will get roughly $1.34 \times 10^{-3} = 0.00134 \ M$.

$$\text{Degree of ionization} = \frac{0.00134}{0.1} = 0.0134$$

The question also asks for pH of the solution.

$$pH = -\log [H^+]$$

The hydrogen ion concentration is $0.00134 \ M$. By substituting in the pH formula you should get the following result.

The pH of the solution is 2.87.

Base-ionization Constant (K_b)

Just like the acid-ionization constant, there is also the base-ionization constant. Consider the ionization of ammonia in water.

$$NH_3 \ (aq) \quad + \quad H_2O \ (l) \ \rightleftharpoons \ NH_4 \ (aq) + \ ^-OH \ (aq)$$

For the above reaction, we can write the base-ionization constant (K_b) for the above reaction as follows:

$$\text{Base-ionization constant, } K_b = \frac{[NH_4^+][OH^-]}{[NH_3]}$$

H. DISSOCIATION OF POLYPROTIC ACIDS

Some acids have two or more protons that can be released upon dissociation. Such acids are called polyprotic acids. For example, phosphoric acid (H_3PO_4) can lose up to three protons in aqueous solution.

Sulfuric acid is a polyprotic acid that can lose two protons in solution. The first ionization is complete because sulfuric acid is a strong acid.

$$H_2SO_4\ (aq) \longrightarrow H^+(aq) + HSO_4^-(aq) \qquad \text{Dissociation constant, } K_a1 = \text{very large}$$

The second proton comes off as depicted by the next equation. In this case, an equilibrium exists because hydrogen sulfate ion (HSO_4^-) is not as strong as H_2SO_4.

$$HSO_4^-\ (aq) \rightleftharpoons H^+(aq) + SO_4^{2-}(aq) \qquad \text{Dissociation constant, } K_a2 = 1.2 \times 10^{-2}$$

It is clear from this example that the second dissociation constant is always lower than the first dissociation constant. Thus, it is easier to remove a proton from an uncharged species (H_2SO_4) than from a charged species (HSO_4^-).

Based on the Bronsted-Lowry definition of acids and bases, an acid is a proton donor and base is a proton acceptor. A species (charged or uncharged) that can gain or lose a proton is called amphoteric or amphiprotic species. For example, (bicarbonate ion) HCO_3^- can donate a proton acting as an acid. The same species can accept a proton acting as a base. Hence, amphoteric species can act as an acid or a base depending on the surrounding conditions.

under basic conditions, HCO_3^- can act as a Bronsted-acid

$$HCO_3^-\ (aq) \rightleftharpoons H^+(aq) + CO_3^{2-}(aq)$$
$$+$$
$$H^+(aq)$$
$$\updownarrow$$
$$H_2CO_3\ (aq)$$

under acidic conditions, HCO_3^- can act as a Bronsted-base

I. DIFFERENTIATING ACIDIC AND BASIC SALTS

Salt solutions can be acidic, neutral, or basic. Let's consider a salt solution of NaF. NaF dissolves in water to form sodium and fluoride ions.

$$NaF(s) \xrightarrow[H_2O]{} Na^+(aq) + F^-(aq)$$

While the sodium ion is not reactive to water, the fluoride ion is reactive to water (fluoride is the conjugate base of a weak acid, HF). The fluoride ion can act as a base by accepting a proton from H2O by the process of hydrolysis. The reaction is shown below.

$$H_2O(l) + F^-(aq) \rightleftharpoons HF(aq) + OH^-(aq)$$

The increased presence of hydroxide ions (notice the formation of hydroxide ions as one of products of the hydrolysis reaction) makes the solution basic. This strategy can be used to predict whether a salt solution is acidic, basic, or neutral.

1. A salt of a strong base and a strong acid gives a neutral aqueous solution.
   Eg: NaCl is a salt of a strong acid (HCl) and a strong base (NaOH).
2. A salt of a weak acid and a strong base gives a basic aqueous solution.
   Eg: NaCN is a salt of a weak acid (HCN) and a strong base (NaOH).
3. A salt of a weak base and a strong acid gives an acidic aqueous solution.
   Eg: $Zn(NO)_3$ is salt of a weak base ($Zn(OH)_2$) and a strong acid (HNO_3).

J. BUFFERS

A solution which resists changes in pH when small amounts of acid or base are added to it is called a buffer solution. A buffer solution is usually a mixture of a weak acid and its conjugate base or a weak base and its conjugate acid. A buffer solution contains equilibrium amounts of acid and base species. Consider a buffer solution containing equal molar amounts of a weak acid (H_2CO_3) and its conjugate base (HCO_3^-).

$$H_2CO_3(aq) \rightleftharpoons H^+(aq) \;+\; HCO_3^-(aq)$$

If a strong acid is added to this buffer solution, the H^+ concentration increases and they react with the base (HCO_3^-) thereby decreasing the H^+ concentration and maintaining the initial pH. On the other hand, if a strong base is added, the OH^- ions supplied by it will react with the H^+ so that more of H_2CO_3 will dissociate thereby restoring the initial pH. In this case, when a strong acid is added, the equilibrium shifts to the left. When a strong base is added, the equilibrium shifts to the right. In both cases, the pH or the hydrogen ion concentration is maintained. This does not mean that a buffer solution can maintain a constant pH no matter how much acid or base is added. In other words, buffers do not have unlimited capacity to resist pH-change. The *buffer capacity* of a buffer depends on the nature of the buffer and the amount of acid and conjugate base present in the solution. The buffering capacity (the amount of acid or base the buffer can resist) of a buffer can be increased by increasing the concentration of the acid-conjugate pair. The Henderson-Hasselbalch equation can be used to relate the pH of a buffer and the concentrations of base and acid.

For a weak acid-conjugate base buffer, $pH = pK_a + \log \dfrac{[\text{conjugate base}]}{[\text{weak acid}]}$

In a weak acid buffer solution, when the concentrations of the weak acid and its conjugate base are equal the pH of the solution is equal to the pKa of the weak acid.

For a weak base-conjugate acid buffer, $pOH = pK_b + \log \dfrac{[\text{conjugate acid}]}{[\text{weak base}]}$

In a weak base buffer solution, when the concentrations of the weak base and its conjugate acid are equal the pOH of the solution is equal to the pKb of the weak base.

K. TITRATION CURVES OF ACIDS AND BASES

Acid-base titrations are reactions by which we can determine the amount of acid or base present in a solution. This is done by reacting the solution with a base or acid (of known concentration), and by measuring the volume of the known acid or base used up in the process. The reaction data is usually plotted with the volume of the substance (concentration known) in the x-axis, and the pH of the solution in the y-axis. The graph is called a titration curve.

Take a look at the first titration plot (Figure 9-1) given. You will see a steep region in the plot. The center of this steep region is called the equivalence point. The **equivalence point** denotes the point at which equivalent amounts of acid and base have reacted. To know the equivalence point, we usually add an indicator which will change its color close to the equivalence point. We can use the following relation to equate the amount of acid or base present in a solution against the volume of acid or base added whose concentration is known.

$$N_1 V_1 = N_2 V_2$$

where N_1 is the normality of the unknown acid or base,
N_2 is the normality of the known base or acid,
V_1 is the volume of unknown acid or base, and
V_2 is the volume of the known base or acid.

Indicators

An indicator is usually used to detect the equivalence point in an acid-base reaction or titration. The most common indicators used are weak organic acids or bases that change color in response to a change from acidic to basic medium or vice versa. The pH at which the color change occurs is characteristic of each indicator. For an acid-base reaction, the indicator is chosen based on the pH at which the equivalence point is expected to occur. Consider the hypothetical dissociation reaction of an indicator represented by HIn.

$$HIn \rightleftharpoons H^+ + In^-$$
yellow   blue
color   color

Let's consider a scenario in which the indicator is in an acidic solution. Acidic solution means there is excess H^+. So the equilibrium will shift to the left (LeChatelier's principle), and the predominant species will be HIn making the indicator show yellow color. On the other hand, in a basic solution, the equilibrium will shift favoring the forward reaction and the predominant species will be In⁻(blue color). Because HIn (acid form) and In have different colors, this can indicate the equivalence point of acid-base reactions. You might be thinking that the dissociation of the indicator used itself might change or affect the pH of the tested solution. But this is negligible because only a tiny amount of the indicator is needed to show a visible color change.

Table 9-2
Some Common Indicators

Indicator	Approx. pH Range of Color Change	Color Change
Thymol blue	1.2-2.8	Red to Yellow
Methyl Orange	3.2-4.4	Red to Yellow
Cresol Red	7.1-8.9	Yellow to Red
Thymol Blue	8.0-9.7	Yellow to Blue
Phenophthalein	8.3-10.0	Colorless to Pink
Alizarin Yellow	10.0-12.0	Yellow to red

Titration of a Strong Acid with a Strong Base

Consider the titration reaction involving HCl against NaOH. Let's say that we have 50 ml of a 0.1 M solution of HCl, titrated with 0.1 M solution of NaOH. As we add NaOH into the solution of HCl, initially the pH increase will not be very drastic. The pH increases slowly. When certain amount of NaOH is added, the change in pH becomes more drastic and the plot becomes very steep, as indicated in the plot (Figure 9-1). At this steep region, the equivalence point is reached. Can you guess the pH at the equivalence point? If you guessed 7, you are right. At the equivalence point of this titration you have a salt which is neutral, and hence the pH is 7.

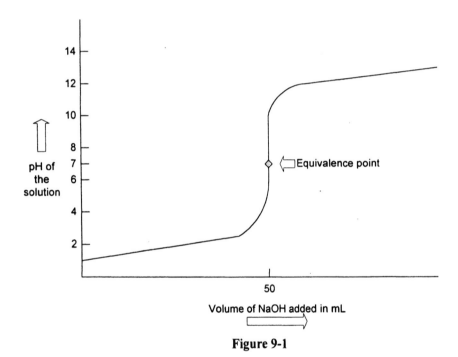

Figure 9-1

Titration of a Weak Acid with a Strong Base

The curve of a weak acid-strong base titration is different from that of the plot we learned for the strong acid-strong base titration. Unlike the previous curve, this plot will have a region which has buffering properties. Besides that, the equivalence point will be above the pH value 7. The general shape of the curve is shown in Figure 9-2.

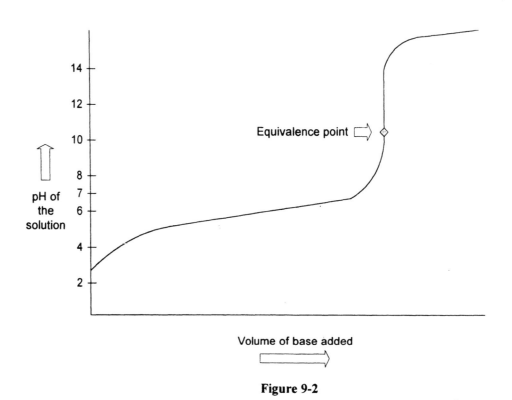

Figure 9-2

Titration of a Weak Base with a Strong Acid

The trend seen in the weak base-strong acid titration curve is somewhat similar to that of the weak acid-strong base curve. At first, as we add the acid, the pH slowly decreases. Then the decrease in pH becomes drastic, as you can see in Figure 9-3.

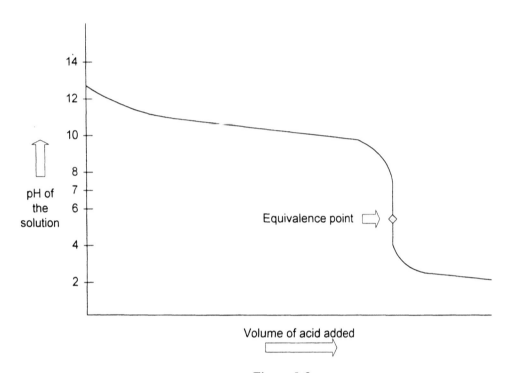

Figure 9-3

CHAPTER 9 PRACTICE QUESTIONS

1. If the pH of a solution is 2.5, what is the concentration of H_3O^+ in that solution?

   A. 2.9×10^{-1}
   B. 3.2×10^{-3}
   C. 3.8×10^{-2}
   D. 6.3×10^{-5}

2. NaCl solution is most likely:

   A. acidic.
   B. basic.
   C. neutral.
   D. cannot be predicted.

3. Which of the following is NOT a polyprotic acid?

   A. H_2SO_4
   B. $H_2PO_4^-$
   C. H_3AsO_4
   D. None of the above

4. Based on the equation,

   $$pOH = pK_b + \log \frac{[conjugate\ acid]}{[base]}$$

   which of the following is NOT valid?

   A. $\log K_b = \log [OH^-] + \log \dfrac{[conjugate\ acid]}{[base]}$

   B. $\log K_b = \log [OH^-] - \log \dfrac{[base]}{[conjugate\ acid]}$

   C. $\log K_b + \log [OH^-] = \log \dfrac{[conjugate\ acid]}{[base]}$

   D. None of the above are valid.

5. Which of the following species has the highest pKa value?

   A. $H_2PO_4^-$
   B. H_3PO_4
   C. HPO_4^{2-}
   D. All the above species have almost the same pKa values, since they all have the same type of phosphate anionic counterpart.

Questions 6-10 are based on the following passage.

Passage 1

   Strong acids and bases ionize completely in aqueous solutions. Weak acids and bases ionize only partially in aqueous solutions. An acid-base reaction is shown below. A titration was done by adding a base to a known concentration and fixed volume of an acid. The reaction follows:

Reaction 1

$$HClO_4\ (aq) + NaOH\ (aq) \longrightarrow NaClO_4\ (aq) + H_2O\ (l)$$

The dissociation of a weak acid can be represented as:

$$HA\ (aq) \longrightarrow H^+\ (aq) + A^-$$

Chemists often use Henderson-Hasselbach equation to calculate the pH of solutions containing a weak acid of known pKa, provided that the other concentrations are known. Henderson-Hasselbach equation is:

$$pH = pKa + \log \frac{[A^-]}{[HA]}$$

This equation is also used to calculate the buffering capability of solutions. It is roughly estimated that a given buffer is most likely to be effective at pH levels between (pKa + 1) and (pKa − 1).

6. The net ionic equation of Reaction 1 is:

A. $H^+ (aq) + OH^- (aq) \longrightarrow H_2O (l)$

B. $Na^+ (aq) + ClO_4^- (aq) \longrightarrow NaClO_4 (aq)$

C. $H^+ (aq) + ClO_4^- (aq) + Na^+(aq) + OH^-(aq)$
$\longrightarrow Na^+ (aq) + ClO_4^- (aq) + H_2O (l)$

D. Perchloric acid is a weak acid and cannot ionize completely, so that net ionic equation cannot be written.

7. The titration curve of the acid-base reaction (Reaction 1) is best represented by:

A.

B.

C.

D.

8. What are the base-to-acid ratios corresponding to the lower and upper limits of pH values which make the best buffer?

   A. 10 and 1
   B. 100 and 1
   C. 0.01 and 10
   D. 0.1 and 10

9. What is the pH of a 3.2×10^{-4} M solution
   of HCl?

   A. 2.7
   B. 3.5
   C. 4
   D. 4.4

10. The pH at which the base and the acid con-
    centrations equal in a buffer system is called
    the:

    A. equivalence point.
    B. pKa.
    C. neutralization point.
    D. non-buffering zone.

10

Thermodynamics

A. INTRODUCTION

In this chapter, the review will mainly focus on the laws of thermodynamics and their implications. The discussion includes concepts such as enthalpy, entropy, specific heat, heat capacity, Gibbs free energy, spontaneity of reactions, and related aspects. We have many ideas to discuss. So buckle up!

What is Thermodynamics?

In our busy modern life, we often forget about the fundamental aspects of today's life that make it so unique. Everyday we use machines and gadgets, big and small, which depend on some type of energy. We harvest the available energy and use it in many ways. But how is this done? We use natural energy sources such as coal, petroleum products, and nuclear energy. The question is, what are the fundamental principles regarding the harvesting of energy from these sources? It is by chemical reactions that we make use of the hidden energy available from these sources. What we learn from thermodynamics is the dynamics of energy (heat) transfer during chemical changes. In this chapter, we will review the various aspects of thermodynamics and the related principles.

B. THE FIRST LAW OF THERMODYNAMICS

According to the **first law of thermodynamics**, energy is neither created nor destroyed, which also implies that the total energy present in the whole universe is constant. Based on this law, we can say that the energy is just taken from one form and converted to another form. This is exactly what we are doing when we are burning fuels such as gasoline to get sufficient energy to run the internal combustion engine, or when we are using nuclear reactions to turn the turbines of a nuclear power plant to make electricity.

Basic Aspects of Thermodynamics

First, let's talk about internal energy. **Internal energy** of a substance is the total energy present in the particular quantity of that substance. For a chemical reaction or a physical change of reactants, the change in internal energy (ΔE) of the reactants is expressed as follows:

Change in internal energy,

ΔE = Final internal energy (E_{final}) – Initial internal energy ($E_{initial}$)

$$\Delta E = Q + W$$

Here, Q represents the heat and W represents the work done.

Based on the above equation, these conventions are followed:

When heat is absorbed by a system, heat (Q) is positive.
When heat is given off by a system, heat (Q) is negative.
When work is done on a system, work (W) is positive.
When work is done by a system, work (W) is negative.

C. ENDOTHERMIC AND EXOTHERMIC REACTIONS

The change in heat for chemical reactions at constant pressure is called **enthalpy change**, denoted by ΔH. The change in enthalpy (ΔH) of a reaction is represented as shown below:

$$\Delta H = H_{products} - H_{reactants}$$

If the reaction is **endothermic**, the change in enthalpy is positive. In an endothermic reaction, the enthalpy of the reactants is less than the enthalpy of the products. So the reaction is accomplished by supplying energy to the reaction. On the other hand, the change in enthalpy is negative if the reaction is **exothermic**. Energy is released in this case. Also it is worth remembering that in an exothermic reaction, the enthalpy of the reactants is greater than the enthalpy of the products. Hence, if we have the enthalpy data, we can predict whether the reaction is endothermic or exothermic.

D. LAW OF HEAT SUMMATION

According to the **law of heat summation** put forth by Henri Hess, we can find the total enthalpy of a reaction by adding the enthalpy changes of the individual steps in a reaction. It doesn't really matter if the reaction occurs in many steps or in one step. As long as the enthalpy values that we sum up are correct, we will get the overall enthalpy change.

> *Law of heat summation: The total enthalpy of a reaction can be derived by adding the enthalpy changes of the individual steps in the reaction.*

Example 10-1

Calculate the ΔH of the reaction between HCl and fluorine, forming HF and chlorine. The enthalpies of the related reactions are also given.

$$2\,HCl\,(g) \;+\; F_2 \longrightarrow 2\,HF\,(l) \;+\; Cl_2\,(g)$$

		ΔH
(Reaction 1)	$HCl\,(g) + 1/4\,O_2\,(g) \longrightarrow 1/2\,H_2O\,(l) + 1/2\,Cl_2\,(g)$	-37.1 kJ/mol
(Reaction 2)	$2\,HF\,(l) \longrightarrow H_2\,(g) + F_2\,(g)$	$+1200$ kJ/mol
(Reaction 3)	$H_2\,(g) + 1/2\,O_2\,(g) \longrightarrow H_2O\,(l)$	-285.8 kJ/mol

Solution:

	ΔH
$2\,HCl\,(g) + 1/2\,O_2\,(g) \longrightarrow H_2O\,(l) + Cl_2\,(g)$	-74.2 kJ/mol
$H_2\,(g) + F_2\,(g) \longrightarrow 2\,HF\,(l)$	-1200 kJ/mol
$H_2O\,(l) \longrightarrow H_2\,(g) + 1/2\,O_2\,(g)$	$+285.8$ kJ/mol
Overall reaction: $2\,HCl\,(g) + F_2 \longrightarrow 2\,HF\,(l) + Cl_2\,(g)$	-988.4 kJ/mol

The individual reactions that are given have to be reversed if necessary, so that the sum of the sub-reactions will add up to the overall equation. Reaction 1 should be multiplied by 2. The second and third reactions should be reversed. This applies to the corresponding enthalpy values as well. That means, if the reaction is reversed the sign of the corresponding change in enthalpy should also be reversed. The enthalpy of the overall reaction is −988.4 kJ/mol.

E. THE SECOND LAW OF THERMODYNAMICS

We learned how to predict the mode of a reaction in terms of whether the reaction will be endothermic or exothermic. In this section, we will explore the dynamics and the factors that influence the spontaneity of reactions. For that, we have to be familiar with the term "entropy."

Entropy (S) is the measure of how disordered a system is. The entropy is dependent on the prevailing conditions such as pressure and temperature. From the MCAT point view, the values of entropy and related aspects that you will be dealing with are at standard state. The standard state refers to 1 atm and 25° C.

> *Entropy of a system is the measure of disorder or randomness of the system.*

Let's talk more about entropy. The higher the disorder is, the greater the entropy of that system. In terms of the phases of matter, think about which phases will have a higher entropy. We can generalize that the gas phase of a substance has higher entropy than its liquid phase, and the liquid phase has higher entropy than its corresponding solid phase. Thus, as the temperature increases the entropy increases. The change in entropy (ΔS) is equal to the final entropy minus the initial entropy.

$$\Delta S = S_{final} - S_{initial}$$

According to the **second law of thermodynamics**, there is an overall natural tendency toward disorder. You have to understand that we are talking about the overall entropy. Do not confuse this with the fact that we sometimes look at individual systems or reactions and categorize them as having either increasing entropy or decreasing entropy. But the overall entropy of all the events together is increasing.

Example 10-2

Predict whether the entropy is increasing or decreasing for the following change.

$$CO_2\ (s) \longrightarrow CO_2\ (g)$$

Solution:

The question asks whether the entropy of the system is increasing or decreasing for the above written equation. Your response should be that there is an increase in entropy. Why? As we discussed, the change in phase is the key aspect to watch here. Carbon dioxide is changing from its solid form to gaseous form. Hence, the randomness of the system is increasing. So the entropy is increasing.

Example 10-3

Predict whether the entropy of the system is increasing as the reaction given below goes to completion.

$$2\ C_2H_2\ (g)\ +\ 5\ O_2\ (g)\ \longrightarrow\ 4\ CO_2\ (g)\ +\ 2\ H_2O\ (g)$$

Solution:

The reaction shown above is the combustion reaction of acetylene. This reaction is made use of in welding, commonly called the "acetylene torch." Tremendous amount of heat is liberated as a result of this reaction and is used for welding purposes. As you can see from the equation, the number of moles of the reactants is greater than the number of moles of the products. Thus, as the reaction proceeds, there is a decrease in the number of moles of gas. If you predicted a decrease in entropy, your answer is correct.

F. THE THIRD LAW OF THERMODYNAMICS

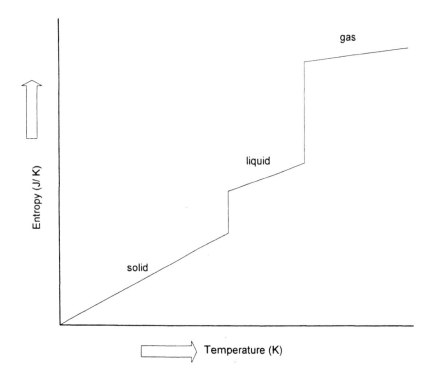

Figure 10-1 Entropy versus temperature

Let's state the **third law of thermodynamics**. The law states that pure and perfect crystalline substances have an entropy of zero at 0 Kelvin. What does that mean? It means that a pure crystalline substance will have perfect order at absolute zero temperature. An increase in temperature will destroy this zero entropy. By looking at the graph (Figure 10-1), it is clear that an increase in temperature increases the entropy.

G. FREE ENERGY

Free energy denoted by the letter G is a thermodynamic quantity, with which we can predict the spontaneity of a reaction. The change in free energy (ΔG) is related to the changes in enthalpy and entropy, and temperature as indicated by the equation:

$$\Delta G = \Delta H - T\Delta S$$

Here, ΔG represents the change in free energy, ΔH represents the change in enthalpy, ΔS represents the change in entropy, and T represents the temperature.

How Can We Predict Spontaneity?

On the basis of free energy change we can predict the spontaneity of a reaction. You should be able to manipulate the above mentioned equation, and once you have found the free energy change, you can do the prediction using the following guidelines.

If ΔG is positive, the reaction generally is nonspontaneous. If ΔG is negative, then the reaction is generally spontaneous. The changes in free energy and spontaneity depend on the change in enthalpy as well as the change in entropy. Besides these two important factors, the temperature at which the reaction takes place also plays a major role in dictating the spontaneity of reactions. Take a look at Table 10-1.

Table 10-1

ΔG	ΔH	ΔS
Spontaneous at all temperatures	–	+
Spontaneous at low temperatures	–	–
Spontaneous at high temperatures	+	+
Nonspontaneous at all temperatures	+	–

H. TEMPERATURE – SOME BASICS

We use the term temperature quite a lot in Chemistry, but how can we define it? Students often get confused with the terms temperature and heat. Even though temperature and heat are related, they are not the same. Let us consider two objects that are at different temperatures; a hot object and a cold object. Let's say we kept them in close proximity for some time. The heat passes from the hot object to the cold one, until they reach equilibrium. So it is the heat (energy) that passes from the hot object to the cold one resulting in a change in temperature.

The common scales used to denote temperature are the Celsius scale and the Kelvin scale (K). The SI unit of temperature is actually kelvin (K). The Celsius and the Kelvin scales can be easily converted back and forth, and are related by the following simple relations:

$$K = \,^{\circ}C \,+\, 273.15$$
$$or$$
$$^{\circ}C = K - 273.15$$

The other temperature scale that we are more familiar with is the Fahrenheit scale. Temperature denoted in degree Celsius can be converted to degree Fahrenheit using the following relation:

$$F = (\,^{\circ}C \times 1.8\,) \,+\, 32$$

You are expected to know these conversions at this level of study in college. So know them!

CHAPTER 10 PRACTICE QUESTIONS

1. Bomb calorimeter is a device used to determine the energy changes associated with reactions. The calorimeter measures the heat absorbed or evolved during a reaction. Which of the following is true with respect to bomb calorimeter?

   A. The measurements are done at constant volume.
   B. The measurements are not done at constant volume, because we cannot keep the volume constant.
   C. Theoretically work is done during the reaction in a bomb calorimeter.
   D. None of the above.

2. Consider the figure shown below in which ice is melted to form water. Which of the following is true regarding this conversion?

   A. Entropy is decreased.
   B. Entropy is increased.

   C. Entropy is not affected since the change does not constitute an actual reaction, but only a change in physical state of H_2O.
   D. Randomness is decreased.

3. If the change in free energy of a reaction is zero at constant temperature and pressure, what is true regarding such a system?

   A. The reaction is spontaneous.
   B. The reaction is nonspontaneous.
   C. The reaction is at its equilibrium state.
   D. Cannot be predicted.

4. Mercury sulfide can be converted to mercury by heating while exposed to air. What is probably true about this reaction?

   $$HgS\ (s)\ +\ O_2\ (g)\ \longrightarrow Hg\ (l)\ +\ SO_2\ (g)$$

   A. The reaction is nonspontaneous.
   B. The reaction is endothermic.
   C. O_2 acts as the catalyst.
   D. None of the above can be ascertained without further data.

5. All the following are FALSE regarding entropy, EXCEPT:

   A. the entropy of pure substance at 0 K temperature is greater than 1.
   B. the entropy of pure substance at 0 K temperature is between 0 & 1.
   C. the entropy of pure substance at 0 K temperature is 0.
   D. the entropy of pure substance at 0 K temperature is a negative number.

11

Equilibrium and Kinetics

A. INTRODUCTION

Different chemical reactions occur at different rates. Some reactions occur very fast, whereas some others take years and years to complete. A better understanding of chemical kinetics (the study of reaction rates) and equilibrium enables chemists to optimize the production of desirable products. This exploration of chemical kinetics has increased the understanding of biochemical pathways and other pharmaceutical endeavors. We will also discuss catalysts and their effects on reactions.

B. RATE OF REACTION

The rate of a reaction depends on many factors such as the concentration of reactants, the temperature at the time of the reaction, the states of reactants, and catalysts. The **rate of a reaction** is defined as the change of reactant or product concentration in unit time. If we were to define the rate of a reaction in terms of the reactants, we should define the rate as the rate of disappearance of reactants. If we were to define the rate in terms of the products formed, we should define it as the rate of appearance of products.

For further exploration of this concept, let's look at a hypothetical reaction. In the hypothetical representative reaction shown below, the small letters denote the coefficients of the corresponding capital letter reactants or products. In this reaction, A and B are reactants, and a and b their coefficients respectively. X and Y are the products, and x and y their coefficients respectively.

$$a\,A + b\,B \longrightarrow x\,X + y\,Y$$

For this reaction, we can represent the rate in terms of the disappearance of each reactant or appearance of each product. The numerators are the concentrations of either the reactant or the product, and Δt represents the elapsed time.

$$\text{Rate} = -\frac{\Delta [A]}{\Delta t}$$

We can also represent it in terms of reactant B. That looks the same as the rate in terms of concentration of A. In order to express it in terms of B's concentration, substitute the numerator with the concentration of B. The minus sign convention indicates that the rate is expressed in terms of the rate of disappearance (decreasing concentration) of the reactants.

$$\text{Rate} = -\frac{\Delta [B]}{\Delta t}$$

Also shown below are the representations of the rate in terms of the products:

$$\text{Rate} = \frac{\Delta [X]}{\Delta t} \qquad\qquad \text{Rate} = \frac{\Delta [Y]}{\Delta t}$$

Rate Law

Rate law is an expression that we can find experimentally, which relates the concentration of reactants and the rate of a reaction. Let's consider the same hypothetical equation:

$$a\,A + b\,B \longrightarrow x\,X + y\,Y$$

For this reaction, we can write the rate as follows:

$$\text{Rate} = k\,[A]^m\,[B]^n$$

Here, k is the rate constant,
m and n are the corresponding exponential values, and
[A] and [B] are the concentrations of reactants A and B.

Note that the rate constant and the exponents of a reaction are found experimentally. For questions related to finding the actual rate expression of a reaction, you will be given the relevant experimental data. We will look at some examples to familiarize ourselves with this concept.

We mentioned the exponent values (for this reaction, we represented them as m and n) in the rate law. Those exponents represent the order with respect to a particular reactant, or by adding all the exponents, you will get overall **order of the reaction**. For our hypothetical reaction, the reaction order with respect to reactant A is m. The order with respect to reactant B is n. The overall order of the reaction is m+n. That is one way to determine the order of a reaction. Chemists categorize them as first order, second order, etc. You may have heard of zero order. In some reactions, even if a reactant appears in the balanced equation of a reaction, it may not appear in the experimentally found rate expression. The reason for this is that the particular reactant that does not appear in the rate expression has an exponent of 0. So the order with respect to that reactant is zero.

Example 11-1

From the given experimental data, determine the rate law of the hypothetical reaction indicated below:

$$P + 2Q \longrightarrow PQ_2$$

Experiment	Initial concentration of P	Initial concentration of Q	Initial Rate of product formation
1	0.20 M	0.20 M	0.012 M/min
2	0.20 M	0.40 M	0.048 M/min
3	0.40 M	0.40 M	0.096 M/min

Solution:

The rate of the reaction will have the general look as shown. Assume that the rate law of the reaction is:

$$Rate = k[P]^m[Q]^n.$$

The plan is to find out the actual values of m and n from the given data. Let's do it step by step.

Look at the given experimental data. If we compare Experiments 1 and 2, we can see that the concentration of Q is doubled in Experiment 2. But the concentration of P is kept constant. With these changes, we see the quadrupling of the rate. That means the exponent of Q is 2. At this point we can rewrite the rate law as follows:

$$Rate = k\,[\,P\,]^m\,[\,Q\,]^2$$

Now compare Experiments 2 and 3. Here the concentration of Q is kept constant, but the concentration of P is doubled. The rate is doubling because of this change. So the exponent of P is 1. We can now write the completed rate law of the reaction.

$$Rate = k\,[\,P\,]\,[\,Q\,]^2$$

C. TRANSITION STATE

From our earlier discussions, we know that exothermic reactions release energy and endothermic reactions consume energy. Here, we will plot the potential energy diagrams of exothermic and endothermic reactions. Before we do that, we will discuss the concept of transition state. Consider the hypothetical reaction shown below:

$$A + B \longrightarrow X + Y + \text{heat energy}$$

Can you say what type of reaction this is? It is an exothermic reaction. For reactions to proceed, there should be breaking of bonds and formation of bonds. For many reactions, the stability barrier that originally made the reactant molecules stable should be overcome. This is achieved by the formation of an energy-state that has higher energy than the reactants and the products. This high-energy state is often referred as **transition state**. These transition states have a relatively short life span, and once this highly unstable transition state is formed, it quickly disintegrates to form the products. For a reaction to reach this transition energy level, a certain amount of energy is required. This energy is called the **activation energy** or the energy of activation.

In the diagram (Figure 11-1), the activation energy depicted in both Figures (a) and (b) are for the forward reactions.

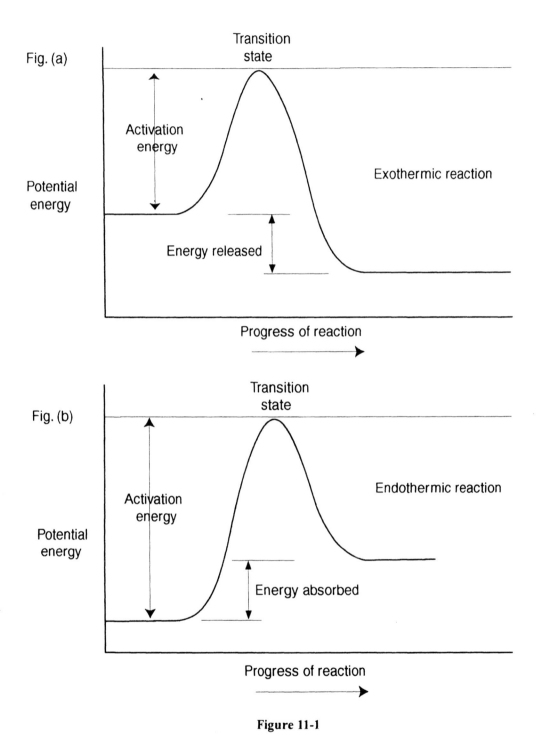

Figure 11-1

D. TEMPERATURE DEPENDANCE OF RATE

The rate of a reaction depends on the prevailing temperature. Hence, the rate law is dependent on the temperature at which the reaction takes place. The reactants must attain a high energy form (transition state) in order for the reaction to occur. For this, the activated reactive species must collide (with feasible orientation) with each other with a minimum kinetic energy which is greater than that of the reactants. This kinetic energy depends on the temperature of the system in which the reaction takes place. At a particular temperature, some of the reactants will attain the activation energy to undergo the reaction. If we increase the temperature, more reactant molecules will attain this energy. More reactants attaining the required energy level means more reaction is taking place.

A mathematical relationship was introduced by Arrhenius. The expression relating the rate constant and the energy of activation is:

$$k = A\,e^{-E_a/RT},$$

where k is the rate constant of the reaction,
E_a is the activation energy,
R is the gas constant (8.31 J/mol.K), and
T is the temperature.

There is no need to memorize this equation, but you should understand how to work with the equation conceptually.

E. A BRIEF LOOK AT CATALYSTS

We all have heard of catalysts. In lay terms we know that catalysts speed up reactions. But the question is how do they accomplish this? Consider the formal definition of a catalyst.

A catalyst is a chemical substance that can increase the rate of a reaction. Even if the catalyst is involved in the reaction, by the end of the reaction you will get the catalyst intact. In other words, the catalyst retains its identity. If a substance changes its identity and does not have the original nature after the reaction has occurred, it is not a catalyst, but a reactant.

As we said earlier, the **activation energy** is the minimum energy required by the reactants to reach the transition state. A catalyst lowers the activation energy of a reaction. Thus it provides a lower energy pathway for the reaction to occur. So the transition state bump in the potential energy diagram (see Figure 11-2) is lowered in a catalyzed reaction, compared to the corresponding uncatalyzed reaction.

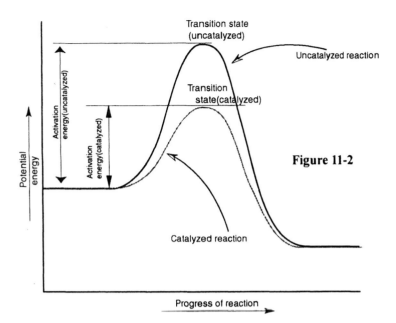

Figure 11-2

Catalysts are often classified on the basis of the phases (solid, liquid, and gas) in which they exist during a chemical reaction. If a catalyst exists in the same phase as the reactants of a reaction, then it is called a homogeneous catalyst. If a catalyst's phase is different from that of the reactants of a reaction, then it is called a heterogeneous catalyst.

F. CHEMICAL EQUILIBRIUM

Many reactions are reversible. **Reversible reactions** are reactions in which there are both forward and backward reactions. Consider an experiment in which two reactants have been mixed. At first, the reaction proceeds with considerable rate in the forward direction (forward reaction favored). Before the reaction goes on to completion, the backward reaction takes place. Then again the forward reaction takes place, followed by the backward reaction and so on. These uneven back-and-forth directional changes take place until the reaction mixture reaches the equilibrium. At the equilibrium, the rate will be the same for both forward and backward reactions.

The Equilibrium Constant

We already talked about the rate of a reaction and its general expression. For reactions involving simple one-step mechanisms, we can easily write the rates of forward and backward reactions. Examine a one-step hypothetical reaction represented by the equation (balanced) given below:

$$a \, A + b \, B \longrightarrow c \, C + d \, D$$

The **equilibrium constant** of a reversible reaction is equal to the ratio of the product of the concentrations of the products raised to their corresponding coefficients, to the product of the concentrations of the reactants raised to their corresponding coefficients. Keep in mind that the coefficients are taken from the balanced equation. To further clarify this concept, take a look at the mathematical expression for equilibrium constant (K_c) shown below:

$$Kc = \frac{[C]^c[D]^d}{[A]^a[B]^b}$$

The best way to find out the equilibrium constant of a particular reaction at a given condition is to do it experimentally. Equilibrium constant depends on temperature, and hence it differs with change in temperature. You should also ask yourself this question. Does the initial concentration of the reactants dictate the equilibrium constant? The answer is no.

We can also explore the meaning of equilibrium constant in terms of forward and backward reactions. A small value (less than one) for the equilibrium constant indicates that the forward reaction is not favored. A value greater than one for the equilibrium constant indicates that the forward reaction is favored.

G. FACTORS THAT AFFECT THE EQUILIBRIUM OF REACTIONS

The equilibrium of a reaction is affected by factors such as changes in concentration, pressure, and temperature. The likely resulting changes in equilibrium can be predicted on the basis of Le Chatelier's principle which can be stated as follows:

If we change the conditions (factors such as the ones mentioned above) of a reaction system in equilibrium, the system will shift in such a way as to reduce the imbalance caused by the stress. This is Le Chatelier's principle.

Based on this principle, we will look at some of the factors that affect the equilibrium of reactions.

Effect of Temperature

What is your first instinct when you think of a reaction scenario in which the temperature is changed? It is true that the reaction rate will change. We might even think that the reaction rates of all reactions invariably increase. This is not true. Even though many reactions speed up with the increase in temperature, that is not always the case. Consider the reaction given below:

$$N_2\,(g) + 3\,H_2\,(g) \rightleftharpoons 2\,NH_3\,(g) + heat$$

The reaction between nitrogen and hydrogen to give ammonia is an exo-thermic reaction. The reaction produces heat energy during the forward reac-tion. For this reaction at equilibrium, if we increase the temperature, it will only facilitate the backward reaction. Now we will consider another reaction.

$$C \ (s) \ + \ H_2O \ (g) \ + \ heat \ \rightleftharpoons \ CO \ (g) \ + \ H_2 \ (g)$$

For this reaction, we are supplying heat. So what kind of reaction is it? It is an endothermic reaction. If we subject this reaction in equilibrium to an increase in temperature, the forward reaction will be favored. We can generalize our observations as follows:

An increase in temperature favors endothermic reactions. An increase in temperature decreases the reaction rate, if the reaction is exothermic.

Effect of Pressure

The effects of pressure are significant in reactions involving gases. Think about what happens when we increase the pressure of a reaction in equilibrium. When the pressure is increased, the equilibrium no longer exists. Consider the reaction given below.

$$N_2 \ (g) \ + \ 3 \ H_2 \ (g) \ \rightleftharpoons \ 2 \ NH_3 \ (g)$$

The direction of reactions can be predicted based on Le Chatelier's principle. For the above reaction, if the pressure is increased the forward reaction is favored. Why is the forward reaction favored? The reason is that the forward reaction will result in less moles of gas, thereby decreasing the strain caused by the increased pressure. This influence of pressure will not affect the reaction if the total number of moles of reactants and the total number of moles of products are equal. The influence of pressure is not seen with reactants or products which are either in their solid or liquid state because they are almost non-compressible.

CHAPTER 11 PRACTICE QUESTIONS

1. Choose the correct equilibrium expression for the following reaction.

$$N_2 \,(g) + 3\,H_2 \,(g) \rightleftharpoons 2\,NH_3 \,(g)$$

A. $K = \dfrac{[\,NH_3]}{[\,N_2\,]\,[\,H_2\,]}$

B. $K = \dfrac{[\,N_2\,]\,[\,H_2\,]^3}{[\,NH_3]^2}$

C. $K = \dfrac{[\,N_2\,]\,[\,H_2\,]}{[\,NH_3]}$

D. $K = \dfrac{[\,NH_3]^2}{[\,N_2\,]\,[\,H_2\,]^3}$

2. Based on the given data, what is the rate law of the following hypothetical reaction?

$$X + Y \rightarrow Z$$

Concentration of X	Concentration of Y	Initial Rate
0.02	0.02	2.0×10^{-5}
0.02	0.04	4.0×10^{-5}
0.04	0.04	1.6×10^{-4}
0.04	0.08	3.2×10^{-4}

A. Rate = k [Y]
B. Rate = k [X] [Y]
C. Rate = k [X]² [Y]
D. Rate = k [X] [Y]²

3. Which of the following factors will affect the rate of a reaction?

A. The concentration of reactants
B. Temperature
C. The state of reactants
D. All the above

4. Figure 1 represents the potential energy diagram of a reaction. Pick the true statement regarding this reaction.

Fig. 1

P.E.

Time (reaction coordinate)

A. The reaction requires no activation energy, since it is spontaneous.
B. There is a net absorption of energy by the reaction.
C. Reactants have lower energy than that of the products.
D. None of the above.

5. Which of the following is true regarding catalysts?

   A. Catalysts can change the rate of a reaction.
   B. Catalysts increase the activation energy.
   C. Catalysts are often consumed completely by the reactants.
   D. All the above.

Questions 6-13 are based on the following passage.

Passage 1

At this point of advancements in science, chemists have a good understanding of the kinetics of reactions. They can predict the effects of changes in pH, temperature, and concentration in chemical reactions.

Experiment 1

In a cylinder, there is a reaction mixture of hydrogen and iodine. The hydrogen and the iodine react to form hydrogen iodide.

$$H_2(g) \;+\; I_2(g) \;\rightleftharpoons\; 2HI(g) \qquad \text{(Reaction 1)}$$

The industrial production of ammonia is done by a process called Haber process. The reaction occurs as shown below, and is usually done in the presence of an iron catalyst.

$$N_2(g) \;+\; 3H_2(g) \;\rightleftharpoons\; 2NH_3(g) \qquad \text{(Reaction 2)}$$
$$\Delta H = -92kJ$$

6. If the reverse reaction of Reaction 1 is endothermic, what is the sign of ΔH of the reaction in which HI is on the product side?

   A. Positive
   B. Negative
   C. Neither positive nor negative, because the reaction is reversible
   D. Cannot be predicted, because more data is required regarding the individual enthalpy values

7. Which of the following is most likely to occur, if we take away H_2 from the reaction mixture in Reaction 1?

   A. The reaction will proceed to the right.
   B. The reaction will suddenly reach equilibrium.
   C. The reaction will proceed to the left.
   D. No apparent effect will be observed.

8. If the pressure applied to Reaction 1 is decreased, what is the most likely effect?

   A. The equilibrium will shift toward the left.
   B. The equilibrium will shift toward the right.
   C. There will be no effect on the equilibrium.
   D. The volume of the system will decrease.

9. A student researcher conducted experiments on the effects of changes in the conditions on reactions. The student did the experiments with Reaction 2, by increasing the pressure on the cylinder where the reaction mixture was present. Which of the following are completely true regarding the experiment?

   I. The reaction will shift toward the right, because there are more moles on the product side.
   II. The reaction will shift toward the left, because there are more moles on the reactant side.
   III. The reaction will have increased production of ammonia, because there are more moles on the reactant side.

   A. I only
   B. II only
   C. III only
   D. II & III

10. Which of the following best explains the theory behind the predictions of the effects of increasing the concentrations of reactants or products in a reaction system?

    A. Dalton's law
    B. Markovnikov's principle
    C. De Broglie principle
    D. Le Chatelier's principle

11. If 70 g of nitrogen is reacted with hydrogen, how many grams of ammonia will be produced ? (The weight of hydrogen used =10 g)

    A. 42.5 g
    B. 57 g
    C. 85 g
    D. 17 g

12. In Reaction 2 for the production of ammonia from nitrogen and hydrogen, what is most likely to be true about entropy?

    A. Entropy increases and is positive
    B. Entropy decreases and is negative
    C. Entropy increases and is negative
    D. Entropy increases and is positive

13. In the Haber process for the production of ammonia, what can you say about the spontaneity of the reaction with the available information in the passage?

    A. The reaction is definitely spontaneous.
    B. The reaction is definitely nonspontaneous.
    C. The reaction is endothermic, and definitely spontaneous.
    D. Cannot be predicted accurately without further data.

12

Electrochemistry

A. INTRODUCTION

Electrochemistry is the study of chemical reactions that result in the production of electric current, and chemical reactions that occur when subjected to electric current. Electrochemical applications are part of everybody's day-to-day life. Energy storing batteries that we use for TV remotes, flashlights, automobiles are a few examples. Electroplating is another achievement among many others. In this chapter, our discussion will revolve around two types of electrochemical cells – the electrolytic cell and the galvanic cell.

B. ELECTROLYTIC CELL

In an electrolytic cell, electric current drives the chemical reaction. The chemical reaction involved in an electrolytic cell is nonspontaneous. Electric current is used to drive the reaction. This process is called **electrolysis** and hence the name, electrolytic cell. The reaction involves the transfer of electrons and thus it is a redox reaction. For further understanding of the functioning of an electrolytic cell, we will look at an example of an electrolytic cell involving the electrolysis of molten sodium chloride. Molten sodium chloride is a good conductor of electricity. The melting point of NaCl is around $800°$ C.

The cell contains molten sodium chloride into which two electrodes are immersed, as shown in Figure 12-1. One electrode is connected to the positive terminal of the battery, and the other is connected to the negative terminal of the battery. The electrode that is connected to the positive terminal of the battery is the anode. The other electrode is the cathode. **Reduction** occurs at the cathode, and **oxidation** occurs at the anode. When the current starts flowing the reaction starts, as described below:

Figure 12-1 Electrolytic cell set up showing the electrolysis of molten NaCl

As the reaction proceeds, the sodium ions (Na^+) are reduced to sodium (Na) at the cathode, and the sodium metal is deposited at the cathode. On the other hand, the chloride (Cl^-) ions are oxidized at the anode forming chlorine gas (Cl_2). The half-reactions and the overall reaction are represented below:

$$Cl^-(l) \longrightarrow \tfrac{1}{2}Cl_2\,(g) \;+\; e^- \qquad \text{Anode}$$

$$Na^+(l) + e^- \longrightarrow Na\,(l) \qquad\qquad \text{Cathode}$$

$$\overline{Na^+(l) \;+\; Cl^- \longrightarrow Na\,(l) \;+\; \tfrac{1}{2}\,Cl_2\,(g)} \qquad \text{Overall reaction}$$

C. FARADAY'S LAW

According to **Faraday's law**, the amount of substance that undergoes oxidation-reduction reaction at the electrodes is directly proportional to the amount of electric current that the reaction is subjected to. Faraday constant is equal to the charge of one mol of electrons, and is numerically equal to 96500 coulombs. You probably remember 'coulombs' from your physics undergraduate courses. The unit coulomb is related to the unit *ampere* (*SI* unit of current).

> amperes × seconds = coulombs
> current × time = charge

D. GALVANIC CELL

Galvanic cell is also known as voltaic cell. The major difference between an electrolytic cell and a galvanic cell is that the reaction in a galvanic cell is spontaneous, and the reaction produces electric current. The batteries that we use in TV remotes and flash lights are galvanic cells. Galvanic cells convert the stored chemical energy into electrical energy for usage.

A galvanic cell has two half-cells. Each half-cell consists of a metal electrode immersed in a solution containing the same ions. The two half-cells are connected by a wire as shown in Figure 12-2. As we mentioned earlier, the galvanic cell produces electric current. Thus the voltage developed can be measured by setting a voltmeter along the connecting wire, as seen in the figure.

Here, we will look at a cell setup which uses zinc and copper as the electrodes. In addition to the electrodes, the two containers which hold the appropriate solutions and the connecting wire, there is a salt bridge which connects the two solutions. The **salt bridge** is usually dipped into the solutions of the two half-cells. It contains a gel in which an electrolyte is present. The electrolyte present in the salt bridge will neutralize the buildup of ionic charge in the cells; a buildup which will otherwise slow down and stop the reaction from proceeding.

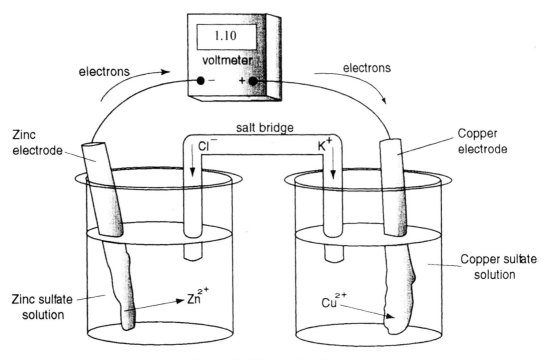

Figure 12-2 Galvanic cell

In the zinc half-cell, a zinc electrode is immersed in zinc sulfate solution. In the copper half-cell, a copper electrode is immersed in copper sulfate solution. The two electrodes are connected by a wire through which there will be flow of electrons resulting from the reaction. The half-reactions are shown below:

$$Zn\ (s) \longrightarrow Zn^{2+}\ (aq)\ +\ 2e^-\qquad \text{(Oxidation half-reaction)}$$

$$Cu^{2+}\ (aq)\ +\ 2e^- \longrightarrow Cu\ (s)\qquad \text{(Reduction half-reaction)}$$

$$Cu^{2+}\ (aq)\ +\ Zn\ (s) \longrightarrow Cu\ (s)\ +\ Zn^{2+}\ (aq)\qquad \text{(Overall reaction)}$$

The process of **oxidation** occurs at the **anode** and the process of **reduction** occurs at the **cathode**. So the first half-reaction (oxidation half-reaction) occurs at the anode, and second half-reaction (reduction half-reaction) occurs at the cathode. The overall reaction can be obtained by adding the two half reactions. Here, the zinc electrode is the anode, and the copper electrode is the cathode. In a galvanic cell, the anode is the negative electrode and the cathode is the positive electrode. As far as electron flow is concerned, the flow is always from the anode to the cathode.

Let's take a look at Figure 12-2 again. Notice the irregular edges of the electrodes. Why is that so? The reason is simple. As the reaction proceeds, zinc is stripped away from the zinc electrode, and thus it becomes thinner and thinner until the reaction stops (when it is at equilibrium). On the other hand, the copper electrode becomes thicker and thicker due to the deposition of metal copper on the copper electrode.

The half-reactions are often represented by the notation shown below. By convention, the oxidation reaction is written on the left of the symbol denoting the salt bridge, and the reduction reaction is written on the right side of the salt bridge symbol.

Anode half-reaction   Cathode half-reaction

$$Zn \mid Zn^{2+} \parallel Cu^{2+} \mid Cu$$

$\parallel$ denotes salt bridge

Note: See Table 12-2 at the end of this chapter for electrolytic versus galvanic cell comparison.

E. STANDARD ELECTRODE POTENTIALS

Before we discuss standard electrode potential, we will talk about electromotive force (emf). The **electromotive force** of a cell is the potential difference between the two electrodes. This can be measured using a voltmeter. The maximum voltage of a cell can be calculated using experimentally determined values called **standard electrode potentials**. By convention, the standard electrode potentials are usually represented in terms of reduction half-reactions for 1 molar solute concentration. The standard electrode potential values are set under ideal and standard-state conditions (1 atm pressure and 25°C temperature). From the MCAT point of view, you can assume that the conditions are standard, unless stated otherwise. Table 12-1 shows a list of standard electrode potentials (in aqueous solution) at 25°C.

The standard electrode potential at the above mentioned standard state conditions is denoted by $E°$. For the MCAT, the values of the standard electrode (reduction) potentials will be given to you if you are required to solve such a question. Do not try to memorize those values. The standard electrode potentials are based on an arbitration with reference to standard hydrogen electrode. The standard hydrogen electrode potential is considered to be 0 volt.

Table 12-1 Some Standard Electrode (Reduction) Potentials

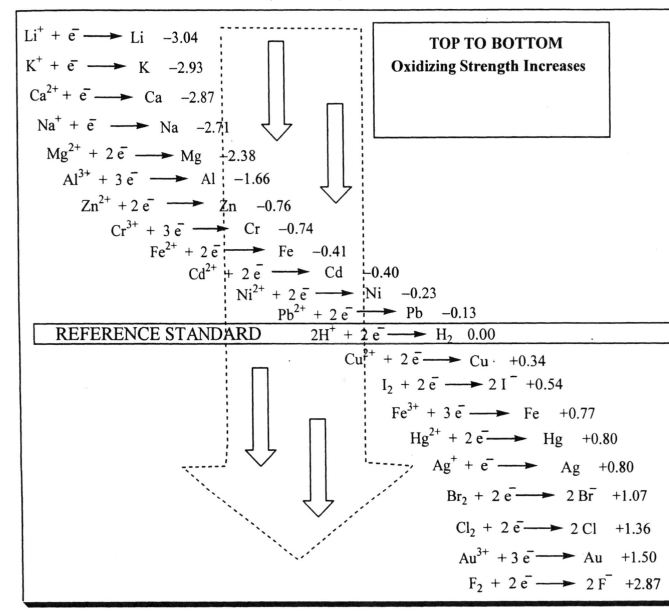

$Li^+ + e^- \longrightarrow Li \quad -3.04$

$K^+ + e^- \longrightarrow K \quad -2.93$

$Ca^{2+} + e^- \longrightarrow Ca \quad -2.87$

$Na^+ + e^- \longrightarrow Na \quad -2.71$

$Mg^{2+} + 2e^- \longrightarrow Mg \quad -2.38$

$Al^{3+} + 3e^- \longrightarrow Al \quad -1.66$

$Zn^{2+} + 2e^- \longrightarrow Zn \quad -0.76$

$Cr^{3+} + 3e^- \longrightarrow Cr \quad -0.74$

$Fe^{2+} + 2e^- \longrightarrow Fe \quad -0.41$

$Cd^{2+} + 2e^- \longrightarrow Cd \quad -0.40$

$Ni^{2+} + 2e^- \longrightarrow Ni \quad -0.23$

$Pb^{2+} + 2e^- \longrightarrow Pb \quad -0.13$

TOP TO BOTTOM
Oxidizing Strength Increases

REFERENCE STANDARD $\qquad 2H^+ + 2e^- \longrightarrow H_2 \quad 0.00$

$Cu^{2+} + 2e^- \longrightarrow Cu \quad +0.34$

$I_2 + 2e^- \longrightarrow 2I^- \quad +0.54$

$Fe^{3+} + 3e^- \longrightarrow Fe \quad +0.77$

$Hg^{2+} + 2e^- \longrightarrow Hg \quad +0.80$

$Ag^+ + e^- \longrightarrow Ag \quad +0.80$

$Br_2 + 2e^- \longrightarrow 2Br^- \quad +1.07$

$Cl_2 + 2e^- \longrightarrow 2Cl^- \quad +1.36$

$Au^{3+} + 3e^- \longrightarrow Au \quad +1.50$

$F_2 + 2e^- \longrightarrow 2F^- \quad +2.87$

Finding the emf of a Cell

The emf of a cell can be calculated from the standard electrode potentials of the half-reactions. In order to find the emf, we have to look at the two half-reactions involved in the reaction. Then, set up the two half-reactions so that when they are added we will get the net reaction. Once we have set the equations properly and assigned the proper potentials to those half-reactions, we can add the standard electrode potentials. A common mistake that students make is that they forget the fact that the standard electrode potentials are given in terms of reduction reactions. Redox reactions involve both oxidation and reduction. If one half-reaction is reduction, the other should be oxidation. So we must be careful about the signs of the half-reaction potentials, before we add the two half-reaction potentials to get the emf value. Do the next example.

Example 12-1

Calculate the emf of the cell, based on the following net reaction.

$$Cu^{2+} (aq) \quad + \quad Zn (s) \quad \longrightarrow \quad Cu (s) \quad + \quad Zn^{2+} (aq)$$

Standard Electrode Potentials of the half-cells

Half-reaction	E^o (volts)
$Zn^{2+} (aq) \; + \; 2 \, e^- \; \longrightarrow \; Zn (s)$	$^-0.76$
$Cu^{2+} (aq) \; + \; 2 \, e^- \; \longrightarrow \; Cu (s)$	0.34

Solution:

First, we have to write the half-reactions as indicated below.

$$Zn (s) \quad \longrightarrow \quad Zn^{2+} (aq) \quad + \quad 2 \, e^- \qquad \text{(Oxidation half-reaction)}$$

$$Cu^{2+} (aq) \quad + \quad 2 \, e^- \quad \longrightarrow \quad Cu (s) \qquad \text{(Reduction half-reaction)}$$

From Table 12-1, we can take the standard electrode potential values. The cell containing the copper electrode has a standard potential value of 0.34 V. For the other half-cell, the reaction is oxidation. Since the value given in the table is in terms of reduction half-reactions, we have to reverse the sign of the standard electrode potential given. The correct value for the oxidation half-cell is +0.76 V instead of –0.76 V. Now, you can add the two values to get the emf of the whole setup.

$$emf = 0.34 + 0.76 = 1.10 \text{ V}$$

The answer is 1.10 V.

Table 12-2   Electrolytic cell & Galvanic cell - A comparison

	ELECTROLYTIC CELL	GALVANIC CELL
Spontaneity?	Nonspontaneous	Spontaneous
Cathode	Negative electrode	Positive electrode
Anode	Positive electrode	Negative electrode
Oxidation	Anode	Anode
Reduction	Cathode	Cathode
Energy dynamics	Electrical to chemical	Chemical to electrical

F. THE FREE ENERGY-EMF RELATION

The change in free energy (ΔG) is the maximum amount of energy that is available to do useful work. In an electrochemical cell, this free energy is equal to electrical work which is equal to the product of the number electrons, the Faraday constant, and the electrochemical cell's emf.

$$\Delta G = - n \, FE^0_{cell}$$

In this equation, n is the number of equivalents of electrons transferred in the reaction, F is the Faraday constant (96,500 coulombs), and E^0_{cell} (cell's emf). From this equation, we can deduce that if the emf is positive, the corresponding change in free energy (ΔG) will be negative. In other words, if the emf is positive the reaction is most likely to be spontaneous. On the other hand, if the emf of a cell is negative, the ΔG will be positive indicating a nonspontaneous reaction.

Example 12-2

Calculate the standard free energy change at 25°C for the redox reaction in Example 12-1. (Faraday constant = 96,500 coulombs)

Solution:

$$Cu^{2+}(aq) + Zn(s) \longrightarrow Cu(s) + Zn^{2+}(aq)$$

From the previous example, we know that the emf of this reaction is 1.10 V. The formula for ΔG in terms of the potential difference is:

coulombs × volts = joules

$$\Delta G = -n\,FE^0_{cell}$$

Here, the number of electrons transferred is 2. This number is obtained by examining the balanced equation and evaluating the change in oxidation numbers. For example, copper ions with +2 oxidation state changed to copper (solid) with an oxidation state of 0. In other words, each half-reaction involves two electrons.

$$\Delta G = -n\,FE^0_{cell} = -2 \times 96500\ C \times 1.10\ V = -2.12 \times 10^5\ Joules$$

Notice that the change in free energy is negative and this indicates that the reaction is likely to be spontaneous.

CHAPTER 12 PRACTICE QUESTIONS

1. Given below is the standard electrode potential (E°) of the following redox reaction. Predict the most feasible event, if the reaction occurred spontaneously.

$$Zn^{2+}(s) + Sn(s) \longrightarrow Zn(s) + Sn^{2+}$$

$$E^\circ = {}^-0.62 \ V$$

   A. Zn^{2+} was reduced.
   B. Sn was oxidized.
   C. Zn lost electrons.
   D. Ether was used as the solvent medium.

2. In an electrochemical cell, the redox reaction involved the change of oxidation state of chromium from +2 to +3. This half-reaction most likely must have occured at the:

   A. anode, because it is oxidation.
   B. anode, because it is reduction.
   C. cathode, because it is oxidation.
   D. cathode, because it is reduction.

3. The standard potential E° is related to equilibrium constant K by the following relation:

$$-nFE^\circ = -RT \ \ln K$$

   In a reaction occurring at standard state conditions, if the concentrations of the products are greater than that of the reactants at equilibrium, which of the following is true?

   A. K is negative.
   B. E° is negative.
   C. The reaction is nonspontaneous.
   D. None of the above

4. In an electrolytic cell, 5 A of current passes for about 3.5 minutes. The amount of electric charge equals:

   A. 17.5 coulombs.
   B. 85.7 coulombs.
   C. 1050 coulombs.
   D. $96500 \times 5 \times 3.5$ coulombs.

Questions 5-10 are based on the following passage.

Passage 1

Table 1	
Half-reaction	E^0 (V)
$F_2 + 2\bar{e} \rightarrow 2\bar{F}$	+2.87
$Cl_2 + 2\bar{e} \rightarrow 2\bar{Cl}$	+1.36
$Ag^+ + \bar{e} \rightarrow Ag$	+0.80
$Cu^{2+} + 2\bar{e} \rightarrow Cu$	+0.34
$2H^+ + 2\bar{e} \rightarrow H_2$	0.00
$Pb^{2+} + 2\bar{e} \rightarrow Pb$	-0.13
$Ni^{2+} + 2\bar{e} \rightarrow Ni$	-0.25
$Cr^{3+} + 3\bar{e} \rightarrow Cr$	-0.74
$Zn^{2+} + 2\bar{e} \rightarrow Zn$	-0.76
$Mg^{2+} + 2\bar{e} \rightarrow Mg$	-2.38
$Na^+ + \bar{e} \rightarrow Na$	-2.71
$K^+ + \bar{e} \rightarrow K$	-2.92
$Li^+ + \bar{e} \rightarrow Li$	-3.05

By comparing standard reduction potentials, we can compare the reduction and oxidation powers of elements or ionic species. Some standard reduction potential values are given in Table 1.

5. Which of the following processes is most likely to be a spontaneous process?

   A. Oxidation of copper
   B. Reduction of chlorine
   C. Oxidation of fluoride ion
   D. Reduction of zinc ion

6. What is the overall cell potential for a cell which is formed with Ni/Ni^{2+} and Ag/Ag^+ half-cells?

   A. +1.85 V
   B. +0.55 V
   C. −1.85 V
   D. +1.05 V

7. In a galvanic cell, usually a salt bridge is used. What is the most likely purpose of this?

   A. To conduct electricity
   B. To prevent corrosion
   C. To regulate electricity
   D. To maintain neutrality in the half-cells

8. Which of the following will act as an oxidizing agent the most?

   A. Na^+
   B. Ag^+
   C. Cl_2
   D. Pb^{2+}

9. Which of the following species has the highest oxidation potential?

   A. Cr
   B. K
   C. Cu
   D. Ag

10. The process of corrosion is a redox reaction. Consider the rusting of the body panel of automobiles. Certain parts of the object that are undergoing corrosion act as if they were half cells. For the corrosion of iron, iron is changed to Fe^{2+} ions. Which of the following best represents the area where this change occurs?

    A. Cathode
    B. Anode
    C. Both anode and cathode
    D. Cannot be predicted without more data

13

Radioactivity

A. INTRODUCTION

This is the last chapter in Part I of the general chemistry review. In this chapter, we will discuss the different aspects of radioactivity. Radioactivity is a nuclear phenomenon. It results from natural nuclear instability or externally induced nuclear instability. We will limit our discussion of nuclear chemistry to the basic aspects of radioactivity involving radioactive emissions such as alpha emission, beta emission, gamma rays, positron emission, and electron capture. We will also review other ideas such as the half-lives of radioactive substances and the mass-energy equation.

B. STABILITY OF NUCLEUS

The nucleus is not involved in normal chemical reactions. In radioactivity, it is the nucleus that is undergoes the changes. Nuclear forces are extremely strong forces that hold the nuclear particles together. These forces make the nucleus very stable. Remember that the protons are positively charged and can exert repulsive forces among themselves. It has been found out that there are certain predictable behavioral patterns in elements as the atomic number increases. As the atomic number increases, the neutron-to-proton ratio increases and as more and more protons are present in the nucleus, the stabilizing forces are not sufficient to keep the nucleus stable. Thus the stability of the nucleus decreases as the neutron-to-proton ratio increases.

C. RADIOACTIVE DECAY

Atoms with unstable nuclei can undergo radioactive decay to become atoms which are more stable than their parent atoms. In the process, different types of particles are emitted. We will discuss some of the important ones that you have to know from the MCAT point of view.

Alpha emission: Alpha emission (α) is a low-penetrating emission. It is actually helium nucleus and is often represented as $_2^4 He$. An example of radioactive decay of radium-226 is given below:

$$_{88}^{226} Ra \rightarrow\ _{86}^{222} Rn\ +\ _2^4 He$$

As you can see, the resulting atom has both mass number and atomic number changed. The atomic number decreases by 2, and the mass number decreases by 4.

Beta emission: Beta particles (β^-) are emissions having medium level penetration. They are fast traveling electrons. As a result of beta emission, the resulting atom will have an increase in the atomic number by 1. There is no change in the mass number. In the process, there is also a proton formation from the neutron inside the nucleus, along with the electron formation. In the following example, thorium-234 decays to protactinium-234 by emitting a beta particle.

$$_{90}^{234} Th \longrightarrow\ _{91}^{234} Pa\ +\ _{-1}^0 e$$

Positron emission: Positron emission (β^+) is the positive counterpart of an electron emission. A positron has the exact mass of an electron, but has a positive charge. During this event, a proton is converted to a neutron and a positron. The product of a positron decay will have an atomic number less than that of the decayed atom by one unit. There is no change in mass number.

Electron capture: As a result of electron capture, a proton is converted into a neutron. The electron is usually captured from the innermost shell of the atom. The atomic number of the product will be one less than that of the original atom. There is no change in mass number.

Gamma emission: Gamma (γ) emissions or gamma rays, as they are commonly referred to, are highly penetrating and dangerous emissions. They are high frequency electromagnetic rays. Gamma rays travel at the speed of light. The resulting product atom has the same atomic and mass numbers as those of the parent atom from which the gamma rays are emitted. Gamma rays have no charge.

D. HALF-LIFE

All radioactive elements do not decay at the same pace. They have drastically different rates of decay. The radioactive decay time is expressed in terms of half-life period. The **half-life** of a radioactive substance is the time required for the decay of half the substance present in a sample of that substance.

Regardless of the amount of a particular radioactive substance we have, it takes the same time (half-life) to complete the decay of half the number of nuclei in that sample.

> *The half-life of a radioactive substance is the time required for the complete decay of exactly half the amount of that substance.*

Example 13-1

Calculate the amount of time (in years) it takes for the decay of 75% of a given sample of carbon-14. Carbon-14 has a half-life of approximately 5700 years.

Solution:

After the first 5700 years of decay, 50% of the original sample is left. After 5700 more years, 50% of that sample will have decayed, which means that there is now 25% of the original intact sample. This is the amount of time that the question is asking for. To be clear about our analysis, let's rephrase what we have said. We have 25% of the original sample left at this point. Thus the decay of 75% of the original sample is complete. So the answer is $5700 \times 2 = 11400$ years.

Table 13-1 Summary of changes in the parent nucleus due to different decay modes.

M = mass number of the parent nucleus undergoing decay.
Z = atomic number of the parent nucleus undergoing decay.

TYPE OF DECAY	MASS NUMBER OF THE DAUGHTER NUCLEUS	ATOMIC NUMBER OF THE DAUGHTER NUCLEUS
Alpha decay	M – 4	Z – 2
Beta⁻ decay	M	Z +1
Beta⁺ decay (Positron)	M	Z – 1
Electron capture	M	Z – 1
Gamma decay	M	Z

CHAPTER 13 PRACTICE QUESTIONS

1. Radium 226 can undergo radioactive decay to form Radon 222. Which of the following is the most likely type of particle that is emitted?

   A. Beta particle
   B. Alpha particle
   C. Gamma particle
   D. Positron particle

2. Consider the radioactive-decay equation given below. What is the most likely identity of X?

$$^{22}_{11}Na \rightarrow \, ^{22}_{10}Ne \; + \; X$$

   A. Alpha particle
   B. Beta particle
   C. Positron particle
   D. Neutron

3. Which of the following emissions travels at the speed of light?

   A. Gamma ray
   B. Beta particle
   C. Alpha particle
   D. Antineutrino

4. Which of the following has the highest penetrating power?

   A. Alpha particles
   B. Beta particles
   C. Gamma rays
   D. All the above have the same penetrating power

5. Substance X has a radioactive half-life of 12 years. How much time must have elapsed if only 9 grams is left from an original sample of 150 grams?

   A. 12 years
   B. 24 years
   C. 36 years
   D. 48 years

Questions 6-11 are based on the following passage.

Passage 1

In nuclear reactions, significant changes occur in the composition of the nuclei of the atoms involved. These reactions usually release tremendous amounts of energy. One of the reasons for the nuclear changes can be attributed to the stability of the nucleus.

The formation of nucleus from the subatomic particles – neutrons and protons, results in the release of energy. The mass of these individual particles in the nucleus is greater than that of the actual nucleus that is formed. This loss of mass is due to the change of mass into energy. The energy-mass relation can be represented in terms of the equation:

$$E = mc^2,$$

where m represents the mass, and c represents the speed of light (3×10^8 m/s).

If the nucleus of an atom is not stable, it can get transformed into another nucleus. A plot of the number of neutrons versus the number of protons is often used to assess the stability trends of elements. If the number of protons and neutrons are equal, the nucleus is considered to be reasonably stable. As the atomic number increases, the trend changes.

Isotopes of elements having atomic numbers above ≈83 are unstable atoms. These unstable atoms can undergo disintegrations. The half-lives of some radioactive elements are shown in Table 1.

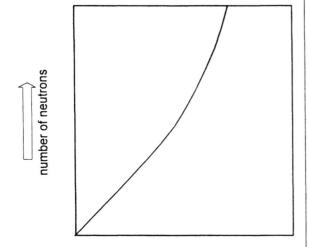

number of protons

TABLE 1

atom	half-life
Carbon 14	5.73×10^3 years
Uranium 238	4.47×10^9 years
Radon 222	3.82 days
Radium 226	1.6×10^3 years
Krypton 89	3.2 minutes

6. A sample of ^{226}Ra disintegrates to 3% of its original quantity. How many half-lives have this sample passed?

   A. two
   B. three
   C. four
   D. five

7. ^{234}Th undergoes radioactive decay. If the thorium nucleus emitted a β-particle during its decay, what is the identity of the element that is formed?

   A. ^{234}Pa
   B. ^{234}Ac
   C. ^{234}Ra
   D. ^{232}U

8. All the following are true regarding radio-active rays, EXCEPT:

   A. α-particles are positively charged.
   B. β-particles are negatively charged.
   C. γ rays are electromagnetic rays and can be deflected by an electric field.
   D. There are radioactive emissions in which the mass number is not affected.

9. Which of the following is true regarding radioactivity?

    A. As the atomic number increases, eventually the neutron-proton ratio values become ≤ 1.
    B. As the atomic number increases, eventually the neutron-proton ratio values become ≥ 1.
    C. As the atomic number increases, eventually the proton-neutron ratio values become ≥ 1.
    D. None of the above

10. When a helium nucleus is formed, there is always some degree of loss of mass. If the loss of mass equals 3.1×10^{-5} kg during the formation of one mol of it, what is the binding energy?

    A. 3.1×10^{-5} J
    B. 1.8×10^{19} J
    C. 9.3×10^{3} J
    D. 2.8×10^{12} J

11. The most probable set of particles that were given off during the series of nuclear changes from ^{232}Th to ^{224}Ra are:

    A. two alpha particles and one beta particle.
    B. one alpha particle and two beta particle.
    C. one alpha particle and three beta particles.
    D. two alpha particles and two beta particles.

PART II

ORGANIC CHEMISTRY

General Concepts

A. INTRODUCTION

Organic Chemistry is the study of carbon compounds. Carbon can form a wide array of compounds, because of its size and ability to form covalent bonds with other carbon atoms. In addition, carbon can form bonds with many other elements. This property of carbon increases the facility of forming multitudes of different compounds. The particular electronegativity of carbon also plays a key role in its versatility. In this chapter, we will review some of the fundamental aspects of carbon atom and the main types of hybridizations involving carbon compounds.

B. THE CARBON ATOM

Electrons are found in regions around the nucleus in an atom, and those regions are called **orbitals**. The orbitals can be defined and differentiated by size, shape, and orientation. **Valence electrons** are electrons that are found in the outermost shell. The carbon atom has four valence electrons. These valence electrons are involved in chemical reactions and bonding.

The electronic configuration:

Carbon:	Atomic number	–	6
	Electronic configuration	–	$1s^2 2s^2 2p^2$

C. BONDING

Ionic bond – Ionic bond is formed between an electropositive and electronegative atom (ion), or generally we can define it as an attractive force between a positive and a negative ion (e.g., KCl).

Covalent bond – Covalent bond is formed by the sharing of a pair of electrons between two atoms. Carbon compounds generally contain covalent bonds.

For a more detailed discussion of this topic see the general chemistry section of this book – Chapter 5.

D. HYBRIDIZATION OF ORBITALS

The six electrons of a carbon atom are distributed in the orbitals as follows:

Electronic configuration   – $1s^2 2s^2 2p^2$

Ground state carbon atom

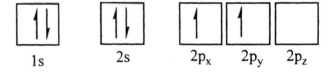

1s   2s $2p_x$ $2p_y$ $2p_z$

sp^3 Hybridization

The carbon atoms of alkanes (e.g., methane, ethane) are sp^3 hybridized. In order to form the four bonds in methane, a carbon atom needs four half-filled orbitals. In order to have more free half-filled orbitals, the carbon atoms undergo hybridization.

METHANE

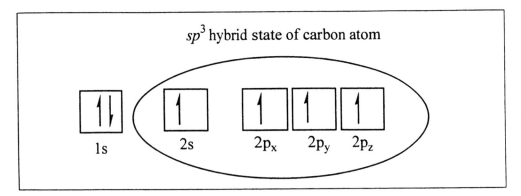

The hybridization results in one half-filled $2s$ orbital, and three half-filled $2p$ orbitals (a total of four half-filled orbitals). These unpaired electrons form the sp^3 hybridized carbon, which can form the four covalent bonds in the methane molecule. The four sp^3 hybrids are directed to the corners of a tetrahedron with bond angles of 109.5^0.

sp^2 Hybridization

In carbon-carbon double bonds, the carbons undergo another type of hybridization called the sp^2 hybridization. In this hybridization, only one $2s$, and two $2p$ orbitals are involved. The C=C contains a sigma (σ) bond and a pi (π) bond. The pi bond is formed by the unhybridized $2p$ orbital overlap. The three equal hybrids lie in an xy-plane with bond angles of 120^0.

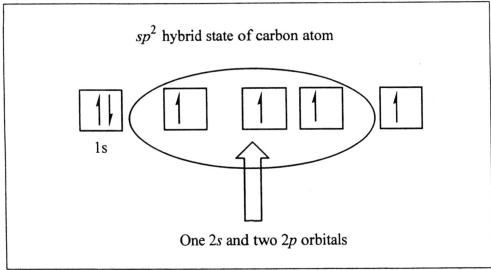

sp Hybridization

Yet another hybridization called the *sp* hybridization exists in carbon-carbon triple bonds. An *sp* hybridized carbon atom is bonded only to two other atoms. In this type of hybridization, one 2s orbital and one 2p orbital are involved. A carbon-carbon triple bond contains one sigma bond and two pi bonds.

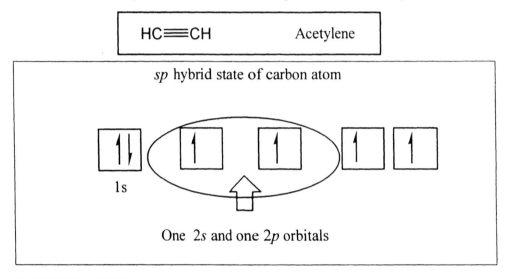

E. RESONANCE

Resonance is an important aspect in Organic chemistry. Though we represent definite Lewis structures of molecules, in reality the electrons are not localized. They are shared and delocalized by the atoms in a molecule to have the most stable electron distribution. This is called **resonance**. Resonance promotes stability.

F. FUNCTIONAL GROUPS

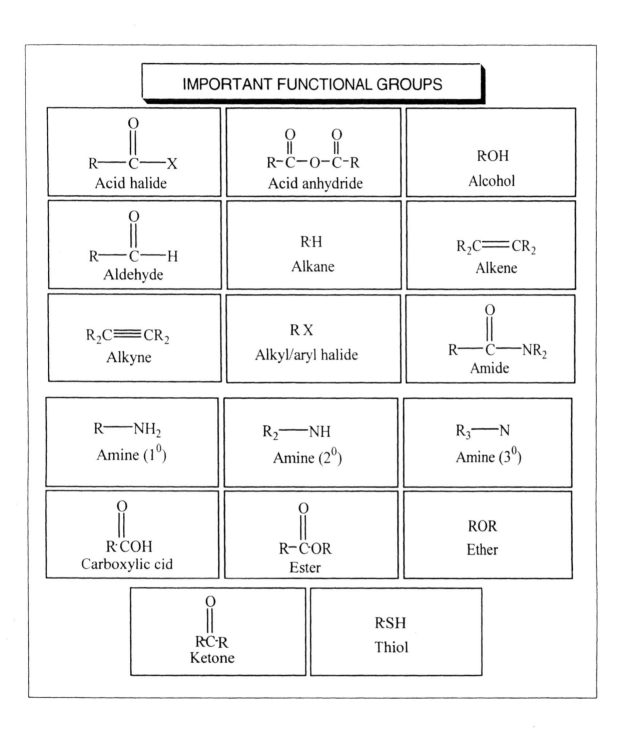

CHAPTER 14 PRACTICE QUESTIONS

1. The carbon indicated by the arrow has which of the following hybridizations?

$$CH_3CH_2CH_2CH = CH_2$$

   A. *sp* hybridization
   B. sp^2 hybridization
   C. sp^3 hybridization
   D. sp^3d^2 hybridization

2. In acetylene, how many sigma bonds are present between the two carbons?

   A. One
   B. Two
   C. Three
   D. Four

3. The triple bond of 2-propyne contains:

   A. one sigma bond and one pi bond.
   B. one sigma bond and two pi bonds.
   C. two sigma bonds and one pi bond.
   D. three sigma bonds.

4. Which of the following represents the arrangement of the sp^3 hybrid orbitals in methane?

   A. Planar
   B. Tetragonal planar
   C. Tetrahedral
   D. Bipyramidal

5. How many electrons are actually involved in the carbon-carbon bond of acetylene?

   A. 2
   B. 3
   C. 4
   D. 6

6. Which of the following best represents the hydrogen-carbon-hydrogen bond angles in methane?

   A. 90°
   B. 109.5°
   C. 120°
   D. 180°

7. Which of the following bonds indicated by the arrows has the shortest bond length?

A. a
B. b
C. c
D. d

Figure for Q-7

8. The carbon-hydrogen bond in propane can be best described as:

A. an ionic bond.
B. a covalent bond.
C. a hydrogen bond.
D. a dipole-dipole bond.

Alkanes

A. INTRODUCTION

Hydrocarbons are compounds containing only carbon and hydrogen. They are classified into **aliphatic** and **aromatic hydrocarbons**. Aliphatic hydrocarbons can be divided into three major groups – **alkanes**, **alkenes**, and **alkynes**. Alkanes come under saturated hydrocarbons, because they have carbon-carbon single bonds. Alkenes and alkynes are unsaturated hydrocarbons, since they have carbon-carbon double and triple bonds, respectively.

B. ALKANES

Alkanes have the general molecular formula C_nH_{2n+2}. Hence, if we know the number of carbons present in an alkane, we can calculate the number of hydrogens in it or vice versa. Methane is the first member of the alkane family. It has a molecular formula of CH_4. Natural gases which are found in petroleum deposits contain gases such as methane, ethane, and propane. They are the first three members of the alkane family.

ALKANES WITH 1-12 CARBON ATOMS

Methane	CH_4	Heptane	C_7H_{16}
Ethane	C_2H_6	Octane	C_8H_{18}
Propane	C_3H_8	Nonane	C_9H_{20}
Butane	C_4H_{10}	Decane	$C_{10}H_{22}$
Pentane	C_5H_{12}	Undecane	$C_{11}H_{24}$
Hexane	C_6H_{14}	Dodecane	$C_{12}H_{26}$

Methane is a colorless, odorless gas. Ethane, propane, and butane are also gases, with butane having the highest boiling point among these. What kind of trend can we see from these observations? As the number of carbons and hydrogens increases, the boiling point increases. Each carbon in an alkane is sp^3 hybridized.

C. PROPERTIES OF ALKANES

At room temperature, the first four members of the alkane family are gases. The straight chain alkanes from pentane and up are liquids, and octadecane (18 carbons) and up in the alkane family are solids. As the number of carbons increases, the boiling point increases. Branched alkanes have lesser boiling points than their unbranched or less branched isomeric counterparts. The reason for this is that the unbranched molecules have more intermolecular interactions than the branched ones.

D. STRAIGHT CHAIN AND BRANCHED ALKANES

Butane (C_4H_{10}) and the other alkanes above it can exhibit **constitutional isomerism**. If the alkane is unbranched and has a straight chain, it is called *n*-alkane. For example, the straight chain pentane is called *n*-Pentane.

n-Pentane $CH_3CH_2CH_2CH_2CH_3$

n-Butane $CH_3CH_2CH_2CH_3$

Constitutional (structural) isomers are isomers with the same molecular formula, but are different in terms of the order in which the atoms are connected.

Butane has two possible isomers: *n*-Butane and Isobutane

n-Butane   Isobutane

$CH_3CH_2CH_2CH_3$

$$H_3C\!-\!\overset{\displaystyle H}{\underset{\displaystyle CH_3}{C}}\!-\!CH_3$$

Pentane has three isomers: *n*-Pentane, Isopentane, and neopentane

$$CH_3CH_2CH_2CH_2CH_3 \qquad CH_3\overset{\overset{\displaystyle CH_3}{|}}{C}HCH_2CH_3 \qquad CH_3-\overset{\overset{\displaystyle CH_3}{|}}{\underset{\underset{\displaystyle CH_3}{|}}{C}}-CH_3$$

      n-Pentane   Isopentane   Neopentane

The best way to find the number of possible isomers is by drawing out the structures sequencially and systematically, starting from the straight chain compound. There is no simple general formula to calculate the number of possible isomers of an alkane.

E. ALKYL GROUPS

Alkyl groups are groups which lack one hydrogen atom compared to its parent alkane. For example, methyl group is CH_3-, which lacks one hydrogen atom with respect to its parent alkane, methane (CH_4). Similarly, ethyl group (C_2H_5-) lacks one hydrogen atom compared to ethane (C_2H_6).

Some common alkyl groups

$$CH_3CH_2CH_2- \qquad CH_3\overset{\overset{\displaystyle CH_3}{|}}{C}H- \qquad CH_3CH_2CH_2CH_2- \qquad CH_3\overset{\overset{\displaystyle CH_3}{|}}{C}HCH_2-$$

propyl (*n*-propyl)   isopropyl   butyl   isobutyl

$$CH_3CH_2\overset{\overset{\displaystyle CH_3}{|}}{C}H- \qquad CH_3-\overset{\overset{\displaystyle CH_3}{|}}{\underset{\underset{\displaystyle CH_3}{|}}{C}}-$$

       sec-butyl   *tert*-butyl

F. THE IUPAC NAMING OF ALKANES

Main rules and strategies for the IUPAC naming of alkanes

1. Write out the expanded structural formula, if it is not given in the expanded form.
2. Find the longest carbon chain and then identify the alkyl or other substituents that are connected to this long chain.
3. The numbering of carbons should start from the specific end of the long chain, so that the numbers assigned for the substituents are the lowest.

$$\text{H}_3\text{C}\underset{1}{\rule{0pt}{0pt}}\text{---}\underset{2}{\text{HC}}\text{---}\underset{3}{\text{H}_2\text{C}}\text{---}\underset{4}{\text{H}_2\text{C}}\text{---}\underset{5}{\text{H}_2\text{C}}\text{---}\underset{6}{\text{CH}_3}$$

with CH$_3$ attached to carbon 2

2-methyl hexane

4-ethyl-2-methyl heptane

2,2-dimethyl-4-ethyl heptane

G. CYCLOALKANES

Cycloalkanes are cyclic compounds with ring structures. The general molecular formula of a cycloalkane is C_nH_{2n}.

or   Cyclopropane

Cyclopentane

Cyclohexane

H. REACTIONS OF ALKANES

Combustion

Hydrocarbons undergo combustion reactions in the presence of oxygen to form carbondioxide and water as products. Combustion reactions are very exothermic giving out energy, as they burn in the presence of oxygen.

Sample reaction 15-1

$$CH_4 + 2O_2 \longrightarrow CO_2 + 2H_2O \qquad \Delta H^0 = -890 \text{ kJ}$$

Halogenation

The **halogenation reaction** can be generalized as follows:

$$\textbf{RH} + \textbf{X}_2 \longrightarrow \textbf{RX} + \textbf{HX}$$

In this substitution reaction, the halogen (fluorine, chlorine, bromine, iodine) substitutes one hydrogen atom in the alkane, forming hydrogen halide and alkyl halide as the products. The reactivity of halogens in the halogenation reactions is as follows:

Fluorine > Chlorine > Bromine > Iodine

Fluorine is the most reactive among halogens in halogenation reactions, and iodine is the least reactive.

I. MECHANISM OF FREE RADICAL SUBSTITUTION OF ALKANES

Halogenation reactions occur via a mechanism called **free radical substitution**. There are three main steps in the free radical mechanism. They are:

(1) initiation
(2) propagation
(3) termination.

The overall reaction of chlorination of methane.

$$CH_4 + Cl_2 \longrightarrow CH_3Cl + HCl$$

(1) Initiation

This step involves the dissociation of the halogen molecule (e.g., chlorine molecule) into two chlorine atoms. Even though the total reaction is exothermic, initially energy should be supplied for the reaction to proceed.

Chlorine
molecule

2 Chlorine
atoms

(2) Propagation steps

During the propagation step, the hydrogen atom is abstracted from methane by a chlorine atom. This is followed by the reaction between the methyl radical and the chlorine molecule.

Chlorine atom   Methane

2 Chlorine
atoms

Methyl
radical

$$:\ddot{C}l:\ddot{C}l: \; + \; CH_3\cdot \quad \longrightarrow \quad \cdot\ddot{C}l: \; + \; CH_3:\ddot{C}l:$$

| Chlorine molecule | Methyl radical | | Chlorine atom | Methyl chloride |

(3) Termination

The termination steps involve the combination of the radicals.

$$:\ddot{C}l\cdot \; + \; CH_3\cdot \quad \longrightarrow \quad CH_3:\ddot{C}l:$$

$$:\ddot{C}l\cdot \; + \; :\ddot{C}l\cdot \quad \longrightarrow \quad Cl_2$$

$$\cdot CH_3 \; + \; CH_3\cdot \quad \longrightarrow \quad H_3C\!-\!CH_3$$

J. REACTIVITY OF ALKANES

Primary, Secondary, and Tertiary Carbons

A carbon which is attached directly to only one other carbon is called a primary (1^0) carbon. If it is attached directly to two other carbons, it is a secondary (2^0) carbon. A carbon is called a tertiary (3^0) carbon, if it is directly attached to three other carbons.

Though alkanes are not so reactive, they can undergo some reactions by forming intermediates. These intermediates can be alkyl radicals, carbocations, or carbanions. Alkyl radicals are intermediates of free radical reactions. Carbocations (carbonium ions) are species with a positive charge on one of the carbon atoms. A carbanion has a negative charge on one of its carbon atoms. Some major trends are given below:

Carbocation/Alkyl radical stability $3^0 > 2^0 > 1^0 > $ methyl
Carbocation/Akyl radical reactivity $3^0 < 2^0 < 1^0 < $ methyl
Carbanion stability $3^0 < 2^0 < 1^0 < $ methyl
Carbanion reactivity $3^0 > 2^0 > 1^0 > $ methyl

K. CONFORMATION AND STABILITY OF ALKANES

Conformations

Alkanes can have different conformations. By analyzing the structure of ethane, we can define certain aspects regarding its conformations. **Conformations** are different arrangements of the atoms in a molecule, as a result of rotation around a single bond.

Figure 15-1   STAGGERED CONFORMATION

SAWHORSE REPRESENTATION   NEWMAN PROJECTION

In **staggered conformation**, the torsional angle is 60°. In **eclipsed conformation**, each carbon-hydrogen bond is aligned with the carbon-hydrogen bond of the next carbon.

Figure 15-2   ECLIPSED CONFORMATION

SAWHORSE REPRESENTATION   NEWMAN PROJECTION

In eclipsed conformations, the torsional angle is 0°. In staggered conformations, the torsional angles can either be 60° **(gauche)** or 180° **(anti)**. The anti conformation is more stable than the gauche conformation. We should also consider the fact that in this analysis of staggered conformation, the ethane molecule looks the same in the Newman projections, whether it is gauche or anti. Reason: There are no substituents other than just hydrogens. To denote the positional significance, the hydrogens are indicated in bold in the diagrams shown in Figure 15-4.

Eclipsed

0^0

ANGLE OF TORSION
IS 0^0
Figure 15-3

Gauche

60^0

Anti

180^0

ANGLE OF TORSION
IS 60^0

ANGLE OF TORSION
IS 180^0

Figure 15-4

L. CONFORMATION AND STABILITY OF CYCLOALKANES

According to Baeyer strain theory, the stability of a cycloalkane is based on how close its angles are to 109.5°. The closer the angle is to 109.5°, the more stable the cycloalkane. Deviation from this angle can cause angle strain. An increase in the angle strain means a decrease in the stability of the molecule.

Conformations of Cyclohexane

Cyclohexane has a non-planar structure that makes it almost free from ring strain. The most important conformations that it can have include **chair conformation** and **boat conformation**. The chair conformation is more stable than the boat conformation. The boat conformation can sometimes be more stable than it usually is, by a slight rotation in the C-C bonds and is called the **twist boat conformation**. Nevertheless, the chair conformation is the most stable cyclohexane form.

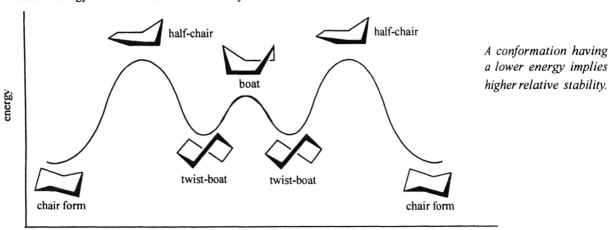

Figure 15-5

Relative energy levels of the conformations of cyclohexane

A conformation having a lower energy implies higher relative stability.

Based on the energy diagram of cyclohexane, the following inference can be made regarding the stability of the conformations:

chair conformation >twist boat conformation > boat conformation > half-chair conformation

increasing stability

In the chair form of cyclohexane, there are two different kinds of carbon-hydrogen bonds. Of the twelve carbon hydrogen bonds in a cyclohexane, six bonds are pointed up or down and are called axial bonds. The remaining six carbon-hydrogen bonds are pointed at an angle out of the ring and are called equatorial bonds. Each carbon atom in the ring is attached to one hydrogen atom by an axial bond, and to the other hydrogen atom by an equatorial bond.

(a) axial position

(e) equatorial position

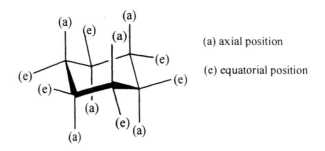

When ring flipping occurs between conformers, equatorial groups become axial, and axial groups become equatorial.

Experimental analysis has confirmed that among the two chair conformations of methylcyclohexane, 95% of the molecules have their methyl group in the equatorial position. In other words, the methyl group being in the equatorial position is more stable than methyl group in the axial position. The lower stability of the axial position can be attributed to the fact that there is an increased steric hindrance because of the proximity of the axial methyl group to the axial hydrogens that are attached to carbon atoms 3 and 5. This interaction called 1,3-diaxial interaction results in steric strain. This accounts for the increased relative stability of the conformation when the methyl group is in the equatorial position.

cis-1,2-dimethylcyclohexane

trans-1,2-dimethylcyclohexane

Example 15-1

The *cis*-geometric isomer of 1,3-dimethylcyclohexane is more stable than its *trans*-isomer. Why?

Solution:

To understand why the *cis*-isomer is more stable, let's draw the possible chair forms of 1,3-dimethylcyclohexane.

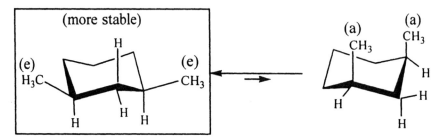

cis-1,3-dimethylcyclohexane

trans-1,3-dimethylcyclohexane

When the two methyl substituents are in 1,3 positions, the *cis*-isomer can have both substituents in equatorial position. In the *trans*-isomer, one methyl group must always be axial.

CHAPTER 15 PRACTICE QUESTIONS

1. A student is assigned to identify an unknown compound in an organic chemistry class. She is sure that the compound contains only carbon and hydrogen atoms. In addition, the unknown compound is a saturated hydrocarbon. If there are fourteen hydrogens in a molecule of this unknown compound, and it does not have a ring structure, what is the most likely number of carbons in this compound?

   A. 3
   B. 6
   C. 7
   D. 14

2. Which of the following represents the general formula of an alkane?

   A. C_nH_{2n+2}
   B. C_nH_{2n}
   C. C_nH_{2n-2}
   D. C_nH_n

3. n-Butane and isobutane are best described as:

   A. stereoisomers.
   B. anomers.
   C. diastereomers.
   D. constitutional isomers.

4. Choose the correct name of the following compound from the choices given below.

   A. 2-propyl-5-methyl heptane
   B. 3-methyl-6-propyl heptane
   C. 3,6-dimethyl nonane
   D. 4,7-dimethyl nonane

5. In the combustion reaction of butane, how many moles of carbon dioxide are formed, if one mole of butane undergoes complete combustion in a controlled environment in the presence of excess oxygen?

   A. one
   B. two
   C. four
   D. eight

6. Which of the following represents secondary carbons?

A. I & II only
B. I & III only
C. II & IV only
D. I, II, III & IV

7. Carbonium ions have:

A. a positive charge.
B. a negative charge.
C. no charge.
D. either a positive or a negative charge.

8. The gauche conformation is a form of:

A. eclipsed conformation.
B. anti-conformation.
C. staggered conformation.
D. none of the above conformations.

9. In cycloalkanes which of the following bond angles will have the least angle strain?

A. 90°
B. 110°

C. 125°
D. 180°

10. Which of the following alkanes has the highest boiling point?

A. I
B. II
C. III
D. IV

Questions 11-15 are based on the following passage.

Passage 1

Hydrocarbons are compounds composed of carbon and hydrogen atoms. Alkanes are hydrocarbons. As the number of carbons increases in straight-chain alkanes, there is a steady gradation of properties which can be easily compared and predicted. The properties of branched alkanes vary considerably and are hard to predict because of other intervening forces that come into play. The boiling points of a few alkanes are given below:

methane	−161.6° C
propane	−88.6° C
pentane	36.1° C
hexane	68.7° C
octane	125.6° C
3-methylpentane	63.3° C

11. Which of the following intermolecular forces are important with respect to alkanes?

  A. Hydrogen bonding
  B. Dipole-dipole electrostatic forces
  C. Ionic forces
  D. Van der Waals forces

12. The melting point of butane is close to:

  A. 37.5° C.
  B. 55.1° C.
  C. 24° C.
  D. −138° C.

13. Alkenes can undergo free radical substitution reactions with halogens. Which of the following best represents a chain propagation step during the free radical chlorination of methane?

  A. $Cl_2 \longrightarrow 2 \ :\!\overset{..}{\underset{..}{Cl}}\!\cdot$

  B. $\cdot CH_3 + \ :\!\overset{..}{\underset{..}{Cl}}\!\cdot \longrightarrow CH_3Cl$

  C. $\cdot CH_3 + Cl_2 \longrightarrow CH_3Cl + \ :\!\overset{..}{\underset{..}{Cl}}\!\cdot$

  D. $\cdot CH_3 + \cdot CH_3 \longrightarrow CH_3CH_3$

14. What is the most likely boiling point of 2,3-dimethylbutane?

  A. 58° C
  B. 63.3° C
  C. 68.7° C
  D. 75.8° C

15. The total number of possible structural isomers of heptane is:

  A. three.
  B. seven.
  C. nine.
  D. twelve.

16

Alkenes

A. INTRODUCTION

Alkenes are hydrocarbon compounds that contain carbon-carbon double bonds. The first member of the alkene family is ethene (ethylene), similar to ethane of the alkane family in terms of the basic name, though the ending is -ene rather than -ane. The general molecular formula of alkenes is C_nH_{2n}.

B. NAMING OF ALKENES

Ethene (Ethylene) $CH_2=CH_2$

Propene (Propylene) $CH_2=CH-CH_3$

From the third member (butene) of the alkene family onward, there is a need to specify the location of the double bond to recognize the correct structure denoted by the name. When naming alkenes, the numbering should begin from the carbon chain end which gives the double bond position the lowest number.

Watch the numbering of carbons in the following examples.

$$\overset{1}{C}H_2=\overset{2}{C}H\overset{3}{C}H_2\overset{4}{C}H_3 \quad \text{1-Butene}$$

$$\overset{1}{C}H_2=\overset{2}{C}H\overset{3}{C}H_2\overset{4}{C}H_2\overset{5}{C}H_3 \quad \text{1-Pentene}$$

$$\overset{7}{C}H_3\overset{6}{C}H_2\overset{5}{C}H_2\overset{4}{C}H_2\overset{3}{C}H=\overset{2}{C}H\overset{1}{C}H_3 \quad \text{2-Heptene}$$

$$\overset{7}{C}H_3\overset{6}{C}H_2\overset{5}{C}H_2\overset{4}{C}H_2\overset{3}{C}H=\overset{2}{C}H\overset{1}{C}H_3 \quad \text{6-Methyl-2-heptene}$$
$$CH_3$$

C. STRUCTURAL INTEGRITY AND ISOMERISM OF ALKENES

The carbon atoms which contain the double bonds in alkenes are *sp²* **hybridized**. Each carbon-carbon double bond is made of one sigma and one pi bond.

Isomerism

Any compound with a carbon-carbon double bond can exhibit cis-trans isomerism, provided that the carbons involved in the double bond do not have two of the same groups or atoms attached to each of them. 2-Butene is the simplest alkene that can have cis-trans isomerism. Trans isomers are generally more stable than their cis counterparts. Alkyl groups are mildly electron-donating toward the double bond. This can lead to polarity. For instance, *cis*-2-butene has a net dipole moment as shown in the diagram given below. On the other hand, in *trans*-2-butene the net dipole is zero since the dipole moments cancel out (the vector sum of the dipole moments is zero).

More substituted alkenes are usually more stable than less substituted alkenes.

net dipole= yes   net dipole= no

Both *cis* and *trans*-2-butene have van der Waals attractive forces. But, only the *cis*-isomer can have dipole-dipole interactions because it has a net dipole moment. Hence, *cis*-2-butene has a higher boiling point than *trans*-2-butene.

The E-Z System of Naming Alkenes

Sometimes we are not able to categorize alkenes into trans and cis isomers. The following example will reveal why that is the case.

For compounds such as the ones shown above, we have to prioritize the substituents, and that is the only way to name and identify these compounds. A new system was proposed by scientists, which categorizes these compounds under **E *(entgegen)***, and **Z *(zusammen)*** configurations. **E configuration** describes *opposite*, whereas **Z configuration** describes *same side*. Study the following examples to get familiarized with this system of naming alkenes. In order to recognize which substituent is higher or lower, you have to compare their atomic numbers. That means an atom with a higher atomic number takes precedence over an atom with a lower atomic number.

One key aspect to remember is that when we compare which substituent is higher or lower, we should compare the substitutions in the same carbon. In the above example, it is easy to see that on the left substitution, obviously bromine is higher (higher in the atomic number sense) than hydrogen. On the right side, chlorine is higher (atomic number:17) than carbon (atomic number:6). So the compound shown in Fig. (a) has an **E configuration**, and the one shown in Fig.(b) has a **Z configuration**.

D. GENERAL PROPERTIES OF ALKENES

Just like alkanes, the melting and boiling points of alkenes increase with an increase in the number of carbons (increase in chain length). Carbon-carbon double bonds are shorter than carbon-carbon single bonds. Alkenes are insoluble in water, but are soluble in nonpolar solvents such as hexane, and ethers.

E. SYNTHESIS OF ALKENES

We can synthesize alkenes by processes such as dehydrogenation of alkanes, dehydrohalogenation of alkyl halides, and dehydration of alcohols.

From Alkanes

An alkene can be synthesized by the process of dehydrogenation (removal of hydrogen atoms), by heating an alkane up to about $700-750^\circ$.

Sample reaction 16-1

$$CH_3\text{-}CH_3 \xrightarrow[\quad 750^\circ \quad]{} CH_2\text{=}CH_2 + H_2$$

Ethane   Ethylene   Hydrogen

From Alcohols

When alcohols undergo dehydration reactions, alkenes are generated. There is a chance of rearrangement of the carbocation intermediates to form more stable carbocation intermediates, whenever possible, resulting in the formation of more than one type of alkenes. The mechanisms of such rearrangements are discussed in Chapter 21.

Sample reaction 16-2

$$CH_3CH_2OH \xrightarrow[H_2SO_4,\ heat]{} CH_2\text{=}CH_2 + H_2O$$

The order of carbocation stability: $3^\circ > 2^\circ > 1^\circ$

The only product in the above reaction is ethylene, since there is no rearrangement. This is because the intermediate formed in this reaction is a primary carbocation, and rearrangement cannot produce a more stable carbocation since there are only two carbons in the cation intermediate formed from ethanol.

From Alkyl Halides by Dehydrohalogenation

Alkenes can be synthesized by reacting the corresponding alkyl halides with a suitable strong base that can abstract a proton from one of the carbon atoms, while the leaving group attached to the adjacent carbon leaves. The general mechanism is shown below.

According to Zaitsev's rule, the major alkene product is the one that is the most highly substituted. Consider the following example involving 2-bromobutane with potassium hydroxide.

Sample reaction 16-3

minor product(20%)

CH_3CH_2CH=CH_2 monosubstituted alkene

+

CH_3CH=$CHCH_3$ disubstituted alkene

major product(80%)

If bulky bases are used, the least substituted alkene may predominate as the product. In the next example, the base used is *tert*-butoxide ion. Since it is a bulky base it will preferentially abstract the less hindered hydrogen, leading to the formation of the least substituted alkene–the Hofmann product.

Sample reaction 16-4

Zaitsev product (minor)

+

Hoffman product (major)

From Vicinal Dibromides by Dehalogenation

Vicinal dibromides have two bromines on adjacent carbon atoms. Vicinal dibromides can be converted to alkenes by reduction with zinc or iodide ion. A sample reaction is given below.

Sample Reaction 16-5

NaI or

Zn/Acetic acid

Alkene

Vicinal dibromide

F. REACTIONS OF ALKENES

Hydrogenation

In hydrogenation reactions, H_2 is added to the unsaturated (carbon-carbon double or triple bonds) bonds. The resulting product of hydrogenation of a pure alkene is an alkane.

$$CH_2=CHCH_2CH_2CH_2CH_3 + H_2 \longrightarrow CH_3CH_2CH_2CH_2CH_2CH_3$$

Usually, catalysts like platinum, palladium, or nickel are used for these types of hydrogenation reactions. Hydrogenation reactions are exothermic. Thus heat is generated as result of hydrogenation and is called **heat of hydrogenation.**

The greater the substitution of the carbon-carbon double bond is, the lesser the heat of hydrogenation, and higher the stability of the alkene.

Alkenes with Hydrogen Halides

Alkenes undergo electrophilic addition reactions with hydrogen halides, to form alkyl halides.

Sample reaction 16-6

$$CH_2=CH_2 \quad + \quad HX \longrightarrow \quad CH_3-CH_2X$$
Ethylene $\qquad$ Hydrogen halide $\qquad$ Ethyl halide

In the process, the hydrogen halide attacks the double bond in the alkene, and the pi electrons in the double bond are transferred to the electrophile, resulting in a carbocation intermediate. This is followed by the formation of the alkyl halide.

$$CH_2=CH_2 \quad + \quad HX \longrightarrow \quad CH_3-CH_2X$$
Ethylene $\qquad$ Hydrogen halide $\qquad$ Ethyl halide

(1)

Alkene   Hydrogen halide   Carbocation   Chloride ion

(2)

Carbocation   Chloride ion   Alkyl halide

If the alkene used is not symmetrical, the possibility of different products from hydrogen halide addition is an issue. In such cases, the hydrogen from the hydrogen halide adds to the double-bonded carbon that already has the greater number of hydrogens. This is Markovnikov's rule. Based on this rule, we can predict the major product in such reactions. Consider the following reaction involving 2-methyl-2-butene with hydrogen bromide.

2-methyl-2-butene
(an unsymmetrical alkene)

the hydrogen from the hydrogen halide can add here resulting in a tertiary carbocation

the hydrogen from the hydrogen halide can add here resulting in a secondary carbocation

not observed

less stable

more stable

Markovnikov product
(major product)

An example of a Markovnikov addition is shown below. Watch where the hydrogen and the bromine are added.

Sample reaction 16-7

Markovnikov addition of hydrogen and bromine

Sample reaction 16-8

H goes to the double-bonded carbon that has the greatest number of hydrogens

Anti-Markovnikov Addition

Hydrogen bromide in the presence of peroxides can add to an unsymmetrical alkene resulting in anti-Markovnikov products. The change in trend can be explained based on the mechanistic difference of HBr addition in the presence of peroxides. Peroxides can easily form free radicals, since the oxygen-oxygen bond in peroxides is weak. This type of addition is not seen with HCl or HI. The mechanism of HBr addition to an alkene in the presence of a peroxide is shown below.

Formation of Br radical

$$ROOR \xrightarrow[heat]{} 2 \, RO \cdot$$

$$RO \cdot \; + \; HBr \longrightarrow ROH \; + \; Br\cdot$$

Addition of Br radical to alkene (formation of alkyl radical)

3° radical (more stable)

anti-Markovnikov product

2° radical (less stable)

Notice that when the bromine radical adds to the double-bonded carbon that contains the most number of hydrogens, the resulting alkyl radical is more stable (here, tertiary radical is formed). Remember that free radical stability parallels carbocation stability. A tertiary radical is more stable than a secondary radical which is more stable than a primary radical.

Alkenes with Halogens

We will consider the reaction of ethylene with chlorine.

Sample reaction 16-9

The overall reaction:

$$CH_2=CH_2 + Cl_2 \longrightarrow ClCH_2CH_2Cl$$

The mechanism of the reaction:

This is an example of electrophilic addition of Cl_2 to an alkene. The mechanism of this reaction involves the following steps. In the first step, the ethylene reacts with chlorine to form the cyclic ethylene chloronium ion (intermediate) and chloride ion. Note that in this cyclic intermediate, the chlorine has a positive charge. This step is followed by the nucleophilic attack by chloride ion on the chloronium ion. The reaction is enhanced by electron-donating substituents such as alkyl groups on the carbon-carbon double bond, since such groups can further stabilize the formation of the transition state which results in the formation of the chloronium ion. Halogen addition is usually an *anti* addition process.

Halogen addition is usually an *anti* addition process. See the next reaction that exemplifies this aspect.

Sample reaction 16-10

Alkenes with Halogens in Aqueous Medium

When a halogen is reacted with an alkene in the presence of water, an organic product called halohydrin is formed by the addition of a halogen atom and a hydroxyl group to the double bond. The reaction proceeds by the attack of halogen resulting in a halonium ion. Once the halonium ion is formed, the nucleophile (water) will attack the halonium ion resulting in a halohydrin. The reaction follows an anti addition pattern. If the alkene is unsymmetrical, the nucleophilic attack of water will be on the most highly substituted carbon.

Sample reaction 16-11

$$CH_2=CH_2 + Cl_2 + H_2O \longrightarrow HOCH_2CH_2Cl + HCl$$

Ethylene   Chlorine   Halohydrin   Hydrogen chloride

Sample reaction 16-12

anti addition product

Epoxidation

Sample reaction 16-13

(Peroxyacid)

$$CH_2{=}CH_2 \xrightarrow{\quad RC\text{-}OOH \quad} H_2C\text{---}CH_2 \quad + \quad RC\text{-}OH$$

Ethylene

Epoxide

Carboxylic acid

Alkenes react with peroxy acids to form epoxides and carboxylic acids as products.

Ozonolysis

Alkenes react with O_3 (Ozone) to form ozonides, which on hydrolysis with water form aldehydes or ketones or both, depending on the type of the reacting alkene. This is illustrated by the sample reactions.

Sample reaction 16-14

$$\begin{array}{c} H \\ H \end{array}\!C{=}C\!\begin{array}{c} H \\ H \end{array} \xrightarrow[\textbf{2. H}_2\textbf{O/ Zn}]{\textbf{1. O}_3} \begin{array}{c} H \\ H \end{array}\!C{=}O$$

AN ALDEHYDE

Sample reaction 16-15

$$\begin{array}{c} H_3C \\ H_3C \end{array}\!C{=}C\!\begin{array}{c} CH_3 \\ H \end{array} \xrightarrow[\textbf{2. H}_2\textbf{O/ Zn}]{\textbf{1. O}_3} \begin{array}{c} H_3C \\ H_3C \end{array}\!C{=}O \quad + \quad \begin{array}{c} H_3C \\ H \end{array}\!C{=}O$$

A KETONE

AN ALDEHYDE

Hydroxylation using Osmium Tetroxide

Sample reaction 16-16

Cyclic osmate   Glycol(diol)

Osmium tetroxide can undergo reaction with alkenes to form a cyclic osmate, which in the presence of hydrogen peroxide results in a glycol (diol). Hydrogen peroxide oxidizes the osmium back to osmium tetroxide, while hydrolyzing the cyclic osmate to glycol. The predominant product is a *syn* addition product.

Acid Catalyzed Reaction

Sample reaction 16-17

$$H_3C \diagdown \diagup CH_3$$
$$C = C$$
$$H_3C \diagup \diagdown H$$

$\xrightarrow{\text{H}_2\text{SO}_4/\text{ H}_2\text{O}}$

$$\begin{array}{c} CH_3 \\ | \\ HO - C - CH_2CH_3 \\ | \\ CH_3 \end{array}$$
(major product)

Alkenes react with aqueous acidic solutions to form alcohols. The reaction intermediate is a carbocation. There is possibility of rearrangement of the intermediates. The major product can be predicted using Markovnikov's rule.

Hydroboration-Oxidation

Sample reaction 16-18

$$CH_3CH_2CH_2CH == CH_2 \xrightarrow[\text{2. H}_2\text{O}_2, \text{ NaOH}]{\text{1. B}_2\text{H}_6}$$ $CH_3CH_2CH_2CH_2CH_2OH$
(major product)

Oxidation followed by hydroboration of alkenes results in alcohols. This reaction takes place in an anti-Markovnikov fashion. Notice that the hydrogen atom, instead of attaching to the carbon contained in the double bond with the highest number of hydrogen substituents, attaches to the carbon with the least number of hydrogen substituents.

Diborane (B_2H_6), a dimer of borane (BH_3), is usually used complexed together with tetrahydrofuran (THF) since diborane by itself is a toxic, and flammable gas. Borane entity actually adds to one of the double-bonded carbons resulting in an alkylborane. BH_3 is a strong electrophile and adds to the least highly substituted double-bonded carbon. This preference makes sense because in the transition state, the electron deprived boron pulls electrons from the pi cloud resulting in a partial positive charge to the other carbon atom. This partial positive charge is better stabilized on the more highly substituted carbon. Hydrogen peroxide under basic conditions oxidizes the alkylborane to an alcohol. In effect, the addition in hydroboration-oxidation is anti-Markovnikov.

Sample reaction 16-19

The addition of hydrogen and boron is simultaneous, and they must add to the same side of the double bond. Hence, this addition reaction involves *syn* addition or same-side addition. Study the next reaction.

Sample reaction 16-20

Oxymercuration-Demercuration

Sample reaction 16-21

Alkenes can be converted into alcohols by oxymercuration-demercuration. The addition of H and OH is in accordance with the Markovnikov's rule. There is no rearrangement of the intermediates in this process.

In the oxymercuration process, the electrophilic addition of the mercuric species occurs resulting in a mercurinium ion which is a three-membered ring. This is followed by the nucleophilic attack of water and as the proton leaves, an organomercuric alcohol (addition product) is formed. The next step, demercuration, occurs when sodium borohydride (NaBH$_4$) substitutes the mercuric acetate substituent with hydrogen. If an alkene is unsymmetric, Oxymercuration-demercuration results in Markovnikov addition. The addition of mercuric species and water follows an *anti* (opposite side) addition pattern. This reaction has good yield, since there is no possibility of rearrangement unlike acid-catalyzed hydration of alkenes.

Sample reaction 16-22

1-methyl-1-cyclopentanol

organomercuric alcohol

The Diels-Alder Reaction

The Diels-Alder reaction is an addition reaction involving an alkene and a diene. Let's look at a representative Diels-Alder reaction involving 1,3-butadiene and an alkene (dienophile means diene-lover). The reaction involves a cyclic transition state. The product is usually a cyclic addition product. Study the representative reaction given below. Pay close attention to how the new bonds are formed in relation to the reactants.

| 1,3-Butadiene | Alkene (dienophile) | The cyclic transition state | Cycloaddition product |

Notice that the substituents in the alkene remain the same way in the product. In other words, *cis* substituents remain *cis* in the cycloaddition product. Hence, the Diels-Alder reaction is stereospecific.

Sample reaction 16-23

Diene   Maleic anhydride (dienophile)   →   Product

Diels-Alder product

The MCAT Chemistry Book

CHAPTER 16 PRACTICE QUESTIONS

1. All the following are possible products of the acid-catalyzed dehydration reaction of the compound shown below, EXCEPT:

A.

B.

C.

D.

2. A student researcher calculated the number of moles of hydrogen used per mol for the hydrogenation of an unsaturated (only double bonds) aliphatic non-cyclic hydrocarbon compound. If the number of moles of hydrogen used for the complete hydrogenation of each mol of the hydrocarbon is eight, how many double bonds were there in the compound that was hydrogenated?

   A. two
   B. four
   C. eight
   D. sixteen

3. Choose the product of the following reaction.

H_3C, H_3C $C=C$ CH_3, H $\xrightarrow{\text{1. O}_3 \quad\quad}{\text{2. H}_2\text{O/ Zn}}$

A. $CH_3CH_2CH_2CH_2CH_3$

B.
$$CH_3 \quad CH_3$$
$$H_3C-C-C-H$$
$$OH \quad OH$$

C.
$$O$$
$$\|$$
$$H_3C-C-CH_3$$
and
$$O$$
$$\|$$
$$H_3C-C-OH$$

D.
$$O$$
$$\|$$
$$H_3C-C-CH_3 \quad \text{and}$$
$$O$$
$$\|$$
$$H-C-CH_3$$

4. Which of the following is the most likely product of the reaction indicated below?

$$CH_3CH_2CH=CH_2 \xrightarrow{\underset{\underset{O}{\|}}{CH_3COOH}}$$

A.
$$OHOH$$
$$|\ |$$
$$CH_3CHCHCH_3$$

B. H_3CH_2CHC—CH_2 over O (epoxide)

C.
$$H_3C$$
$$H_3C$$ $C=O$

D. none of the above

5. Which of the following is the major product of the hydroboration-oxidation of 1-butene?

A. $CH_3CH_2CH_2CHO$

B. $CH_3CH_2CH_2OHCH_3$

C. $CH_3CH_2CH_2CH_2OH$

D. CH_3CH_2CH—CH_2 over O

6. Which of the following compounds has the highest heat of hydrogenation?

A. ethylene
B. propene
C. 1-butene
D. 1-hexene

7. The major product that results in a reaction involving 1-propene with hydrogen bromide, in the presence of peroxides is:

   A. 1-bromopropane
   B. 1,2-dibromopropane
   C. 2-bromopropane
   D. 1,3-dibromopropane

8. Which of the following is true regarding a reaction of cis-2-pentene with $KMnO_4$?

   A. A trans diol will be formed.
   B. A cis diol will be formed.
   C. The reagent is not strong enough to oxidize cis-2-pentene.
   D. The double bond will be broken, and is followed by a ring closure or ring formation.

9. In the acid catalyzed dehydration reaction of an alcohol, which of the following aspects listed can definitely be true?

   A. There can be no rearrangement of the intermediate, regardless of the alcohol involved.
   B. There can be rearrangement involved, resulting in less stable intermediates from more stable intermediates.
   C. If possible, the major product is the most substituted product because of its higher stability.
   D. None of the above.

10. In the acid-catalyzed dehydration of alcohols to alkenes, which of the following are true?

    I)   A carbanion intermediate is involved.
    II) A carbocation intermediate is involved.

III) There is no intermediate involved.
IV) Methyl shifts can occur in the intermediates.
V) Hydride shift can occur in the intermediates.

   A. I, IV & V only
   B. II, IV & V only
   C. III only
   D. II & V only

Questions 11-15 are based on the following passage.

Passage 1

The following synthesis reactions involving alkenes were done in a lab.

Reaction 1

$$H_2C = CH_2 \xrightarrow{H_2SO_4} CH_3CH_2OSO_3H$$

Reaction 2

Reaction 3

Reaction 4

$$CH_3C\equiv CCH_3$$

H₂
Lindlar
catalyst

Product X

Na/ NH₃ (*l*)

Product Y

11. Which of the following can be the oxidation product of an alkene?

   A. CH_3CH_2CHO
   B. $HOCH_2CH_2OH$
   C. $CH_3CH_2CH_2COOH$
   D. All the above

12. Ethylene oxide in the presence of H_2O can be converted to ethylene glycol by oxidation. In the process, the ring in ethylene oxide is attacked by water. Which of the following best describes the role of water?

   A. Electrophile
   B. Nucleophile
   C. Merely a solvent
   D. No active part in the reaction other than being a spectator molecule

13. In Reaction 2, what is the identity of Product A?

   A. Acetic acid
   B. Carbon dioxide
   C. Methane
   D. None of the above

14. Products X and Y in Reaction 4 are best described as:

   A. mirror images.
   B. tautomers.
   C. anomers.
   D. geometrical isomers.

15. What is the correct name of the compound shown below?

A. (E)-2-bromo-1-nitropropene
B. (Z)-2-bromo-1-nitropropene
C. (E)-2-bromo-1-nitrobutene
D. (Z)-2-bromo-1-nitrobutene

17

Alkynes

A. INTRODUCTION

Alkynes are hydrocarbons that contain carbon-carbon triple bonds. The general formula of alkynes is C_nH_{2n-2}.

$$HC\equiv CH \qquad \text{Acetylene}$$

In acetylene, the carbon is *sp* **hybridized**. The triple bond is composed of one sigma bond, and two pi bonds. The bond angle is $180°$. We should also realize that the sigma bonds are formed by *sp* hybrid orbitals, and the pi bonds are formed by the *p* orbitals.

If the triple bond in an alkyne is at the end of a carbon chain, it is called a terminal alkyne. If the triple bond is not at the end of a carbon chain, it is called an internal alkyne.

$$HC\equiv CCH_2CH_2CH_3 \qquad\qquad H_3CH_2CH_2CC\equiv CCH_2CH_3$$

A terminal alkyne   An internal alkyne

B. NAMING OF ALKYNES

The naming of alkynes is similar to that of alkenes.

sp hybridized

$$HC\equiv CH \qquad\qquad HC\equiv CCH_3 \qquad\qquad HC\equiv CCHCH_2CH_2CH_3$$

with CH_3 branch on the third carbon

Ethyne (Acetylene)   Propyne   3-methyl-1-hexyne

C. SYNTHESIS OF ALKYNES

Acetylene Synthesis by Adding H_2O to CaC_2 (calcium carbide)

Sample reaction 17-1

$$CaO \xrightarrow[\text{heat}]{C \text{ (Carbon)}} CaC_2 \xrightarrow{H_2O} HC\equiv CH \;+\; Ca(OH)_2$$

Calcium Oxide · Calcium carbide · Acetylene · Calcium Hydroxide

From Dihalogenoalkanes

Sample reaction 17-2

A representative reaction is given below:

$$R_1-\underset{H}{\overset{Br}{C}}-\underset{Br}{\overset{H}{C}}-R_2 \xrightarrow{KOH, C_2H_2OH} R_1-C\equiv C-R_2$$

A dibromoalkane → Alkyne

From Acetylene

Higher alkynes can be synthesized from acetylene by reacting with $NaNH_2$ followed by treatment with the appropriate alkyl halide. Terminal alkynes can be deprotonated using strong bases such as sodium amide. Hydroxides or alkoxides are not strong enough to deprotonate an acetylenic hydrogen.

$$H_3CH_2CH_2CC\equiv C-H$$

Acetylenic hydrogen(acidic proton)

A terminal alkyne

Sample reaction 17-3

$$HC\equiv CH + NaNH_2 \longrightarrow HC\equiv C{:}^-Na^+ + NH_3$$

Acetylene · Sodium amide · Sodium acetylide · Ammonia

$$HC\equiv C{:}^-Na^+ \xrightarrow{\overset{\delta^+ \; \delta^-}{CH_3CH_2CH_2Br}} HC\equiv CCH_2CH_2CH_3$$

1-Pentyne

D. REACTIONS OF ALKYNES

Hydrogenation

In the presence of catalysts such as palladium, platinum, or nickel, alkynes can be hydrogenated to the corresponding alkanes.

Sample reaction 17-4

$$HC\equiv CCH_2CH_2CH_3 \xrightarrow{H_2 \; / \; Pt} CH_3CH_2CH_2CH_2CH_3$$

1-Pentyne   Pentane

Alkynes can be hydrogenated to alkenes by using specific catalysts such as Lindlar palladium. This reaction is stereoselective resulting in syn addition.

Sample reaction 17-5

$$CH_3C\equiv CCH_2CH_3 \xrightarrow{\substack{H_2/ \; Lindlar \\ Palladium}}$$

cis-2-pentene

2-Pentyne

An alkyne can be hydrogenated to a *trans*-alkene by hydrogenating the alkyne with sodium in liquid ammonia.

Sample reaction 17-6

$$CH_3C\equiv CCH_2CH_3 \xrightarrow{Na \, / \; Liquid \; NH_3}$$

2-Pentyne

trans-2-Pentene

Acid-Catalyzed Hydration

Alkynes can undergo acid-catalyzed hydration reactions. The product is an **enol**, which is an unstable intermediate, and is immediately converted to a **ketone**. The formation of enol is based on Markovnikov addition (hydration).

$$R_1C\equiv CR_2 \longrightarrow R_1CH=CR_2 \longrightarrow R_1CH_2-CR_2$$

Alkyne   Enol   Ketone

Sample reaction 17-7

$$HC\equiv CCH_2CH_2CH_3 \xrightarrow{H_2O,\ H_2SO_4,\ Hg^{++}} CH_3\overset{\overset{\textstyle O}{\|}}{C}CH_2CH_2CH_3$$

1-Pentyne   2-Pentanone

Alkynes with Hydrogen Halides

Alkynes can undergo reactions with hydrogen halides. The reaction follows Markovnikov's addition of hydrogen and halogen to the triple bond. When two moles of hydrogen halide gets added to an alkyne, the reaction follows the same Markovnikov's pattern resulting in a geminal dihalide (two halogen atoms attached to the same carbon atom). Study the reactions given below.

Sample reaction 17-8

$$HC\equiv CCH_2CH_2CH_3 \xrightarrow{HBr} H_2C=\overset{\overset{\textstyle Br}{|}}{C}CH_2CH_2CH_3$$

1-Pentyne   2-Bromo-1-pentene

$$HC\equiv CCH_3 \xrightarrow{HBr} \text{(alkene)} \xrightarrow{HBr} \text{2,2-dibromopropane}$$

2,2-dibromopropane
(A geminal dihalide)

Alkynes with Halogens

Alkynes can undergo reactions with halogens forming di- and tetra-halogenated products.

Sample reaction 17-9

$$CH_3CH_2C\equiv CCH_3 \xrightarrow{Br_2} \text{(dibromoalkene)} \xrightarrow{Br_2} CH_3CH_2\overset{\overset{\textstyle Br}{|}}{\underset{\underset{\textstyle Br}{|}}{C}}\overset{\overset{\textstyle Br}{|}}{\underset{\underset{\textstyle Br}{|}}{C}}CH_3$$

Ozonolysis

Alkynes can undergo ozonolysis. The products formed are carboxylic acids.

Sample reaction 17-10

$$H_3CC \equiv CCH_2CH_2CH_3 \xrightarrow{\text{1. } O_3 \quad \text{2. } H_3O^+} CH_3CH_2CH_2COOH + CH_3COOH$$

2-Hexyne

In this reaction, the products formed are butanoic acid and acetic acid. If a terminal alkyne is used, the products are carbon dioxide and a carboxylic acid. See the example given below.

$$CH_3C \equiv\!\equiv CH \xrightarrow{O_3 / H_3O^+} CH_3COOH + CO_2$$

Reaction Involving the Acidic Hydrogen in an Alkyne

The acidic hydrogen present in terminal alkynes can undergo reactions with Grignard reagents. A sample reaction is shown.

Sample reaction 17-11

Alkyl magnesium halide
(Grignard reagent)

$$RC \equiv\!\equiv CH \xrightarrow{R'MgX} RC \equiv\!\equiv CMgX + R'H$$

The acidic hydrogen

Acetylide with Aldehydes and Ketones

Acetylides are strong bases and are good nucleophiles. So they can add to the carbonyl groups in aldehydes and ketones. The alkoxide ion that is formed during the reaction can be protonated to an alcohol by treating it with aqueous dilute acid.

CHAPTER 17 PRACTICE QUESTIONS

1. In the compound shown above, which of the indicated bonds (arrows) have the shortest carbon-carbon bond?

   A. a
   B. b
   C. c
   D. d

2. If bottle A contains *cis*-2-butene, bottle B contains 1-propyne, and bottle C contains butane, identify the bottle that contains the compound with carbon-carbon bonds of the highest bond energy.

   A. Bottle A
   B. Bottle B
   C. Bottle C
   D. They all have equal bond dissociation energies.

3. Which of following compounds has the lowest pKa value?

   A. Ethane
   B. Ethene
   C. Acetylene
   D. None of the above listed compounds are strong acids, and hence they do not have pKa values

$$CH_3CH_2C \equiv CCH_3$$

4. The compound shown above is treated with hydrogen in the presence of Lindlar catalyst. The major product is:

   A. pentanol.
   B. *cis*-2-pentene.
   C. pentane.
   D. *trans*-2-pentene.

5. 1-Butyne is treated with aqueous sulfuric acid in the presence of mercuric oxide as the catalyst. The major product is:

   A. 1-Butanone.
   B. 2-Butene.
   C. 2-Butanone.
   D. 1-butanol.

6. Which of the following choices represents the product of ozonolysis of 3-Hexyne?

   A. Propanone
   B. Propanal
   C. Hexanoic acid
   D. Propanoic acid

7. Double dehydrohalogenation of an alkyl vicinal dihalide can directly result in:

   A. a carboxylic acid.
   B. an alkyne.
   C. an alcohol.
   D. an ester.

8. The process by which an alkyne can be directly converted into an alkane is called:

   A. dehydrohalogenation.
   B. dehydration.
   C. hydrolysis.
   D. hydrogenation.

9. If liquid ammonia in the presence of sodium is added to an alkyne, the major product is:

   A. a *trans*-alkene.
   B. a *cis*-alkene.
   C. an aldehyde.
   D. a carboxylic acid.

10. Which of the following is true regarding alkynes?

   A. Alkynes have generally higher boiling points than corresponding alkanes.
   B. Alkynes have *sp* hybridized carbons.
   C. Acetylene (an alkyne) can form salts called acetylides when exposed to strong bases.
   D. All the above are true.

Questions 11-16 are based on the following passage.

Passage 1

   Alkynes are hydrocarbons with carbon-carbon triple bonds in them. The simplest alkyne can be prepared by the process shown in Reaction 1.

Reaction 1

$$CaC_2 + 2\,H_2O \longrightarrow HC\equiv CH + Ca(OH)_2$$

Reaction 2

$$\underset{\underset{CH_3CH-CHCH_3}{|\quad\quad|}}{Br\quad\quad Br} \xrightarrow[\triangle]{KOH} CH_3C\equiv CCH_3$$

Also consider the following reactions.

Reaction 3

$$H_3CC\equiv CH \xrightarrow{HBr} \underset{\underset{H_3CC=CH_2}{|}}{Br}$$

Reaction 4

$$H_3CC\equiv CCH_3 \xrightarrow[\substack{Pd/BaSO_4\\Quinoline}]{H_2} \underset{\underset{H_3CC=CH_2}{|}}{Br}$$

Quinoline is a heterocyclic amine.

11. The hybrid orbital that characterizes and differentiates alkynes from other simple hydrocarbons like alkanes and alkenes, is that alkynes have hybrid orbitals which have:

   A. 75% *p* character and 25% *s* character.
   B. 66% *p* character and 33% *s* character.
   C. 50% *p* character and 50% *s* character.
   D. none of the above.

12. Reaction 3 is best described as:

A. a substitution reaction.
B. an addition reaction.
C. an elimination reaction.
D. a dehydrogenation reaction.

13. Which of the following sequences best describes a way to synthesize 1-hexyne from acetylene?

A. 1. $NaNH_2$/liq. ammonia
    2. *n*-propyl bromide

B. 1. $NaNH_2$/liq. ammonia
    2. *tert*-butyl bromide

C. 1. *n*-Propyl bromide
    2. $NaNH_2$/liq. ammonia

D. 1. $NaNH_2$/liq. ammonia
    2. *n*-butyl bromide

14. Lindlar's catalyst is often used for the reduction of alkynes to alkenes. The catalyst consists of palladium which is deposited in a finely divided state of barium sulfate, which is subsequently treated with a heterocyclic amine called quinoline. Which of the following is the most likely function of quinoline?

A. To speed up the reaction so that the alkyne is completely converted to its most reduced form of hydrocarbon
B. To slow down the reaction, because the function of a catalyst is to slow down the reaction
C. To moderate the catalytic activity to facilitate a restrictive reduction
D. It acts as an oxidizing agent so that the alkyne is reduced.

15. Which of the following is the most likely structure of quinoline?

A.

B.

C.

D.

16. Predict the major product of the reaction shown below:

$$H_3CH_2CC\equiv CCH_3 \xrightarrow[\text{Liquid } NH_3]{K}$$

A. $H_3CH_2CC\equiv CCH_2K$

B.

C.

D.

18

Aromatic Compounds

A. INTRODUCTION

Aromatic compounds are compounds which have benzene rings in them. Aromatic hydrocarbons are also called arenes. Some compounds have structures which look like fused benzene rings. Such compounds are called **polycyclic aromatic compounds**.

Benzene

Toluene

Polycyclic aromatic hydrocarbons

Naphthalene

Anthracene

B. BENZENE

Structure of Benzene

The formula of benzene is C_6H_6. The ring structure has alternate double and single bonds as shown in the diagrams below. According to the latest theories, benzene is in resonance between the two structural entities as shown below. Benzene has a structure that is a hybridized form of these two structures.

The hybridized structure is usually represented as shown below:

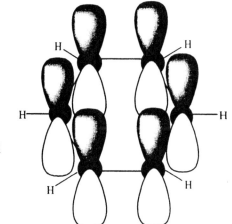

Figure 18-1

The six carbons in the benzene ring have a planar arrangement of a regular hexagon. The carbons are located at the vertices of the hexagon. The carbon-carbon bonds have the same length, and each bond angle is 120°. The hybridization is sp^2. The sigma bonds are formed by the sp^2 hybridized orbitals. However, the unhybridized $2p$ orbitals in each carbon overlap to form a cyclic pi system around the ring. The delocalization of these electrons creates the pi system in aromatic compounds. The electron cloud of the pi system occupies the regions above and below the ring as depicted in Figure 18-1.

In benzene, there are six pi electrons in the ring with overlapping p orbitals.

C. DERIVATIVES OF BENZENE

Many derivatives of benzene are substituted derivative compounds. Some examples of such compounds are shown below:

SOME MONOSUBSTITUTED AROMATIC COMPOUNDS

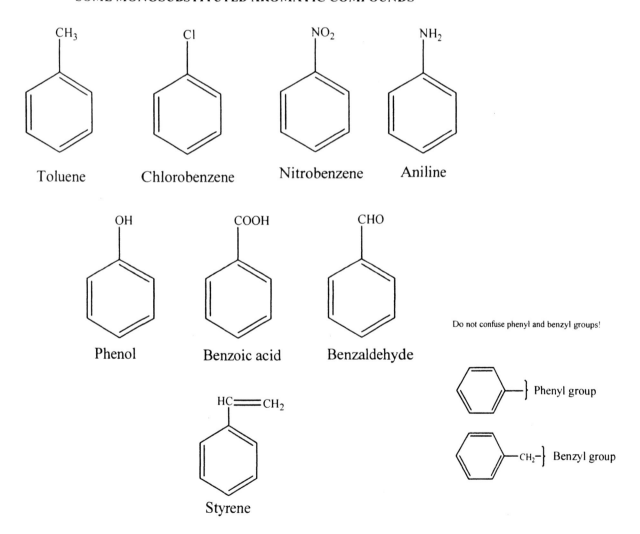

Toluene   Chlorobenzene   Nitrobenzene   Aniline

Phenol   Benzoic acid   Benzaldehyde

Do not confuse phenyl and benzyl groups!

Phenyl group

Benzyl group

Styrene

With respect to the substituent (the methyl group)
arrow (1) indicates the ortho position,
arrow (2) indicates the meta position,
arrow (3) indicates the para position.

o-Xylene   *m*-Xylene   *p*-Xylene

(Xylene is the general name of a dimethyl-substituted benzene)

D. PROPERTIES OF AROMATIC COMPOUNDS

Aromatic hydrocarbons are nonpolar, and are insoluble in water. They commonly undergo reactions like **aromatic electrophilic substitution reactions** and **reduction reactions**.

E. CONCEPT OF AROMATICITY

Aromaticity of compounds is based on certain rules. According to Huckel's rule, the number of pi electrons present should be a number denoted by the formula $4n + 2$, where n is 0, 1, 2, 3, ... Hence, for compounds to be considered aromatic the number of pi electrons should be 2, 6, 10, ... In addition, the structure should also have a cyclic pi system to be aromatic. Atoms in the ring must have unhybridized p orbitals. These unhybridized p orbitals must overlap resulting in a cyclic pi system. For this type of overlap, the structure must have planar (or nearly planar) configuration. In other words, the atoms related or involved in the pi bond should be in the same plane.

Test whether you can recognize the aromaticity of the structures in the examples that follow:

Tips for testing aromaticity

Step 1 – Count the number of pi electrons.
Step 2 – See whether there is a cyclic p orbital overlap.

Predict the aromaticity of the compounds given below:

Compound 1

Number of pi electrons – 6
Cyclic overlap of p orbitals – Yes
Aromatic – Yes

Compound 2

1,3-Cyclopentadiene

Number of pi electrons – 4
Cyclic overlap of p orbitals – No
Aromatic – No

Compound 3

Cyclopentadienyl anion

Number of pi electrons – 6
Cyclic overlap of *p* orbitals – Yes
Aromatic – Yes

Some examples of heterocyclic aromatic compounds

Pyridine

The nonbonded electron pair is in an sp^2 orbital which is perpendicular to the pi system and thus not part of the pi system. Since it has six pi electrons in a planar confirmation, it is aromatic.

Pyrrole

The nonbonded electrons occupy the unhybridized *p* orbital and thus are part of the cyclic pi system. With a total of six pi electrons, pyrrole is aromatic.

Furan

There are two lone pairs of electrons on the oxygen atom in Furan. One of the lone pairs occupies the sp^2 hybrid orbital, while the other pair occupies the unhybridized *p* orbital and forms the overlap with the pi electrons of the carbon atoms to form a continuous ring of six electrons. Hence, furan is aromatic.

F. REACTIONS OF AROMATIC COMPOUNDS

Benzene Stability

Benzene, unlike alkenes, will not react with halogens to form addition products.

This exemplifies the extra stability of the double bonds present in the benzene ring. However, benzene can undergo substitution reactions with halogens in the presence of a Lewis acid catalyst. The Lewis acid enhances the electrophilic nature of the halogen, thus enabling the reaction to proceed.

Electrophilic Substitution Reactions

One of the most characteristic reactions of benzene is the electrophilic substitution reaction, in which a hydrogen is replaced by an electrophile. In such reactions, the benzene acts as the nucleophile.

ELECTROPHILIC AROMATIC SUBSTITUTION REACTION

Benzene   Electrophilic reagent   Substitution products

In a typical aromatic substitution reaction, the electrophile (means electron loving) accepts the electron pair from the pi system of benzene, resulting in a carbocation. This cation of benzene is called the **cyclohexadienyl cation**. Then, the cyclohexadienyl cation loses a proton forming the substitution product.

MECHANISM OF ELECTROPHILIC AROMATIC SUBSTITUTION

Benzene

Electrophile

Cyclohexadienyl cation

· Electrophilic substitution product

Nitration

Benzene can be nitrated by reacting with nitric acid (HNO_3). This is usually done in the presence of sulfuric acid (H_2SO_4).

Sample reaction 18-1

Benzene $\xrightarrow{HNO_3 / H_2SO_4}$ Nitrobenzene $+ H_2O$

In this reaction, nitronium ion (NO_2^+) acts as the electrophile.

Friedel-Crafts Reactions

In Friedel-Crafts reactions, benzene is reacted with acyl or alkyl chlorides, in the presence of metal halides as catalysts. The metal halides act as Lewis acids in these reactions. The two types of Friedel-Crafts reactions are alkylation and acylation.

(1) Alkylation

In Friedel-Crafts alkylation, benzene is reacted with alkyl chlorides in the presence of metal halides ($AlCl_3$, $AlBr_3$) as catalysts. The catalyst serves as Lewis acid and increases the electrophilicity of the alkyl halide. Alkylation is important for the synthesis of alkyl substituted derivatives of benzene. But there is a possibility of rearrangement of the intermediates resulting in undesired products. For example, if primary halides are used in alkylation, they can rearrange to form secondary or tertiary carbocations which are more stable intermediates. This can result in multiple products.

Sample reaction 18-2

| Benzene | Ethyl chloride | | Ethylbenzene | Hydrogen chloride |

The Mechanism of Alkylation Rearrangement

(2) Acylation

In Friedel-Crafts acylation reactions, benzene is reacted with acyl chlorides or acid anhydrides in the presence of metal halides (Lewis acids). The importance of acylation is that there is no rearrangement, unlike alkylation where there is a possibility of rearrangement of the cation intermediates.

The acyl halide forms a complex with the Lewis acid ($AlCl_3$), followed by the leaving of the halogen along with the Lewis acid. The resulting ion, called acylium ion, is resonance stabilized and is strongly electrophilic. This ion reacts with benzene to form an acylbenzene.

Sample reaction 18-3

Benzene   Acyl chloride   Acyl benzene   Hydrogen chloride

Acyl products that are formed can be reduced by reactions such as Clemmenson or Wolf-Kishner reductions.

Clemmenson reduction

Wolf-Kishner reduction

Sample reaction 18-4

Benzene   Acid anhydride

Halogenation

Sample reaction 18-5

Benzene can be halogenated in the presence of Fe. In this reaction, the iron(III) bromide acts as the catalyst, which is formed from the iron and the bromine. The bromine-iron(III) bromide complex that is formed acts as the electrophile which attacks the benzene.

Sulfonation

Benzene can be sulfonated by heating with sulfuric acid.

Sample reaction 18-6

Benzene   Benzenesulfonic acid

G. DIRECTIVE EFFECTS OF SUBSTITUENTS

Consider the reaction of benzene with an electrophile (E).

Notice that the positive charge is spread only on secondary carbons, and thus all resonance structures are equally stable.

The MCAT Chemistry Book

In aromatic substitution reactions, the groups already present in the benzene ring can significantly influence the place of electrophilic attack of the incoming substituent. In other words, the substitution is influenced by the groups that are already present in the benzene ring. There are two types of substituents (groups) – **activators** and **deactivators**. The groups that are activators cause the ring to be increasingly reactive than benzene. The groups that are deactivators cause the ring to be decreasingly reactive than benzene.

Activating Groups

As mentioned above, the activators increase the reactivity of the ring than that of benzene. The substitution primarily occurs in the ortho and para positions of the ring relative to the activating group. For this reason, activators are also called **ortho/para directors**. Let us analyze this with an example. In the following reaction, phenol is nitrated. Notice that phenol contains a hydroxyl group (-OH) which is an ortho/para activator. So the substitution occurs at ortho and para positions with respect to the -OH group.

Sample reaction 18-7

| Phenol | Ortho-Nitrophenol | Para-Nitrophenol |

Now let's us consider an electrophilic attack on toluene.

Ortho attack on toluene

most
favorable

Because the attack on the ortho or para attack results in more stable cation intermediates, those intermediates are formed faster and thus the resulting products from those intermediates are the predominant products.

Para attack on toluene

most favorable

Meta attack on toluene

By observing the resonance forms of the cation intermediates, it is clear that ortho and para attacks are favored. This is because ortho and para attacks have the possibility of spreading or sharing the positive charge by a tertiary carbon. Notice that when the attack is at the meta position, the positive charge is only shared by secondary carbons. A positive charge is better stabilized when it is on a tertiary carbon than on a secondary carbon. The methyl substituent is electron-donating and activates the benzene ring toward electrophilic attack, and the activation is more towards the ortho and para positions than the meta positions. In other words, alkyl groups are electron-donating substituents that are ortho-para directing by donating the electron density and thereby inductively stabilizes the intermediate.

Alkyl groups are electron-donating substituents, but it might seem counterintuitive to think that groups like -OH (hydroxyl) and -OCH3 (methoxy) are also ortho/para activators since oxygen is highly electronegative atom. This is because the oxygen atom that is bonded to the ring carbon has lone electrons or nonbonding electrons. As a result, the positive charge on the carbon atom in the intermediates formed from ortho and para attacks is stabilized through resonance. In other words, such groups can also donate electron density because of the presence of nonbonded electrons.

Deactivating Groups

Deactivators make the ring less reactive than benzene. There are two types of deactivators – **ortho/para** and **meta deactivators**.

1) Ortho/para deactivators

Some deactivators direct the incoming substituents primarily to the ortho and para positions. Halogens (Fluorine, Chlorine, Bromine, Iodine) are ortho/para deactivators.They are electron withdrawing substituents through inductive effect. Furthermore, they have nonbonded electrons that can donate electron density by resonance. Because of the high electronegativity of halogens, they pull the electron density away from the ring, making the ring less susceptible to electrophilic substitution (deactivating property). Halogen substituents have nonbonded electrons which can be donated to a positively charged carbon in the intermediates resulting from ortho and para attacks. Hence, halogens are ortho, para-directing, and deactivating substituents.

Ortho attack

Para attack

2) Meta deactivators

The meta deactivating groups direct the incoming substituents to the meta position. These groups are strongly electron-withdrawing groups. Consider the following example.

Major product
(meta substitution)

The substituent acyl group has a highly polarized carbon-oxygen double bond.

The positively charged carbon withdraws electron density from the benzene ring inductively. This accounts for the deactivation (less reactivity than benzene) of the ring toward electrophilic substitution.

Ortho attack

unstable
(adjacent positve charges)

Para attack

unstable

Meta attack

Both ortho and para attacks result in an intermediate that has adjacent positively charged (polarized) atoms, making it a highly unstable (higher energy) form. On the other hand, meta substitution doesn't result in an intermediate with positively charged atoms adjacent to each other. Thus, meta substitution results in the most stable (lower energy) intermediates. This accounts for the predominance of meta substitution products if acyl or similar groups are present in the ring.

254

Table 18-1 Some Common Directors

ORTHO, PARA DIRECTORS

Activating	Deactivating
-OH	Halogens (-X)
-OR	
-NH$_2$	
-R	
-Ar	
-NHR	
-NR$_2$	
$\overset{\overset{O}{\|}}{-OCR}$	

META DIRECTORS (Deactivating)

-CN
-CO$_2$R
-NO$_2$
-SO$_3$H
+NR$_3$
-CHO
-CO$_2$H
-SO$_2$OR
-CF$_3$

$\overset{\overset{O}{\|}}{-CCl}$

$\overset{\overset{O}{\|}}{-CR}$

CHAPTER 18 PRACTICE QUESTIONS

1. Which of the following compounds is commonly known as xylene?

A. (toluene structure, CH_3)

B. (p-xylene structure, two CH_3)

C. (phenol structure, OH)

D. (styrene structure, $CH=CH_2$)

2. The carbons in the benzene ring are:

A. sp hybridized.
B. sp^2 hybridized.
C. sp^3 hybridized.
D. not hybridized.

3. All the following are monosubstituted aromatic compounds, EXCEPT:

A. phenol.
B. benzoic acid.
C. xylene.
D. toluene.

4. A compound can be aromatic, only if it has a certain number of pi electrons in its ring. All the following numbers can be attributed to the number of pi electrons and aromaticity, EXCEPT:

A. two.
B. four.
C. six.
D. ten.

5. For the reaction involving benzene and nitric acid in the presence of sulfuric acid, which of the following is true?

A. The nitronium ion acts as the electrophile.
B. The reaction is an example of nucleophilic hydrogenation.
C. The reaction is an example of electrophilic addition reaction.
D. None of the above

6. What is the name of the reaction shown below?

A. Clemmenson reaction
B. Williamson synthesis
C. Raman synthesis
D. Friedel-Crafts reaction

Reaction for Q. 7

| Zn (Hg)/ HCl

7. The reaction shown is commonly known as:

A. Clemmenson reduction.
B. Wolff-Kishner reaction.
C. Benedicts reaction.
D. Zaitsev reaction.

8. The group $-NO_2$ can be best described as:

A. an ortho/para activator.
B. a meta activator.
C. an ortho/para deactivator.
D. a meta deactivator.

9. Halogens can be best described as:

A. ortho/para activators.
B. meta activators.
C. ortho/para deactivators.
D. meta deactivators.

10. If the compound shown below was reacted with nitric acid in the presence of sulfuric acid, which of the following is the major product?

A. A para substituted product
B. A meta substituted product
C. An ortho substituted product
D. No net reaction occurs

Questions 11-16 are based on the following passage.

Passage 1

The earliest predictions about the structure of benzene could not completely explain some of its properties. Later it was found that benzene has a cyclic structure which is commonly represented as follows:

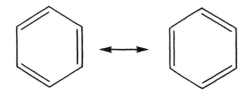

These two structures are resonance structures of benzene. Benzene is also commonly represented as shown below:

A series of reactions were conducted using benzene and other aromatic compounds.

Reaction 1

In Reaction 1, benzene was reacted with *n*-propyl chloride in the presence of $AlCl_3$.

Reaction 2

Nitrobenzene was reacted with nitric acid and sulfuric acid. The reaction occurred as follows:

Compound A + Compound B + Compound C
(major product)

11. Which of the following is true regarding Reaction 1 described in the passage?

A. It is a Friedel-Crafts acylation reaction.
B. It is a reaction which results in a single product.
C. $AlCl_3$ acts as a Lewis base.
D. Rearrangement is possible.

12. Alkoxy group is best described as:

A. an ortho, para-director, and an activating group.
B. an ortho, para-director, and a deactivating group.
C. a meta-director, and an activating group.
D. a meta-director, and a deactivating group.

13. If phenol is reacted with bromine, the major product formed is:

OH

$\xrightarrow[\text{Carbon disulfide}]{\text{Br}_2}$

A.

OH
OBr

B.

OH

Br

C.

OH

Br

D.

OBr

14. The reaction shown here is:

$\xrightarrow[\text{H}^+]{\text{HNO}_3}$

NO$_2$

A. an electrophilic substitution reaction.
B. an electrophilic addition reaction.
C. a reduction-addition reaction.
D. an electrophilic elimination reaction.

15. The inscribed circle in the benzene ring represents:

A. the carbon chain in the cyclic ring.
B. the sigma-system of electrons.
C. the pi-system of electrons.
D. the eight pi-electrons in the cyclic system.

16. All the following are FALSE about Reaction 2, EXCEPT that:

A. Compound A is a meta product.
B. the major product is a 1,2 substituted product.
C. the major product is a para substituted product.
D. Compound C is a 1,3 substituted product.

19

Stereochemistry

A. INTRODUCTION

Stereochemistry is the study of the three-dimensional structures of compounds. In this chapter, we will discuss the various concepts in stereochemistry starting with some simple terms such as isomers. What are isomers? **Isomers** are compounds with the same molecular formula, but with different arrangements of atoms. Stereochemistry takes us further into the intricacies of isomerism in terms of three-dimensional perspectives. Furthermore, stereochemistry helps us understand the differences in activities of molecules that are structurally rather close. In many compounds, the slightest changes in the three-dimensional form of molecules make them active or inactive. This concept is especially important in many biologically significant molecules. Stereochemistry has taken us deep into the secrets of many naturally occurring molecules in our body.

Constitutional isomers have the same molecular formula but different arrangements. Look at the examples shown in Figure 19-1. They are constitutional isomers.

Figure 19-1

Diastereomers

Diastereomers have the same molecular formula, but they do not have a mirror-image relationship to each other. Study the examples in Figure 19-4.

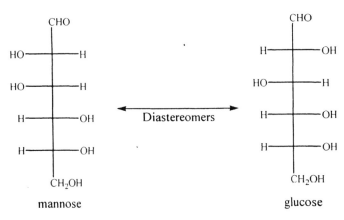

mannose   glucose

Figure 19-4

C. OPTICAL ACTIVITY

The molecular structure and the geometry of a compound dictate many of its properties. The structural integrity of certain molecules makes them capable of rotating the plane of polarized light. In order to make use of this phenomenon, we must have a source of plane polarized light. When light waves are passed through polarizing materials, the electric field vector of the processed light oscillates in one plane. This is plane polarized light.

To examine the chiral properties, experimenters pass plane polarized light through solutions of chiral compounds. The rotation of light is noted with a detector. If the rotation perceived by an observer looking through the solution toward the source of light is clockwise, positive (+) sign is used to denote the optical activity. For counterclockwise rotation, negative (−) sign is used to denote the optical activity. The positive rotation is often referred as *d* (**dextrorotatory**) and negative rotation as *l* (**levorotatory**).

Some Generalizations Regarding Optical Activity

Consider two solutions − A and B. Solution A contains a pure enantiomer, and solution B contains the enantiomer of the compound in solution A. Let's say that solution A exhibited positive rotation.

Since the solution A containing a pure enantiomer exhibits positive rotatory properties, its enantiomer will have negative rotatory properties. What can we conclude about these compounds? Well, we can be certain that both compounds present in the solutions A and B are chiral, since they exhibit optical activity.

263

The specific rotation [α] of a compound at a given wavelength is denoted by

$$[\alpha] = \frac{\alpha}{c\,l},$$

where α is the observed rotation,
c is the concentration in g/ml,
and l is the length (in decimeters) of the polarimeter tube (the optically active solution is taken in the polarimeter tube for the analysis) that is used.

Properties of Enantiomers and Diastereomers

Enantiomers have identical physical properties. So they cannot be distinguished based on their melting points, boiling points, and densities. But enantiomers do differ in terms of optical activity. Enantiomers rotate plane polarized light with the same magnitude, but in opposite directions. Because enantiomers have identical physical properties, separation of enantiomers using conventional methods such as simple distillation and recrystallization is not possible. Enantiomers react the same way with achiral molecules, but react differently with chiral molecules. This difference in reactivity of enantiomers toward chiral molecules is utilized in separating enantiomers. The process is called resolution. The enantiomeric mixture is reacted with a chiral molecule to form a pair of diastereomers. Because diastereomers have different physical properties, they can easily be separated. Diastereomers usually have different solubilities. Followed by the separation of the diastereomers that are formed, the original reaction is reversed to get the original enantiomer corresponding to the diastereomer.

D. CONFIGURATIONS

Chirality and Achirality

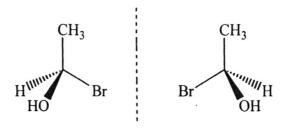

Figure 19-5

If a molecule does not have a plane of symmetry, it is chiral. A chiral molecule is not superimposable on its mirror image. The structures represented in Figure 19-5 are mirror images. These mirror images are non-superimposable. The molecules depicted in Figure 19-5 are chiral.

CH_3 ... CH_3

Figure 19-6

We will now consider Figure 19-6. The mirror images of the molecule depicted are superimposable. Hence it is an achiral molecule. Notice that two of the atoms attached to the central carbon atom are the same, namely the hydrogen atoms.

Achirality can also be recognized by looking at the molecular structure. When we are analyzing the structure of a molecule, we should look and determine whether there is any plane of symmetry in the molecule. Plane of symmetry reflects achirality.

The figure given below shows a stereoisomer of tartaric acid. Notice that this compound has two chiral (stereogenic) centers. But, there is a plane of symmetry and thus the molecule itself is achiral and optically inactive. Such compounds that contain one or more stereogenic centers, but are achiral, are called meso compounds. Hence, having a stereogenic center or chiral carbon does not always lead to chirality of the entire molecule.

meso-tartaric acid

Absolute Configuration

*In three-dimen-
sional repre-
sentation, the
solid wedges
represent bonds
that are point-
ing towards
you.
The dashed
wedges repre-
sent bonds that
are pointing
away from you.*

Fischer projection   Three-dimensional form

Figure 19-7

> *In Fischer projection, the horizontal lines represent bonds that are toward you,
> and the vertical lines represent bonds that are pointing away from you.*

Absolute configuration is the arrangement of substituents around the stereogenic center of a chiral molecule. The Fischer projection and the absolute configuration of the amino acid alanine is shown in Figure 19-7.

R-S System of Representation

The *R-S* system of representation is a convenient and essential way of looking at molecules. The *R-S* convention is done by prioritizing the substituents that are bonded to the chiral carbon.

The following rules will familiarize you with the *R-S* naming of compounds.

1. The orientation of the molecule should be in such a way that the lowest priority group is pointing away from you.

2. First, prioritize each group that is bonded to the chiral carbon. The priority is based on atomic number. Higher the atomic number of the atom (in the group) that is connected to the chiral carbon, higher the priority of that group. For example, if the four groups connected to a chiral carbon are CH_3, H, OH, and Br, then the bromine atom (atomic number 35) has the highest priority. This is followed by the oxygen atom (atomic number 8) of the hydroxyl group, then the carbon atom of the methyl group, followed by the hydrogen atom (atomic number 1). It is important to realize that the priority is determined by the atomic number of the atom that is directly connected to the chiral atom.

3. If two groups that are attached to a chiral carbon are isotopes (same atomic number, different mass numbers), the heavier isotope takes precedence.

4. If two groups have the same atom connected to a chiral carbon, then the next atom along the chain determines the priority. If that too fails (if it is the same atom), then go to the next atom to determine which group has higher priority. For example, -CH$_2$F has a lower priority than -CH$_2$I. If the groups contain unsaturations such as double or triple bonds, consider that the atoms on both ends are duplicated depending on the number of bonds.

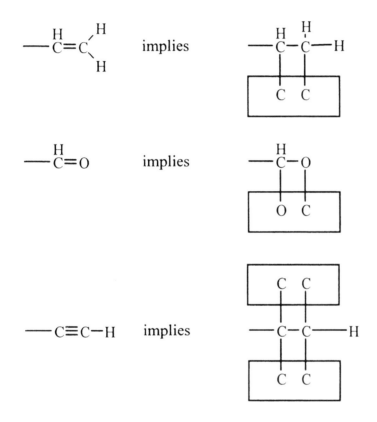

5. After prioritizing, draw an arrow starting from the first priority group to the third priority group through the second priority group. This is illustrated in the example given below.
6. If the arrow points in the clockwise direction, the configuration of that chiral carbon is *R*. If the arrow points in the counterclockwise direction, the configuration of that chiral carbon is *S*.

Notice that the lowest priority group
(H) is pointing away from you.

If the given orientation of a molecule shows the lowest priority group pointing toward the viewer, the orientation should be changed so that the lowest priority group points away from the viewer. In Fischer projection, if the lowest priority group is attached to a vertical bond (the one that points up or down), the molecule should be viewed from another angle so that the lowest priority group points away from the viewer. This can be achieved by doing 2 two-group switches or interchanges. If only 1 two-group interchange is done, the opposite configuration results. See the example given below.

Notice that the lowest priority group (-CH₃) is NOT pointing away from you.

2 two-group interchanges restore the original confuguration

Example 19-1

Find the absolute configuration of the molecule shown below in terms of *R-S* notation.

$$\underset{H_3C}{\overset{\overset{\displaystyle H}{\vdots}}{\underset{\displaystyle}{HO\blacktriangleright C}}}\!\!-\!CH_2CH_3$$

Solution:

First, we have to think about the order of priority of the substituents. The order is as follows:

$$OH > CH_2CH_3 > CH_3 > H$$

We can simplify the structure by looking at the three substituents that determine the configuration. Let's redraw them as shown below:

$$\underset{CH_3}{\overset{HO\qquad CH_2CH_3}{C}}\qquad \text{Clockwise}$$

Since the direction of priority is clockwise, the configuration is *R*.

Some sample conversions to Fischer projection

viewing angle/direction

Fischer projection

Example 19-2

Draw the *L* configuration of the compound shown in Example 19-1.

Solution:

For *L* configuration, the direction of priority should be counterclockwise. So the structure can be best represented as follows:

Counterclockwise

CHAPTER 19 PRACTICE QUESTIONS

1. What is the best term that can be used to express the relationship between the two structures shown below?

A. Diastereomers
B. Enantiomers
C. Mesocompounds
D. Anomers

2. What is the best term that can be used to express the relationship between the two structures shown below?

A. Diastereomers
B. Enantiomers
C. Identical compounds
D. None of the above

3. The structure shown below is that of 2,3,4-trihydroxy glutaric acid. Choose the correct enantiomer of this compound.

```
        COOH
         |
  HO ——— C ——— H
         |
  HO ——— C ——— H
         |
   H ——— C ——— OH
         |
        COOH
```

A.
```
        COOH
         |
  HO ——— C ——— H
         |
  HO ——— C ——— H
         |
   H ——— C ——— OH
         |
        COOH
```

B.
```
        COOH
         |
   H ——— C ——— OH
         |
   H ——— C ——— OH
         |
   H ——— C ——— OH
         |
        COOH
```

C.
```
        COOH
         |
   H ——— C ——— OH
         |
   H ——— C ——— OH
         |
  HO ——— C ——— H
         |
        CHO
```

D.
```
        COOH
         |
   H ——— C ——— OH
         |
   H ——— C ——— OH
         |
  HO ——— C ——— H
         |
        COOH
```

4. All are equivalent structures or representations of the compound given below, EXCEPT:

```
          F
          |
   H₃C ——— C ——— H
          |
          Br
```

A.
```
        CH₃
         |
   F ——— C ——— Br
         |
         H
```

B.
```
         H
         |
  Br ——— C ——— F
         |
        CH₃
```

C.
```
         H
         |
  Br ——— C ——— CH₃
         |
         F
```

D. All the above are equivalent structural representations.

5. What is the name of Compound X?

F
|
H————————Br
|
CH₃

Compound X

A. (S)-1-bromo-1-fluoromethane
B. (R)-1-bromo-1-fluoromethane
C. (S)-1-bromo-1-fluoroethane
D. (R)-1-bromo-1-fluoroethane

6. Which of the following are true?

I. Diastereomers are stereoisomers.
II. All stereoisomers are enantiomers.
III. All enantiomers are stereoisomers.

A. I & II only
B. I & III only
C. II & III only
D. I, II, & III

7. Saw horse representation of a compound is given below. Which of the following is true about this structure?

A. The compound has an eclipsed conformation.
B. The compound has a staggered conformation.
C. The compound has a *cis*-configuration.
D. None of the above

20

Alkyl Halides

A. INTRODUCTION

Alkyl halides are organic compounds with the general formula RX, where R denotes the alkyl group and X denotes the halogen.

B. NAMING OF ALKYL HALIDES

CH_3CH_2Cl	$CH_3CH_2CH_2CH_2Cl$	$CH_3CH_2CHCH_2CH_3$	$CH_3CH_2CCH_2CH_3$
1-Chloroethane	1-Chlorobutane	3-Bromopentane	3-Bromo-3-methyl-pentane
1^0 alkyl halide	1^0 alkyl halide	2^0 alkyl halide	3^0 alkyl halide

We can classify alkyl halides as primary (1^0), secondary (2^0), and tertiary (3^0) alkyl halides. The general formulas for these are as follows:

Primary alkyl halide	RCH_2X
Secondary alkyl halide	R_2CHX
Tertiary alkyl halide	R_3CX

C. PROPERTIES OF ALKYL HALIDES

Alkyl halides have large dipole moments since the carbon-halogen bond is polar. They also have reasonably high boiling points because of the polarity and the high molecular weights.

$$R \overline{} X$$

Alkyl halides are generally insoluble in water. Density of alkyl halides increases as the atomic weight of the halogen present increases. The heavier the halogen is, the higher the density.

Increasing order of density $\Longrightarrow$

$$RF \quad < \quad RCl \quad < \quad RBr \quad < \quad RI$$

D. SYNTHESIS OF ALKYL HALIDES

From Alcohols

Alkyl halides can be prepared from alcohols. The following examples show some representative reactions. The conversion of an alcohol to an alkyl halide is an example of a **nucleophilic substitution** reaction.

Sample reaction 20-1

$$CH_3CH_2OH \xrightarrow{\text{HCl}} CH_3CH_2Cl$$

Ethyl Alcohol   Ethyl chloride

Sample reaction 20-2

$$\underset{\text{2-Butanol}}{CH_3\overset{\overset{\displaystyle OH}{|}}{C}HCH_2CH_3} \xrightarrow{\text{SOCl}_2} \underset{\text{2-Chlorobutane}}{CH_3\overset{\overset{\displaystyle Cl}{|}}{C}HCH_2CH_3}$$

From Alkanes

Alkyl halides can be synthesized from alkanes. In this reaction, one of the alkane's hydrogen atoms is substituted with a halogen atom. The reaction occurs by free radical mechanism.

Sample reaction 20-3

$$\underset{\text{Alkane}}{RH} \xrightarrow{\text{Cl}_2} \underset{\text{Alkyl halide}}{RCl} \quad + \quad HCl$$

From Alkenes

Alkyl halides can be prepared from alkenes.

Sample reaction 20-4

$$CH_2=CH_2 \quad + \quad HX \quad \longrightarrow \quad CH_3\text{-}CH_2X$$
Ethylene   Hydrogen halide   Ethyl halide

Sample reaction 20-5

Markovnikov addition of hydrogen and bromine

Alkene

E. REACTIONS OF ALKYL HALIDES

Nucleophilic Substitution Reactions

In this section, we will discuss the two major substitution reactions — S_N1 and S_N2 reactions. In nucleophilic substitution reactions involving alkyl halides as the substrate, a Lewis base (nucleophile) substitutes the halogen present in the alkyl halide. We will discuss nucleophilic reactions in which alkyl halides react with nucleophiles. A general representation can be done as follows:

(Alkyl halide)   (Substitution
                                  product)

$$RX \quad \longrightarrow \quad RNu \quad + \quad X^-$$
                Nu$^-$
          (Nucleophile)

The S_N2 Reaction

S_N2 stands for bimolecular nucleophilic substitution reaction. Consider the reaction between methyl iodide and sodium hydroxide.

$$CH_3I \quad + \quad NaOH \quad \longrightarrow \quad CH_3OH \quad + \quad NaI$$

This reaction follows S_N2 mechanism. Experimentally, it has been confirmed that the rate of this reaction depends on both the alkyl halide and the nucleophile (OH^-) involved. The reaction rate is written as follows:

$$Rate = k\ [CH_3I]\ [OH^-]$$

The Mechanism of S_N2 Reaction

We will look at the mechanism involved in the reaction between methyl iodide and sodium hydroxide. The S_N2 reaction proceeds via a five-coordinate transition state. This transition state has weak (the weak bonds are indicated by the dotted lines in the mechanism) carbon-iodine and carbon-oxygen bonds. Even though these two are weak bonds, the other three bonds involving the central carbon atom are complete bonds. As the leaving group detaches, there is an inversion of configuration (in chiral molecules) at the carbon where the leaving group was attached.

Figure 20-1 The mechanism of S_N2 reaction

In S_N2 reactions, the nucleophilic attack occurs opposite (backside attack) to the side where the leaving group is present. This type of nucleophilic approach is thermodynamically favored since the backside attack minimizes the electrostatic repulsions between the nucleophile and the leaving group involved. If substituents (especially bulky ones) are present on the carbon where the nucleophilic attack occurs, this can hinder the S_N2 process. Hence, primary alkyl halides are the most reactive among alkyl halides with respect to S_N2 reactions.

S_N2 reactivity:	Methyl > Primary > Secondary > Tertiary

HO⁻ → H₃C⁻ⁿⁿⁿC—Cl̈   →   [HO---C---Cl̈]   →   HO—Cⁿⁿⁿ·CH₃
              | | |
              CH₃CH₂   H₃C   CH₂CH₃   CH₂CH₃
              H   H   H

(S) -2-chlorobutane   transition   (R) -2-butanol   Cl̈⁻
                                 state

inversion of configuration ⟹

As mentioned earlier, the nucleophile and its concentration can influence the rate of S_N2 reactions. So the rate is different for different nucleophiles. Nucleophilicity or the strength of a nucleophile depends on how efficiently it can make the leaving group leave from the alkyl halide or whatever the substrate is. Some generalizations can be made regarding nucleophiles. Along a period (in the periodic table), as basicity decreases, nucleophilicity decreases (e.g., $F^- < RO^- < R_2N^- < R_3C^-$). However, a strong base does not always imply a good nucleophile. For example, the order of basicity of halide ions is $F^- > Cl^- > Br^- > I^-$. But the order of nucleophilicity in solution follows the opposite trend. The important aspect that we should note is that this trend-reversal is seen when polar protic solvents are used. Polar protic solvents (e.g. water, alcohol) have protons that can hydrogen bond to negatively charged nucleophiles. Hence, the size of a nucleophile plays a big part in terms of such a scenario. The smaller the nucleophile (anion), the more strongly it is solvated by a protic solvent. Thus, more energy is required to overcome this wrapping effect of the solvent molecules on the nucleophile, and that can reduce the nucleophilicity of the nucleophile. Fluoride ions, that are much smaller than iodide ions, are strongly solvated. This explains why iodide, even though less basic than fluoride ions, acts as stronger nucleophiles in protic environment. In aprotic solvents, this trend is reversed, and so does when a reaction is conducted in gas phase without a solvent.

Nucleophilicity can also be compared among species having the same nucleophilic atom. A negatively charged conjugate base of a neutral species (conjugate acid) is more nucleophilic than its corresponding neutral species. For example, HO^- is a better nucleophile than H_2O.

A leaving group plays an important role in both substitution and elimination reactions. A good leaving group has a weak, polarized carbon-leaving group (C-X) bond. It should be stable on its own once it leaves the substrate, regardless of whether it stays as an ion or a neutral species. Sometimes solvation helps a leaving group to achieve this. Halides are good leaving groups. The order of leaving group ability is F < Cl < Br < I. In general, less basic the species is, the better the leaving group. Other good leaving groups include mesylate and tosylate.

Common nucleophiles (in polar protic solvents)

The S$_N$1 Reaction

S$_N$1 stands for unimolecular nucleophilic substitution reaction. Let's consider a typical S$_N$1 reaction.

$$(CH_3)_3CI \xrightarrow{\text{H}_2\text{O}} (CH_3)_3COH + HI$$

tert-Butyl iodide *tert*-Butyl alcohol

The rates of S$_N$1 reactions depend only on the substrate (alkyl halide) concentration. The nucleophile does not influence the reaction rate of a typical S$_N$1 reaction. The reaction rate is represented as follows:

$$\text{Rate} = k\,[\,(CH_3)_3CI\,]$$

The Mechanism of S$_N$1 Reaction

In this two-step reaction, the alkyl halide splits to form a carbocation intermediate and a halide ion. During the second step, the cation reacts with the nucleophile to form the final product. Since the carbocation formed is planar, the nucleophile can attack the electrophilic carbon from either side. Thus an S$_N$1 reaction results in racemization.

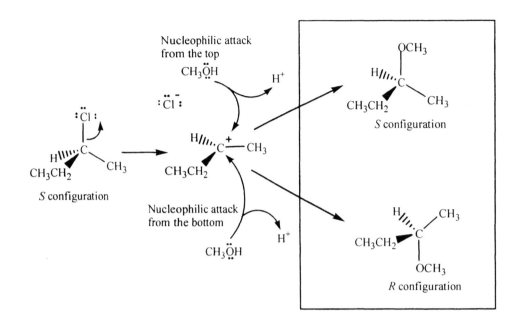

Figure 20-2 The mechanism of S$_N$1 reaction

S$_N$1 reactivity: Methyl < Primary < Secondary < Tertiary

S$_N$2 reaction is favored when the alkyl halide involved is a primary or a secondary alkyl halide. S$_N$1 reaction is favored when the alkyl halide involved is a tertiary or a secondary alkyl halide. In many cases, it is hard to predict the mode of reaction with secondary alkyl halides — it can either be S$_N$1 or S$_N$2, depending on certain other aspects such as the solvent used. The S$_N$1 reaction being favored by tertiary halides is understandable, because of the carbocation intermediate that is formed during the S$_N$1 process.

Polar solvents increase the rate of both types of substitution reactions. Polar solvents which have high dielectric constants can stabilize the transition state and this is highly useful in S$_N$1 reactions. In S$_N$2 reactions, the solvent effects are slightly different. Here what matters is whether the solvent is aprotic. Protic polar solvents such as water and carboxylic acids can undergo hydrogen bonding which in turn can interact with the nucleophile. This can decrease the rate of S$_N$2 reactions. So it is better to use aprotic polar solvents when we are dealing with S$_N$2 reactions. Dimethyl sulfoxide (DMSO) is a polar aprotic solvent.

$$H_3C \diagdown \!\!\!\!\! {}_{S}\!\!=\!\!O \qquad DMSO$$
$$H_3C \diagup$$

Quite often nucleophilic reactions compete with elimination reactions. Next, we will review elimination reactions.

Elimination reactions

There are two types of elimination reactions in general — E1 and E2 reactions. We will first consider an E2 reaction.

The E2 reaction

The E2 reaction mechanism can generally be represented as shown. In the mechanistic representation shown, B stands for the base and X stands for the halogen.

Figure 20-3 The mechanism of E2 reaction

The steps involved in an E2 reaction are the breaking of the carbon-hydrogen bond, the carbon double bond formation, and the breaking away of the carbon-halogen bond.

The rate of the E2 reaction is: Rate = k [RX] [base]

So the reaction rate depends on both the substrate (RX) and the base involved.

In an elimination reaction, the major product formed is the most stable alkene. Usually, the most stable alkene is the most substituted alkene. The increased stability of more highly substituted alkenes can be attributed to **electronic effect**.

The E1 Reaction

Study the mechanism of E1 reaction.

Step 1

Step 2

Figure 20-4 The mechanism of E1 reaction

In step (1), the alkyl halide forms (slow step) the carbocation and the halide ion. In step (2), the base abstracts the proton to form the product (alkene).

> **E1 reactivity**:   Methyl < Primary < Secondary < Tertiary
> (Slowest)   (Fastest)

Substitution versus Elimination

Reaction mechanisms are influenced by many factors. Different combination of factors result in different outcomes. Even though this is the case, let's boil down some of the factors that we can rely on for reasonably judging the outcome of reactions. We will consider some conditions that favor substitution over elimination, and vice versa. The two key factors that we look for are the type of substrate that is undergoing the reaction, and the extent of nucleophilicity or basicity of the anion involved in the reaction.

1) Higher temperatures usually favor elimination over substitution. To be more precise, we can say that elimination is more favored than substitution reactions if the reaction occurs at a high temperature. The latter is more accurate because

both types of reactions are favored by an increase in temperature, but elimination is more favored.

2) Strong bases guide or dictate elimination over substitution in most cases. In general, E2 type of elimination is favored under such conditions.

3) If there is less hindrance or less bulky substituents at the carbon where the leaving group is present, substitution (S_N2) is favored over elimination (E2). Remember that in S_N2 reactions, the transition intermediate is a species in which both the leaving group and the incoming nucleophile are attached to the carbon, where the substitution is taking place.

4) Alkyl halides (tertiary), because of their bulky substituents, mostly prefer elimination rather than substitution provided that a strong base is present. Mild bases can make substitution to predominate even in tertiary alkyl halides. Can you think of a reason why tertiary alkyl halides prefer to undergo elimination? The reason is steric hindrance to the nucleophilic approach.

Note: We have been discussing a number of reactions, both substitution and elimination in terms of alkyl halides. This surely doesn't mean that only alkyl halides undergo these types of reactions.

Nucleophilic Substitution in Alkyl Halides – S_N1 vs S_N2 Comparison

Table 20-1

	S_N1	S_N1
Molecularity	Unimolecular (First order)	Bimolecular (Second order)
Rate	Rate = k [RX]	Rate = k [RX] [Nu]
Stereochemical aspect	Racemization	Inversion of configuration
Rearrangement?	Yes; Carbocation formation	No; No carbocation formation
Rate dependency	Rate independent of nucleophile	Rate dependent on nucleophile
Solvent effect	Best: Polar protic	Best: Polar aprotic
Reactivity	$RX<R_2X<R_3X$	$R_3X<R_2X<RX$
Reactivity of alkyl halides	$RF<<RCl<RBr<RI$	$RF<<RCl<RBr<RI$

CHAPTER 20 PRACTICE QUESTIONS

$$CH_3CH_2\overset{\overset{\displaystyle Cl}{|}}{C}HCH_3$$

1. The compound shown above can be best described as a:

   A. primary alkyl halide.
   B. secondary alkyl halide.
   C. tertiary alkyl halide.
   D. primary alkenyl halide.

2. Pick out the compound with the highest boiling point.

   A. 1-Chloroethane
   B. 1,1-Dichloroethane
   C. 1,1,1-Trichloroethane
   D. Cannot be predicted

3. Alcohols can react with hydrogen halides to form alkyl halides. Which of the following alcohols is the most reactive toward hydrogen halides?

   A. CH_3CH_2OH

   B. $CH_3\overset{\overset{\displaystyle OH}{|}}{C}HCH_3$

   C. CH_3OH

   D. $(CH_3)_3COH$

4. Which of the following is true regarding alkyl halides?

   A. Alkyl halides have relatively very low boiling points, because of its polarity.
   B. Alkyl fluorides have lower densities than those of comparable alkyl bromides.
   C. Alkyl halides are completely soluble in water.
   D. None of the above

Questions 5-9 are based on the following passage.

Passage 1

   Alkyl halides undergo substitution reactions and a variety of other reactions as well. The type of reaction that occurs depends on a variety of factors. The structural integrity of the alkyl group to which the halogen is attached plays an important role in determining the type of product that is likely to result. A reaction involving *t*-butyl bromide is given below:

$$(CH_3)_3CBr \xrightarrow{\overset{\text{Ethyl alcohol/}}{H_2O}} \text{Products}$$

5. Which of the following best represents the increasing rate of bimolecular substitution reaction for the following alkyl halides?

CH_3CH_2Br	= Compound A
CH_3Br	= Compound B
$(CH_3)_3CBr$	= Compound C
$(CH_3)_2CHBr$	= Compound D

A. A < B < C < D
B. C < D < B < A
C. C < D < A < B
D. B < A < D < C

6. Which of the following is true regarding substitution reactions?

A. Tertiary alkyl halides always undergo substitution by S_N2 mechanism.
B. Only alkyl halides can undergo substitution reaction by S_N2 mechanism.
C. S_N2 reactions involve the formation of a carbocation intermediate.
D. None of the above

7. Consider the reaction given in the passage. Which of the following compound is produced as a result of that particular reaction?

A. $H_2C=C(CH_3)CH_3$

B. $(CH_3)_3COH$

C. $CH_3CH_2OC(CH)_3$

D. All the above are possible products.

8. Which of the following is characteristic of a typical S_N2 reaction?

A. Rate = k [alkyl halide]
B. Inversion of configuration
C. Carbocation intermediate
D. Unimolecular mechanism

9. Which of the following is the most reactive by substitution mechanism?

A. CH_3I
B. CH_3F
C. CH_3Cl
D. All are equally reactive.

21

Alcohols

A. INTRODUCTION

Alcohols have the general formula **ROH**.

Some common examples of alcohols:

CH₃OH
methyl alcohol

CH₃CH₂OH
ethyl alcohol

CH₃CH₂CH₂OH
n-propyl alcohol

isopropyl alcohol

isobutyl alcohol

sec-butyl alcohol

tert-butyl alcohol

B. PROPERTIES OF ALCOHOLS

Boiling Point

One of the most important properties of alcohols is their ability to form hydrogen bonds. Since alcohols can form hydrogen bonds, they have very high boiling points. Consider the following comparative analysis to clarify this idea.

The boiling point of ethane (C_2H_6) is − 88.7 ⁰ C.

The boiling point of propane (C_3H_8) is − 42.2 ⁰ C.

The boiling point of ethanol (C_2H_5OH) is 78 ⁰ C.

Note the drastic difference in their boiling points.

By the above comparison, it is clear that some extra forces (here mainly H bonds) are working to increase the boiling points of alcohols.

Hydrogen bonds in alcohols (the arrows point to some of the hydrogen bonds)

Figure 21-1

Solubility in H_2O

Low-molecular weight alcohols are soluble in water. The hydrogen bond formation plays a key role in the solubility of alcohols in water. In other words, hydrogen bonds enhance the solubility of alcohols in H_2O. As the number of carbons increases, the solubility of alcohols decreases as they become more and more similar to hydrocarbons with longer and longer nonpolar hydrocarbon chains.

Acidity of Alcohols

Alcohols are weakly acidic. In fact, they are weaker in acidity than water. Alcohols have K_a values around 10^{-17}.

Alcohols give off the acidic hydrogen to form **alkoxide ions**. Alkoxide ion is the conjugate base of alcohols and they are strong bases.

$$R—OH \xrightarrow{\ OH^- \ } R—O^- + H_2O$$

Alcohol   Alkoxide ion   Water

Among alcohols, primary alcohols are the most acidic, and tertiary alcohols are the least acidic.

Increasing acidity ⟹

3^0 alcohols $<$ 2^0 alcohols $<$ 1^0 alcohols

C. SYNTHESIS OF ALCOHOLS

Acid-Catalyzed Reaction

Sample reaction 21-1

(major product)

Alkenes react with aqueous acidic solutions to form alcohols. The reaction intermediate is a **carbocation**. Hence, there is a possibility of rearrangement of the intermediates in such acid-catalyzed reactions. The reaction follows the **Markovnikov's rule**. Keep in mind that a tertiary carbocation is more stable than a secondary carbocation, which in turn is more stable than a primary carbocation.

Hydroboration-Oxidation

Sample reaction 21-2

$$CH_3CH_2CH_2CH{=\!=\!=}CH_2 \xrightarrow[\text{2. } H_2O_2, \text{ NaOH}]{\text{1. } B_2H_6} CH_3CH_2CH_2CH_2CH_2OH$$
(major product)

Oxidation followed by hydroboration of alkene results in alcohols. The reaction occurs in an **anti-Markovnikov** fashion. Notice that hydrogen, instead of attaching to the carbon with the highest number of hydrogens, attaches to the carbon with the least number of hydrogens.

Oxymercuration-Demercuration

Sample reaction 21-3

$$CH_3CH_2CH_2CH{=\!=\!=}CH_2 \xrightarrow[\text{2. NaBH}_4]{\text{1. HgO}_2CCH_3,H_2O} CH_3CH_2CH_2\overset{\overset{\displaystyle OH}{\displaystyle |}}{C}HCH_3$$

Alkenes can be converted to alcohols by **oxymercuration-demercuration**. The addition of H and OH is in accordance with the **Markovnikov's rule**. There is no rearrangement in this reaction.

From Epoxides

Preparation of an alcohol from an epoxide is shown below. The epoxide (ethylene oxide) ring opens when the nucleophile attacks the carbon-oxygen bond. Note the fact that the nucleophilic carbon is supplied by the Grignard reagent (methyl magnesium bromide).

Sample reaction 21-4

$$\underset{\substack{\text{Ethylene}\\\text{oxide}}}{\overset{CH_2{-\!-\!-}CH_2}{\underset{O}{\diagdown\diagup}}} \xrightarrow[\substack{\text{Diethyl ether}\\H_3O^+}]{\substack{\text{Methyl magnesium bromide}\\CH_3MgBr}} \underset{\text{Propanol}}{CH_3CH_2CH_2OH}$$

Alcohols can also be produced from aldehydes and ketones via Grignard reagents. Other methods to synthesize alcohols include the reduction of aldehydes and ketones. These reactions will be discussed in Chapter 22.

D. REACTIONS OF ALCOHOLS

Formation of Alkoxides

Alcohols when treated with Group I metals like sodium and potassium result in alkoxides.

Sample reaction 21-5

$$\underset{\text{Methanol}}{2\ CH_3OH} \xrightarrow{2\ Na} \underset{\text{Sodium methoxide}}{2\ CH_3ONa} + 2\ H_2$$

Formation of Alkyl Halides

Sample reaction 21-6

2-butanol → (HI) → 2-iodo butane + H_2O

Sample reaction 21-7

(SOCl$_2$) → + SO_2 + HCl

Oxidation of Alcohols

Primary alcohols can be oxidized to aldehydes by reagents like pyridinium dichromate (PDC), and pyridinium chlorochromate (PCC).

Sample reaction 21-8

$$CH_3CH_2CH_2CH_2OH \xrightarrow{PCC} CH_3CH_2CH_2\overset{\overset{\displaystyle O}{\|}}{C}H$$

Butanol → Butanal (aldehyde)

Secondary alcohols can also be oxidized. The product is a ketone.

Sample reaction 21-9

2-Pentanol → (PDC) → 2-Pentanone

Since tertiary alcohols do not have a hydrogen atom in the carbon carrying the hydroxyl group, they cannot be easily oxidized.

Strong oxidizing agents can oxidize alcohols to carboxylic acids. We can use potassium permanganate or chromic acid to do this conversion.

Sample reaction 21-10

$$KMnO_4$$
$$or\ H_2Cr_2O_4$$

Primary alcohol → Carboxylic acid

Primary alcohol [oxidization]→ Aldehyde [oxidization]→ Carboxylic acid

Secondary alcohol [oxidization]→ Ketone

Acid-Catalyzed Dehydration

Alcohols undergo acid-catalyzed dehydration reactions to form alkenes. The reaction is accomplished by the formation of a carbocation intermediate. Thus there is the possibility of rearrangement in the process. First, we will take a look at the mechanism of this reaction.

Mechanism of Acid-Catalyzed Dehydration of Alcohols

Sample reaction 21-11

$$(CH_3)_3COH \xrightarrow{H_3O^+ / heat} (H_3C)_2C{=}CH_2$$

The alcohol is protonated.

Step (1)

$$(CH_3)_3C\ddot{O}H \xrightarrow{H_3O^+} (CH_3)_3C\overset{+}{O}\begin{smallmatrix}H\\H\end{smallmatrix} + H_2O$$

The formation of carbocation.

Step (2)

$$(CH_3)_3C\overset{+}{\underset{H}{O}}{\overset{H}{\diagup}} \xrightarrow[H_3O^+]{} (CH_3)_3C^+ \ + \ H_2O$$

The formation of double bond.

Step (3)

$$(CH_3)_3C^+ \xrightarrow[H_2O]{} H_2C{=}C{\diagup}{\overset{CH_3}{\underset{CH_3}{\diagdown}}} \ + \ H_3O^+$$

Rearrangement – An Example

Organic chemists have conducted experiments to understand the formation of multiple products in acid-catalyzed reactions such as that of 3,3-dimethyl-2-butanol. Let's consider the acid-catalyzed dehydration reaction of 3,3-dimethyl-2-butanol and explore the possibility of rearrangement.

$(CH_3)_3CCHOHCH_3$ 3,3-Dimethyl-2-butanol

Figure 21-2

The major product formed in this reaction is 2,3-Dimethyl-1-butene. Notice (Figure 21-2) the rearrangement that occurs in this reaction. The rearrangement results in a more stable carbocation (A tertiary carbocation is more stable than a secondary carbocation).

CHAPTER 21 PRACTICE QUESTIONS

1. The higher boiling points exhibited by alcohols with respect to comparable alkanes and ethers are primarily due to:

    A. ionic bonds.
    B. covalent bonds.
    C. hydrogen bonds.
    D. none of the above.

2. The conjugate base of alcohols are generally called:

    A. alkyl ions.
    B. alcoholic ions.
    C. alkoxide ions.
    D. vinyl ions.

3. Which of the following is a possible way of making alcohols?

    A. Hydroboration-oxidation of alkenes
    B. Acid catalyzed hydration of alkenes
    C. Oxymercuration-demercuration of alkenes
    D. All the above

4. An organic chemist synthesized and isolated the above represented compound. If this compound undergoes oxymercuration-demercuration reaction, the major product is most likely:

A. —$CH_2CH_2CH_2OH$

B. —CH_2CHCH_3 with OH on the middle carbon

C. —CH_2CH_2CHO

D. —CH_2CH_2COOH

Table X (Question 5)

5. From Table X, the most acidic compound is:

    A. Compound A
    B. Compound B
    C. Compound C
    D. Compound D

6. Direct oxidation of which of the following can result in a carboxylic acid?

    A. Secondary alcohol
    B. Tertiary alcohol
    C. Primary alcohol
    D. All the above

7. Choose the correct product formed as a result of the reduction of a ketone.

    A. A primary alcohol
    B. A secondary alcohol
    C. A tertiary alcohol
    D. None of the above

8. The major product of the following reaction is:

    A. a four-carbon ketone.
    B. a four-carbon halohydrin.
    C. a two-carbon aldehyde.
    D. a four-carbon alcohol.

9. Identify Compound B from the sequence of reactions.

$CH_3CH=CH_2$ $\xrightarrow{B_2H_6 / H_2O_2 \ /OH^-}$ Compound A

Pyridinium dichromate $\longrightarrow$ Compound B

    A. Propanol
    B. Propanal
    C. Acetone
    D. Formaldehyde

10. Reduction of the organic compound shown above results in:

    A. a ketone.
    B. a primary alcohol.
    C. a carboxylic acid.
    D. an ester.

Questions 11-15 are based on the following passage.

Passage 1

    Alcohols are of tremendous use for the synthesis of a wide variety of organic compounds. They also have some very unique properties. Alcohols are in fact slightly weaker acids than water, and have pKa values between 16 and 18.

    An alcohol can loose its acidic hydrogen to form an alkoxide ion.

Reaction 1

$$2\ CH_3CH_2OH \xrightarrow{\ 2\ Na\ } 2\ NaOCH_2CH_3$$

11. The alcohol shown below is:

    A. *cis*-2-ethylcyclohexanol.
    B. *cis*-2-ethylcycloctanol.
    C. *cis*-1-ethyl-2-hydroxycyclopentane.
    D. *trans*-2-ethylcyclohexanol.

12. Which of the following is the most acidic?

    A. $(CH_3)_3COH$
    B. NH_3
    C. $(CH_3)_2CHOH$
    D. CH_3OH

13. In Reaction 1, predict the identity of the other product, if any.

    A. H_2O
    B. O_2
    C. H_2
    D. No other products are produced.

14. Which of the following is the most reactive alcohol toward sodium?

    A. CH_3OH

    B. $(CH_3)_3COH$

    C.

    D. $H_3C-CH-CH\begin{smallmatrix}CH_3\\CH_3\end{smallmatrix}$ with OH on middle CH

15. Which of the following can be used to make propanol directly by oxidation?

    A. CH_3CH_2CHO

    B. CH_3CH_2COOH

    C. $\overset{\overset{\textstyle O}{\|}}{CH_3C}CH_3$

    D.   None of the above

Aldehydes and Ketones

A. INTRODUCTION

Aldehydes and **ketones** are compounds containing the acyl group. The carbonyl group present in them is polar because of the electronegativity of oxygen. It is noteworthy to mention that the carbonyl group in aldehydes and ketones are very reactive.

ALDEHYDE GENERAL FORMULA

KETONE GENERAL FORMULA

ACYL GROUP   CARBONYL GROUP

The partial negative charge on the oxygen is because of its higher electronegativity compared to carbon. This gives the carbonyl carbon a partial positive charge.

B. SOME ALDEHYDES AND KETONES

Methanal
(formaldehyde)

Ethanal
(acetaldehyde)

Butanal
(butanaldehyde)

Acetone

2-pentanone

3-methyl-2-pentanone

C. PROPERTIES OF ALDEHYDES AND KETONES

The carbonyl group present in aldehydes and ketones make them polar in nature. Both aldehydes and ketones have higher boiling points than comparable hydrocarbons. Aldehydes and ketones do not form hydrogen bonds themselves. Hence, they have lower boiling and melting points compared to alcohols with comparable molecular weights. Finally, aldehydes and ketones have higher solubility in water than hydrocarbons, but less solubility than alcohols. Even though aldehydes and ketones cannot undergo hydrogen bonding themselves, they can undergo hydrogen bonding with water molecules.

D. SYNTHESIS OF ALDEHYDES AND KETONES

From Alcohols

Aldehydes can be prepared by the oxidation of primary alcohols. Oxidizing agents such as pyridinium chlorochromate (PCC) or pyridinium dichromate (PDC) can be used for such conversions.

Sample reaction 22-1

$$CH_3CH_2CH_2CH_2OH \xrightarrow{\text{PCC}} CH_3CH_2CH_2\overset{\displaystyle O}{\overset{\displaystyle \|}{C}}H$$

Butanol

Butanal (an aldehyde)

Oxidation of secondary alcohols results in ketones.

Sample reaction 22-2

A secondary alcohol   A ketone

From Alkenes by Ozonolysis

Aldehydes and ketones can be prepared by the ozonolysis of alkenes.

Sample reaction 22-3

AN ALDEHYDE

Sample reaction 22-4

A KETONE   AN ALDEHYDE

E. NUCLEOPHILIC ADDITION TO THE CARBONYL GROUP

The carbon of the carbonyl group is an electrophile. Thus it is susceptible to nucleophilic attack. During most addition reactions of alkenes, it is an electrophile that attacks the pi system. But in an addition reaction involving a carbonyl group, we see that the attack on the carbonyl carbon is made by a nucleophile. Think about why this is the case? One reason for this is the polar nature (due to electronegativity of the oxygen atom) of the carbonyl group. Furthermore, the resonance capability of the carbonyl group also enhances this type of reactive property. A generalized nucleophilic attack is shown below in Figure 22-1.

Figure 22-1

F. REACTIONS OF ALDEHYDES AND KETONES

Formation of Carboxylic Acids

Aldehydes can be oxidized to carboxylic acids using oxidizing agents such as potassium permanganate or potassium dichromate.

Sample reaction 22-5

$$RCHO \xrightarrow{KMnO_4} RCOOH$$

Sample reaction 22-6

$$CH_3CH_2-\overset{\overset{\displaystyle O}{\|}}{C}-H \xrightarrow[\text{/ dil. } H_2SO_4]{Na_2Cr_2O_7} CH_3CH_2-\overset{\overset{\displaystyle O}{\|}}{C}-OH$$

Aldehydes selectively react in a solution of silver-ammonia complex called Tollen's reagent. A sample reaction is given below.

Sample reaction 22-7

$$CH_3CH-\overset{\overset{\displaystyle O}{\|}}{C}-H + \underbrace{2\,Ag(NH_3)_2{}^+ + 3\,OH^-}_{\text{Tollens reagent}} \longrightarrow CH_3CH-\overset{\overset{\displaystyle O}{\|}}{C}-O^- + 4\,NH_3 + 2\,H_2O + 2\,Ag^+\downarrow$$
$$\overset{\displaystyle |}{CH_3} \qquad\qquad \overset{\displaystyle |}{CH_3} \qquad\qquad \text{silver}$$

With Grignard Reagents

Aldehydes and ketones react with Grignard reagents to form alcohols.

> Grignard reagents are organometallic compounds. These reagents can be prepared from organic halides by reacting with magnesium.
>
> $$RBr \xrightarrow{Mg} RMgBr$$
>
> $$CH_3Br \xrightarrow{Mg} CH_3MgBr$$

Formaldehyde reacts with Grignard reagents to form primary alcohols.

Sample reaction 22-8

Formaldehyde   Ethyl alcohol

Other aldehydes react with Grignard reagents to form secondary alcohols.

Sample reaction 22-9

Aldehyde   2-Propanol

Ketones give tertiary alcohols.

Sample reaction 22-10

Ketone   Tertiary alcohol

G. ALDOL ADDITION AND CONDENSATION REACTIONS

In aldol addition reactions, a carbon-carbon bond is formed between the carbonyl carbon of one aldehyde molecule and the α-carbon of another aldehyde molecule. The product is a β-hydroxy aldehyde. After the nucleophilic addition of the enolate ion to the carbonyl group, removal of water of the β-hydroxy aldehyde can occur resulting in an α,β-unsaturated aldehyde. Study Sample reactions 22-11 and 22-12.

Sample reaction 22-11

Propanal

The enolate adds to this carbonyl carbon

OH^- / H_2O

(β–hydroxyaldehyde)
2-Methyl-3-hydroxypentanal
(Aldol addition product)

The new carbon-carbon bond

+

This α– carbon loses one proton
to the base and forms the enolate ion

Sample reaction 22-12

The addition product upon heating will undergo elimination (dehydration) to
form the α,β-unsaturated aldehyde.

H_2O

heat

α,β–Unsaturated aldehyde
(aldol condensation product)

H. REDUCTION REACTIONS OF ALDEHYDES AND KETONES

Conversion to Alcohols

Aldehydes and ketones can be reduced to alcohols using reducing agents such as lithium aluminum hydride ($LiAlH_4$), and sodium borohydride ($NaBH_4$).

Sample reaction 22-13

$$CH_3CH(=O) \xrightarrow[H_2O]{LiAlH_4} CH_3CH_2OH$$

Acetaldehyde → Ethyl alcohol

Sample reaction 22-14

$$CH_3CR'(=O) \xrightarrow[H_2O]{NaBH_4} \text{Secondary alcohol}$$

Ketone

Sodium borohydride ($NaBH_4$) can reduce aldehydes and ketones when reacted in aqueous or alcohol solutions. Carboxylic acids and esters are not reactive to sodium borohydride reduction. Lithium aluminum hydride ($LiAlH_4$), a more powerful reducing agent, can reduce aldehydes, ketones, esters, and carboxylic acids.

Conversion to Hydrocarbons

The carbonyl groups of aldehydes and ketones can be converted to methylene groups by Clemmenson and Wolf-Kishner reduction reactions.

Sample reaction 22-15

$$H_3C-C(=O)-CH_3 \xrightarrow[\text{heat}]{\substack{\text{(Wolff-Kishner reduction)} \\ H_2NNH_2, KOH}} H_3C-\overset{H_2}{C}-CH_3$$

$$C_6H_5-C(=O)-CH_3 \xrightarrow[\text{(Clemmensen reduction)}]{Zinc(Hg) / HCl} C_6H_5-\overset{H_2}{C}-CH_3$$

I. FORMATION OF ACETALS

Aldehydes can undergo reactions with alcohols under acidic conditions. The product of this nucleophilic addition reaction is called **hemiacetal**. Hemiacetal is formed by the nucleophilic addition of alcohol to the carbonyl carbon. Hemiacetal can react with one more mole of alcohol to form an **acetal**.

FORMATION OF CYCLIC STRUCTURE OF GLUCOSE

In monosaccharides (e.g., glucose, fructose), the cyclic ring structure is formed by the intramolecular reaction between the carbonyl and the hydroxyl groups within the same molecule. Glucose (an aldohexose) forms a cyclic hemiacetal by the intramolecular reaction between the aldehyde group of carbon 1 and the hydroxyl group of carbon 5.

CHAPTER 22 PRACTICE QUESTIONS

1. Propanal is treated with ethyl magnesium halide (with diethyl ether & H_3O^+). Which of the following is true regarding this reaction?

    A. A five-carbon ether is the major product.
    B. A five-carbon secondary alcohol is the major product.
    C. A five-carbon ketone is the major product.
    D. None of the above are true.

2. The structure shown below represents:

$$\underset{\underset{OH}{|}}{CH_3CH_2CHOCH_2CH_3}$$

    A. a ketal.
    B. a hemiacetal.
    C. an acetal.
    D. a hemiketal.

3. The Baeyer-Villiger reaction is a very useful synthesis reaction. An example is the reaction of acetone with peroxyacetic acid to give an ester and a carboxylic acid. This reaction can be generalized as:

    A. a reduction reaction.
    B. an oxidation reaction.
    C. a hydrolysis reaction.
    D. an isomerization reaction.

4. Predict the aldol addition product of the structure shown below:

$$CH_3CH_2CH_2CH_2CH_2CHO$$

A.

OH

CHO

B.

OH   CHO

C.

CHO

D.

OH

OH

5. Which of the following carbons indicated by arrows has the most acidic protons?

    a   b   c

    A. a
    B. b
    C. c
    D. No acidic protons are present, since ketones cannot be acidic.

6. The structure represented below can be most appropriately called an:

$$CH_3CH=C \overset{\displaystyle O^-}{\underset{\displaystyle CH_3}{\big<}}$$

   A. alkenyl ion.
   B. acyl ion.
   C. alkoxide cation.
   D. enolate ion.

7. Predict the aldol condensation product (major product) of the following compound.

   A.

   B.

   C.

   D.

8. Which of the following is the conjugate base of a ketone?

   A.

   B.

   C.

   D.

9. A student is trying to prove the identity of a compound that she synthesized. She knows that the compound is a methyl ketone. Which of the following qualitative tests can be used to prove the identity of the synthesized compound as a methyl ketone?

   A. Ignition test
   B. Potassium permanganate test
   C. Beilstein test
   D. Iodoform test

10. Chromic acid test can be used for the identi-fication of:

    A. aldehydes and ketones.
    B. aldehydes only.
    C. ketones only.
    D. carboxylic acids only.

Questions 11-16 are based on the following passage.

Passage 1

    Students of an organic chemistry class conducted several experiments with aldehydes and ketones. Some of the reactions are summarized below:

Experiment 1

Acetophenone was reacted with Reagent A. The product was ethyl benzene.

Experiment 2

Propanal underwent acid-catalyzed reaction with alcohol.

$$CH_3CH_2CHO \xrightarrow[HCl]{(excess)\ CH_3OH} CH_3CH_2CH(OCH_3)_2$$

Experiment 3

$$CH_3CH_2CHO \longrightarrow CH_3CH_2\overset{\overset{\displaystyle OH}{|}}{C}HCH_3$$

Experiment 3 involved merely the analysis of a conversion. Students were asked to discuss a method to accomplish this synthesis reaction.

Experiment 4

The MCAT Chemistry Book

11. Which of the following best represents the general name of the product formed in Experiment 2?

   A. Hemiacetal
   B. Acetal
   C. Ketal
   D. Hemiacetal

12. The conversion presented in Experiment 1 is:

   A. an oxidation reaction.
   B. a reduction reaction.
   C. a dehydrohalogenation reaction.
   D. a dehydrogenation reaction.

13. Which of the following Grignard reagents will serve the purpose for the reaction in Experiment 4?

   A. $(CH_3)_3CMgBr$

   B. $CH_3CH_2CH_2CH_2MgBr$

   C. $CH_3CH(MgBr)CH_3$

   D. $CH_3CH_2CHMgBr$
      $|$
      CH_3

14. In Experiment 3, which of the following is a possible scenario?

   A. Reaction is possible, because propanal can be directly oxidized to form the product indicated.
   B. Reaction is not possible, because you cannot convert an aldehyde to a secondary alcohol.

C. Reaction is possible, if the reactant is treated with an appropriate Grignard reagent followed by hydrolysis.
D. Reaction is not possible, because aldehyde carbonyls are nucleophilic and are thus unreactive.

15. Which of the following is not an organometallic compound?

   A. $H_3CC \equiv CNa$

   B. CH_3CH_2MgBr

   C.

   D. $KOCH_2CH_3$

16. In our body, toxic chemicals are metabolized in the liver. One such process involves the production of acetaldehyde from ethanol. This conversion is best described as:

Ethanol $\rightleftharpoons$ Acetaldehyde (alcohol dehydrogenase)

   A. a dehydrogenation reaction.
   B. a hydrogenation reaction.
   C. an oxidation reaction.
   D. a reduction reaction.

23

Carboxylic Acids

A. INTRODUCTION

Carboxylic acids are compounds with the general formula **RCOOH**.

Carboxyl group

HCOH
Formic acid
(Methanoic acid)

CH_3COH
Acetic acid
(Ethanoic acid)

CH_3CH_2COH

Propanoic acid

—COOH

Benzoic acid

B. PROPERTIES OF CARBOXYLIC ACIDS

It is clear from the name that carboxylic acids are acidic. The hydrogen of the carboxyl group (-COOH) is acidic. The strength of these acids can be explained in terms of the relative stabilities of their conjugate bases. Weaker the conjugate base is, the stronger the acid. Keep in mind the fact that carboxylic acids are weak acids.

$$CH_3C{-}OH \longrightarrow CH_3C{-}O^- \ + \ H^+$$

Acetic acid   Acetate ion

The K_a of acetic acid is to the order of 10^{-5}.

309

The acidity of a carboxylic acid is influenced by its substituents. Substituents which are very electronegative, especially when they are attached to the α-carbon, increase the acidity of carboxylic acids. As the number of electronegative substituents increases, so does the acidity. This increase in acidity is because of the increased stability of the carboxylate ion formed, as a result of the presence of the electronegative substituent. This effect is due to what is known as **inductive effect**. Because of the electron withdrawing effect of the substituent, the charge is dispersed and the ion (carboxylate ion) is stabilized. Study the following gradation of increasing acidity to reinforce the point just made.

INCREASING ACIDITY

$$CH_3CH_2COOH \quad < \quad CH_3CHCOOH \quad < \quad CH_3CCOOH \quad < \quad CH_2CHCOOH$$

Carboxylic acids can undergo extensive hydrogen bonding. So they have higher boiling points than alkanes or even alcohols. Carboxylate ions are resonance stabilized (Figure 23-1). The negative charge in the carboxylate anion is shared by both the oxygens.

Figure 23-1

C. SYNTHESIS OF CARBOXYLIC ACIDS

By Oxidation

Carboxylic acids can be prepared by the oxidation of primary alcohols, and aldehydes. An oxidizing agent such as $KMnO_4$ can accomplish these conversions.

Sample reaction 23-1

$$CH_3CH_2CH_2OH \xrightarrow[\text{2. } H_3O^+]{\text{1. } KMnO_4/OH^-} CH_3CH_2COOH$$

From Grignard Reagents

Another way to synthesize carboxylic acids is to react Grignard reagents with CO_2. The Grignard reagent acts as a nucleophile toward the carbon dioxide. In an acidic medium the carboxylate entity formed is converted to carboxylic acid. Grignard reagents can be prepared by reacting alkyl halides with magnesium.

Sample reaction 23-2

Carboxylic acid

From Alkyl Halides via Nitriles

Primary or secondary alkyl halides can be converted into nitriles (alkyl cyanide) by nucleophilic substitution. The nitriles formed can in turn be converted to carboxylic acids by hydrolysis.

Sample reaction 23-3

$$CH_3CH_2Cl \xrightarrow{NaCN} CH_3CH_2CN \ + \ NaCl$$

$$:C\equiv N: \quad \text{Cyanide ion}$$

The cyanide ion is negatively charged and the negatively charged carbon atom has nucleophilic character. The reaction usually occurs via S_N2 mechanism. The nitrile formed can be hydrolyzed to a carboxylic acid.

$$CH_3CH_2C\equiv N \xrightarrow[\text{heat}]{H_2O, H^+} CH_3CH_2COOH$$

D. REACTIONS OF CARBOXYLIC ACIDS

Esterification

Carboxylic acids and alcohols can react in the presence of an acid catalyst. The products formed are ester and water.

Sample reaction 23-4

$$\text{RCOOH} \quad + \quad \text{R'OH} \quad \xrightarrow{\text{H}_2\text{SO}_4} \quad \text{RCOOR'} \quad + \quad \text{H}_2\text{O}$$

Carboxylic acid   Alcohol   Ester   Water

Decarboxylation

In a decarboxylation reaction, the carboxylic acid loses carbon dioxide. The process usually requires heat to progress.

Sample reaction 23-4

$$\text{HOOCCH}_2\text{COOH} \quad \xrightarrow{\text{Heat}} \quad \text{CO}_2 \quad + \quad \text{CH}_3\text{COOH}$$

Malonic acid   Carbon dioxide   Acetic acid

CHAPTER 23 PRACTICE QUESTIONS

1. An alkyl magnesium halide is reacted with carbon dioxide under very low pH (acidic conditions). Which of the following are true regarding this reaction?

    I) Carbon dioxide acts as the nucleophile in this reaction
    II) Carboxylic acid is one of the products
    III) Grignard reagent acts as the nucleophile

    A. I only
    B. II only
    C. I & III
    D. II & III

2. Predict the major product (Compound B) from the series of reactions shown below.

    NaCN
    H₂O

    Compound A

    H₂SO₄ / H₂O
    Heat

    Compound B

    A. A four carbon carboxylic acid
    B. A four carbon alkene
    C. A five carbon carboxylic acid
    D. A five carbon aldehyde

3. Predict the identity of Compound X from the following reaction.

    CH_3OH / H^+

    Compound X

    A. Butyl methanoate
    B. Butanaldehyde
    C. Methyl butanoate
    D. Butanol

4. Which of the following has the highest boiling point?

    A. Pentanoic acid
    B. Pentanol
    C. Pentane
    D. Pentanone

5. Which of the following is true regarding the acidity of Compounds A & B?

Compound A

Compound B

A. Compound B is more acidic, because ethoxide is resonance stabilized.
B. Compound A is less acidic, because acetate is resonance stabilized.
C. Compound B is less acidic, because ethoxide is resonance stabilized.
D. Compound A is more acidic, because acetate is resonance stabilized.

6. Predict the most acidic compound from the choices below?

A.

B.

C.

D.

7. The product of the following reaction is:

A. toluene.
B. benzene.
C. benzophenone.
D. benzyl alcohol.

8. The general formula indicated below is that of:

RCOOH

A. an alkane.
B. an aldehyde.
C. an ester.
D. a carboxylic acid.

9. Which of the following compounds has the highest boiling point?

A. Propanal
B. Propanoic acid
C. Propanone
D. Propane

10. The name of the structure shown is:

COOH

A. benzaldehyde.
B. benzoic acid.
C. phenyl ethanoic acid.
D. heptanoic acid.

Questions 11-16 are based on the following passage.

Passage

The sequence of reactions shown below were done in a lab.

Reaction 1

CH₃

Reaction 2

COOH

Reaction 3

CH₂OH

Reaction 4

CHO

Some of the reactions were done to synthesize compounds that were used to conduct other reactions. The experiments were also used to analyze the efficiency of these reactions.

11. All the statements given below are true, EXCEPT:

    A. CH_3COOH can undergo hydrogen bonding.
    B. The melting point of carboxylic acids are higher than that of comparable alcohols.
    C. The carbonyl group in carboxylic acids are more electrophilic than that of ketones.
    D. In carboxylic acids, resonance is possible.

12. Which of the following is true about the conversion involved in Reaction 2?

    A. The conversion is an oxidation reaction, and can be accomplished by using $LiAlH_4$.
    B. The conversion is a reduction reaction, and can be accomplished by using $LiAlH_4$.
    C. The conversion is an oxidation reaction, and can be accomplished by using $KMnO_4$.
    D. The conversion is a reduction reaction, and can be accomplished by using $KMnO_4$.

13. If the product of Reaction 2 were converted to an ester, which of the following reagents should be used for this conversion to be done most easily?

    A. $NaBH_4/H_2O$
    B. Alcohol/HCl
    C. Thionyl chloride/heat
    D. Ether/HCl

14. Formaldehyde can be converted to formic acid. What is the correct hybridization of the carbon atom in the formic acid?

    A. sp
    B. sp^3
    C. sp^3d
    D. sp^2

15. Which of the following compounds has the highest pKa value?

    A. FCH_2CH_2COOH
    B. F_2CHCH_2COOH
    C. $FCH_2CH_2(CH_3)CH_2COOH$
    D. FCH_2COOH

16. From the following compounds, choose the compound that is the most acidic?

    A. CH_3COOH

    B. $HC\equiv CH$

    C.

    D. $NaOCH_3$

24

Acid Derivatives

A. INTRODUCTION

Acid chlorides, anhydrides, amides, esters, and ketoacids are some examples of acid derivatives. An acid derivative has an acyl group which is attached to a functional group. If the functional group attached to the acyl group is a hydroxyl group, then it is a carboxylic acid.

Acid derivative

The acyl group is circled.

$R - C(=O) - $ Functional group

$R - C(=O) - Cl$ Acid chloride (Acyl chloride)

$R - C(=O) - O - C(=O) - R$ Acid anhydride

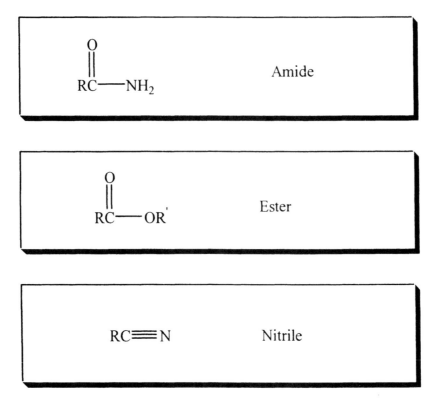

Nitrile is also considered as a carboxylic acid derivative, even though it has no acyl group.

An acid derivative can be converted to the corresponding carboxylic acid by hydrolysis.

$$R-\underset{\substack{\| \\ O}}{C}-X \xrightarrow{H_2O} R-\underset{\substack{\| \\ O}}{C}-OH \quad + \quad HX$$

Acid derivative   Carboxylic acid

This hydrolysis reaction occurs by **nucleophilic substitution**.

Increasing rate of hydrolysis

Amide < Ester < Acid anhydride < Acid chloride

B. ACID CHLORIDES

An acid chloride can be prepared by using thionyl chloride and the corresponding carboxylic acid.

Sample reaction 24-1

$$CH_3CH_2\overset{\overset{\displaystyle O}{\|}}{C}\text{---}OH \xrightarrow{\quad SOCl_2 \quad} CH_3CH_2\overset{\overset{\displaystyle O}{\|}}{C}\text{---}Cl$$

Propanoic acid   Propanoyl chloride

Reactions of Acid chlorides

Acid chlorides form amides when reacted with amines or ammonia.

Sample reaction 24-2

$$H_3C\text{---}\overset{\overset{\displaystyle O}{\|}}{C}\text{---}Cl \xrightarrow{\quad NH_3 \quad} H_3C\text{---}\overset{\overset{\displaystyle O}{\|}}{C}\text{---}NH_2 \quad + \quad NH_4Cl$$

Acid chloride   Amide

Acid chlorides react with alcohols to form esters.

Sample reaction 24-3

$$H_2CH_3C\text{---}\overset{\overset{\displaystyle O}{\|}}{C}\text{---}Cl \xrightarrow[\text{CH}_3\text{OH}]{\text{Alcohol}} H_2CH_3C\text{---}\overset{\overset{\displaystyle O}{\|}}{C}\text{---}OCH_3 \quad + \quad HCl$$

Acid chloride   Ester

C. ACID ANHYDRIDES

Acid anhydrides have important commercial uses. One of the acid anhydrides of such importance is acetic anhydride.

Acetic anhydride

Acetic anhydride can be synthesized by reacting a compound called ketene with acetic acid.

Sample reaction 24-4

$$CH_2=C=O \xrightarrow{\text{Acetic acid} \atop CH_3COOH} CH_3\overset{O}{\overset{||}{C}}O\overset{O}{\overset{||}{C}}CH_3$$

Ketene   Acetic anhydride

Cyclic anhydrides such as succinic anhydride, maleic anhydride, and glutaric anhydride can be prepared by heating the corresponding dicarboxylic acids. The reaction results in intramolecular dehydration and ring formation. Study the following example.

Sample reaction 24-5

Succinic anhydride

Reaction Involving Acid Anhydrides

Acid anhydrides react with alcohols to form esters and carboxylic acids. A general equation representing this type of reaction is shown in the next sample reaction.

Sample reaction 24-6

Acid anhydride   Ester   +   Carboxylic acid

D. AMIDES

Amides can be synthesized from acid chlorides by reacting with ammonia.

Sample reaction 24-7

$$\underset{\text{Acid chloride}}{R-\overset{\overset{\displaystyle O}{\|}}{C}-Cl} \xrightarrow{NH_3} \underset{\text{Amide}}{R-\overset{\overset{\displaystyle O}{\|}}{C}-NH_2} \quad + \quad NH_4Cl$$

Hydrolysis of Amides

In the hydrolysis reaction of an amide in the presence of acids or bases, the products formed are carboxylic acid and amine. This is a nucleophilic acyl substitution reaction.

E. ESTERS

$$\overset{\overset{\displaystyle O}{\|}}{RC}-OR'$$

Esters are compounds having the general structure formula shown above. They have moderate dipole moments, resulting in intermolecular attractive forces. For this reason, they have higher boiling points than the corresponding hydrocarbons of comparable weights. But compared to alcohols, esters have lower boiling points, since they cannot form hydrogen bonds among themselves (Reason: No hydroxyl group). Esters can have hydrogen bonds with other hydroxyl containing compounds such as water and carboxylic acids.

Synthesis of Esters

Esters can be synthesized by reacting carboxylic acids with alcohols, in the presence of acid catalysts.

Sample reaction 24-8

$$\underset{\text{Carboxylic acid}}{RCOOH} + \underset{\text{Alcohol}}{R'OH} \xrightarrow{H_2SO_4} \underset{\text{Ester}}{RCOOR'} + \underset{\text{Water}}{H_2O}$$

F. REACTIONS OF ESTERS

Reduction

Esters can be converted to alcohols by reacting with reducing agents such as lithium aluminum hydride.

Sample reaction 24-9

$$\underset{\text{Ethyl acetate}}{CH_3\overset{\displaystyle O}{\overset{\|}{C}}OCH_2CH_3} \xrightarrow{\quad LiAlH_4/\ H_2O \quad} \underset{\text{Ethyl alcohol}}{CH_3CH_2OH} \ + \ \underset{\text{Acetic acid}}{CH_3\overset{\displaystyle O}{\overset{\|}{C}}OH}$$

Esters with Grignard Reagents

Esters can react with Grignard reagents (two equivalents) to form tertiary alcohols. See the following example.

Sample reaction 24-10

$$CH_3\overset{\displaystyle O}{\overset{\|}{C}}OCH_2CH_3 \ + \ 2CH_3MgBr \longrightarrow \underset{\underset{\displaystyle CH_3}{|}}{CH_3\overset{\displaystyle OH}{\overset{|}{C}}CH_3} \ + \ CH_3CH_2OH$$

Saponification

The hydrolysis of esters in the presence of bases is called **saponification**.

Sample reaction 24-11

Ester → Carboxylate salt + R'OH (NaOH/H₂O, heat)

```
            H
            |
    H———C———OH
            |
    H———C———OH        Glycerol
            |
    H———C———OH
            |
            H
```

Fats are carboxylic acid esters of glycerol. When these esters are hydrolyzed, carboxylic acids with long hydrocarbon chains called fatty acids are
formed, along with the parent alcohol (glycerol).

```
                    H        O
                    |        ||
          O    H———C———O———C———R
          ||         |
    R———C———O———C———H        O
               |             ||
          H———C———O———C———R
               |
               H
```

Fat (triacyl glycerol)

The MCAT Chemistry Book

CHAPTER 24 PRACTICE QUESTIONS

1. Which of the following most readily undergoes hydrolysis among the acid derivatives given below?

A.

B.

C.

D.

2. Which of the following is the major product of the reaction of an acid chloride with an alcohol?

A. An ester
B. An aldehyde
C. A ketone
D. An alkane

3. The reaction of an ester with Grignard reagent (excess) in the presence of an aqueous acid results in:

A. a primary alcohol.
B. a secondary alcohol.
C. a tertiary alcohol.
D. no reaction at all, because esters are not reactive with Grignard reagents.

4. Name the following compound.

A. Methyl propanoate
B. Ethyl butanoate
C. Propionic anhydride
D. Propyl ethanone

5. Predict the product of the reaction shown below.

   A. Ortho-methylbenzyl acetate
   B. Para-methyl benzoic acid
   C. Para-methylbenzyl acetate
   D. Para-methylethylbenzoate

6. The most likely product of an acyl chloride reaction with ammonia is:

   A. a carboxylic acid.
   B. an amide.
   C. an anhydride.
   D. an azide.

7. All the following reactions can be used for the preparation of carboxylic acids, EXCEPT:

   A. ester hydrolysis.
   B. nitrile hydrolysis.
   C. by the reaction of Grignard reagent with carbon dioxide.
   D. by the reduction of aldehydes.

25

Ethers

A. INTRODUCTION

Ethers are compounds with the general formula ROR' (e.g., $CH_3CH_2OCH_2CH_3$).

B. PROPERTIES OF ETHERS

Ethers are polar molecules. Compared to alcohols, ethers have very low boiling points mainly because they cannot form hydrogen bonds (intermolecular). The boiling points of ethers are close to alkanes of comparable weights. Ethers are not very reactive.

C. PREPARATION OF ETHERS

Simple ethers can be prepared by acid-catalyzed intermolecular dehydration of alcohols.

Sample reaction 25-1

$$2 \ C_2H_5OH \ \xrightarrow[\text{heat}]{H_2SO_4} \ C_2H_5OC_2H_5$$

An ether can also be prepared by the nucleophilic substitution of an alkyl halide by an alkoxide. The reaction is an example of S_N2 reaction. The reaction is called Williamson ether synthesis (Sample reaction 25-2).

Sample reaction 25-2

$$CH_3CH_2CH_2ONa \ + \ CH_3CH_2Cl \ \longrightarrow \ CH_3CH_2CH_2OCH_2CH_3 \ + \ NaCl$$

Sodium propoxide ⇧ Propyl ethyl ether

A primary alkyl halide

It is best to use primary alkyl halides in this type of reaction. Other halides most likely undergo elimination rather than substitution reaction.

D. CLEAVAGE OF ETHERS BY ACID

Ethers are cleaved when reacted with hydrogen halides to form alkyl halides and water. A sample reaction is shown:

Sample reaction 25-3

$$CH_3CH_2OCH_3 \ \xrightarrow[\text{heat}]{2\ HI} \ CH_3I \ + \ CH_3CH_2I \ + \ H_2O$$

E. THE BASICITY OF ETHERS

Ethers are weakly basic. The basicity is due to the presence of the unshared electrons that are present on the oxygen atom of ethers.

$$R—\overset{..}{\underset{..}{O}}—R'$$

F. EPOXIDES

Epoxides are three-membered cyclic ethers. Epoxides can be synthesized by the oxidation of corresponding alkenes with peroxy acid.

Ethylene   Peroxy benzoic acid   Ethylene oxide   Benzoic acid

Some Reactions of Epoxides

Epoxides can undergo acid or base-catalyzed ring-opening reactions. If the epoxide used in the reaction is symmetric, the product will be the same under both conditions. But the products will be different, if the epoxide is unsymmetric.

Under Acid-Catalyzed Conditions

Under acidic conditions, the nucleophilic attack is directed to the protonated epoxide. The nucleophile adds to the more highly substituted carbon in the epoxide ring. This is because in the protonated epoxide, the positive charge is shared by the ring-carbon atoms attached to the oxygen. The positive charge is more stabilized when it is on the more highly substituted carbon (stronger electrophile), and thus the attack of the nucleophile is preferentially on the more substituted carbon under acidic conditions.

Under Basic Conditions

In a base-catalyzed ring opening of an epoxide, the nucleophilic attack is on the less substituted (less hindered) carbon atom in the epoxide ring. The mechanism is shown below.

CHAPTER 25 PRACTICE QUESTIONS

1. All the reactions described below CANNOT prepare ethers, EXCEPT:

    A. Williamson synthesis.
    B. dehydrogenation of alkenes.
    C. decarboxylation of carboxylic acids.
    D. Clemmenson reaction.

2. In terms of boiling point, ethers most resemble which of the following types of compounds?

    A. alcohols
    B. water
    C. carboxylic acids
    D. alkanes

3. Which of the following regarding ethers is true?

    A. They are polar.
    B. They are relatively less reactive.
    C. They can be used as solvents in reactions.
    D. All the above

Questions 4-8 are based on the following passage.

Passage 1

Consider the following synthesis reaction.

Reaction 1

$$CH_3CH_2CH_2ONa + RCl \longrightarrow$$

$$CH_3CH_2CH_2OR + NaCl$$

where R represents an alkyl group.

4. Which of the following is true regarding ethers?

    I.   Ethers are not very reactive.
    II. Ethers are extremely reactive.
    III. Ethers are flammable.
    IV. Ethers have higher boiling points than alcohols.

    A. I & III only
    B. II & III only
    C. II, III, an IV only
    D. I & IV only

5. The reaction sequence shown in the passage is most likely to be effective if the reaction runs by S_N2 mechanism. Which of the following is the best suited alkyl halide to conduct this reaction most efficiently?

    A. CH_3Cl

    B. $CH_3\overset{\overset{\displaystyle CH_3}{|}}{C}HCl$

    C. $H_3C\overset{\overset{\displaystyle CH_3}{|}}{\underset{\underset{\displaystyle CH_3}{|}}{C}}Cl$

    D.

The MCAT Chemistry Book

6. All the following alkyl halides can undergo elimination by the reaction represented in Experiment 1, EXCEPT:

A. CH_3CHCH_3 (with I substituent)

B. $(CH_3)_3CI$

C.

D.

7. Predict the major product (Compound M) of the following reaction.

$$CH_3OCH_3 \xrightarrow{conc.HBr} Compound\ M$$

A. CH_3Br
B. CH_3OBr
C. CH_3OBrCH_3
D. No reaction occurs.

8. Which of the following is not an ether?

A.

B. $H_3CC\text{-}OCH_3$ (with =O)

C.

D. $(CH_3)_2CHOCH_2CH_3$

Phenols

A. INTRODUCTION

Phenol is a compound which has a hydroxyl group attached to a benzene ring. Although phenols have similar properties like alcohols (one aspect of similarity is that both phenols and general alcohols have the hydroxyl group), phenols are unique because of their aromatic ring.

Phenol

o-Cresol

m-Cresol

p-Cresol

Salicylic acid
(*o*-hydroxybenzoic acid)

Hydroquinone
(1,4-Benzenediol)

Resorcinol
(1,3-Benzenediol)

B. PROPERTIES OF PHENOLS

Hydrogen bonding is significant in phenols, because of the presence of the hydroxyl group. Phenols can form hydrogen bonds with other phenol molecules and water. Hence the boiling and melting points are relatively high for phenols. Phenols are acidic. In terms of acidity, phenols are in between carboxylic acids and alcohols.

Increasing acidity

ALCOHOLS < PHENOLS < CARBOXYLIC ACIDS

Phenol → Phenoxide anion + H^+

It is important to analyze the fact that the phenoxide ion's negative charge is stabilized by the delocalization of the electrons into the benzene ring. This is one of the reasons for phenols' increased acidity compared to alcohols. In alkoxide ions negative charge is localized in the oxygen atom (not delocalized).

C. EFFECTS OF SUBSTITUENTS ON THE ACIDITY OF PHENOLS

When a phenol has a strongly electron-withdrawing substituent group, the acidity of the phenol is increased. The reason for this increase is the electron-withdrawing group's ability to delocalize the negative charge, more than the phenoxide ion itself.

Increasing acidity

The effect of substituents on the acidity of phenol

On the contrary, electron-donating substituents decrease the acidity of phenols.

D. REACTIONS OF PHENOLS

Formation of Quinones

Oxidation of phenols results in compounds called quinones. They are conjugated, and they contain two carbonyl groups (dicarbonyl). See the example below:

Sample reaction 26-1

The quinone compound

E. ELECTROPHILIC AROMATIC SUBSTITUTION REACTIONS

Certain compounds (electrophilic) can react with phenols (nucleophilic). The nucleophilic activity can be either in the aromatic ring or the oxygen in the hydroxyl group. Examples of electrophilic aromatic substitution include nitration, halogenation, Friedel-Crafts reactions (alkylation and acylation), and sulfonation. The halogenation example shown below is a polysubstitution reaction involving bromine. The polysubstitution usually occurs when polar solvents are used.

Sample reaction 26-2

Phenol

2,4,6-Tribromophenol
(Polysubstitution product)

Monobromination can be achieved by using nonpolar solvents.

Sample reaction 26-3

Phenol

Br$_2$

Carbon disulfide

p-Bromophenol
(major product)

CHAPTER 26 PRACTICE QUESTIONS

1. The product of the reaction sequence shown below is:

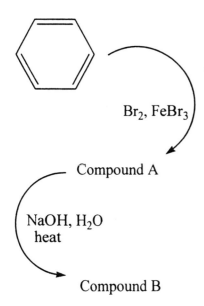

   Br$_2$, FeBr$_3$

   Compound A

   NaOH, H$_2$O
   heat

   Compound B

   A. meta cresol.
   B. phenol.
   C. toluene.
   D. styrene.

2. The reaction of phenol with Br$_2$ / H$_2$O can lead to all the following products in relatively significant quantities, EXCEPT:

   A. *ortho*-Bromophenol.
   B. *meta*-Bromophenol.
   C. 2,4,6-Tribromophenol.
   D. all the above are formed in significant amounts.

3. Which of the following compounds can have significant amounts of intramolecular hydrogen bonding?

   A. *ortho*-nitrophenol
   B. *para*-nitrophenol
   C. phenol
   D. *para*-hydroxy benzaldehyde

27

Amines

A. INTRODUCTION

Amines are derivatives of ammonia. The alkyl derivatives of ammonia are called **alkyl amines**, and the aryl (aromatic) derivatives of ammonia are called **aryl amines**. These nitrogen-containing compounds are unique for their basicity.

Ammonia
NH_3

$R\ddot{N}H_2$	$R_2\ddot{N}H$	$R_3\ddot{N}$
Primary amine	Secondary amine	Tertiary amine
	R= alkyl or aryl group	

B. STRUCTURE OF AMINES

The carbon to which the nitrogen is attached in an alkyl amine is sp^3 hybridized, and in aryl amines it is sp^2 hybridized. The nitrogen in the amines is sp^3 hybridized. As you have probably noticed, the nitrogen present in an amine has an unshared electron pair. In alkyl amines, the substituents attached to the nitrogen atom are arranged in a pyramidal manner around the nitrogen. In aryl amines, this pyramidal mode is more flat compared to alkyl amines. Moreover, the unshared pair of electrons in aryl amines has the advantage of delocalization into the pi electrons in the aromatic ring.

C. PROPERTIES OF AMINES

Amines are somewhat polar. But the polarity is not as high as that of alcohols. As Figure 27-1 indicates, the amines have intermediate boiling points.

Keep in mind that we are comparing the boiling points of amines with comparable alkanes and alcohols. Among amines only primary and secondary amines can form hydrogen bonds. Lower amines are soluble in water.

Alkanes < Amines < Alcohols

Figure 27-1

D. PREPARATION OF AMINES

Alkylation Method

Amines can be prepared by the alkylation of ammonia. In this array of reactions (Figure 27-2), the amines nucleophilically attack the alkyl halides. As shown below, the first reaction yields a primary amine. Primary amines yield secondary amines which in turn yield tertiary amines, and tertiary amines yield quaternary ammonium salts.

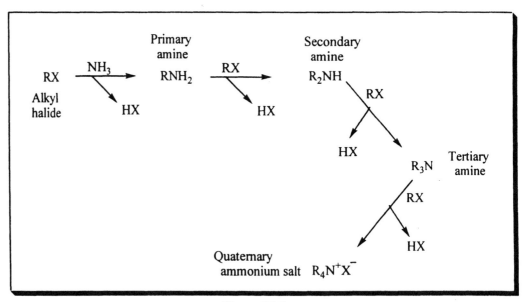

Figure 27-2

E. REACTIONS OF AMINES

Formation of Amides

Amines can react with acid chlorides to form **amides**. A representative reaction (Sample reaction 27-1) is shown. The reaction proceeds by nucleophilic addition to the carbonyl group by the amine.

Sample reaction 27-1

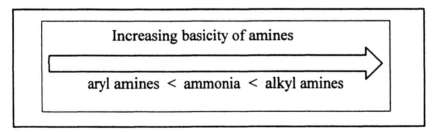

The tetrahedral intermediate

F. BASICITY OF AMINES

Amines are weakly basic compounds. Alkyl amines are more basic than ammonia, and aryl amines are less basic than ammonia.

Increasing basicity of amines

aryl amines < ammonia < alkyl amines

CHAPTER 27 PRACTICE QUESTIONS

1. Arrange the following compounds in the increasing order of boiling points?

    Compound A $CH_3CH_2CH_2COOH$

    Compound B $CH_3CH_2CH_2CH_3$

    Compound C $CH_3CH_2CH_2CH_2OH$

    Compound D $CH_3CH_2CH_2CH_2NH_3$

    A. A<B<C<D
    B. B<D<C<A
    C. B<C<D<A
    D. B<D<A<C

2. Which of the following compounds has the highest basicity?

    A. $CH_3CH_2CH_2NH_2$

    B. NH_3

    C. —NH_2

    D. $(CH_3CH_2)NH$

3. All the following are nitrogen-containing compounds, EXCEPT:

    A. aniline.
    B. quaternary ammonium salt.
    C. oxime.
    D. ester.

    $CH_3CH_2CH_2CN$

    Reaction 1 $\downarrow$

    $CH_3CH_2CH_2CH_2NH_2$

4. The conversion involved in Reaction 1 can be best characterized as:

    A. oxidation.
    B. dehydrogenation.
    C. isomerization.
    D. reduction.

Questions 5-10 are based on the following passage.

Passage 1

Amines range from simple structures to very complex structures. Some simple amines and their K_b values are given below.

K_b of conjugate bases

NH_4^+	1.8×10^{-5}
$CH_3NH_3^+$	4.3×10^{-4}
$(CH_3)_3CNH_3^+$	2.8×10^{-4}
$\text{—}NH_3^+$	3.7×10^{-10}

There are a wide variety of naturally occurring amines. Amines include caffeine, morphine, cocaine, quinine, and amphetamines, just to name a few. Amines are also biologically important. Some of the biologically important amines include thiamine, adrenaline, acetyl choline, and riboflavin.

Gamma-aminobutyrate is an amine and a neurotransmitter. It has mainly an inhibitory function and is extensively found as a neurotransmitter in the Purkinje cells of the central nervous system.

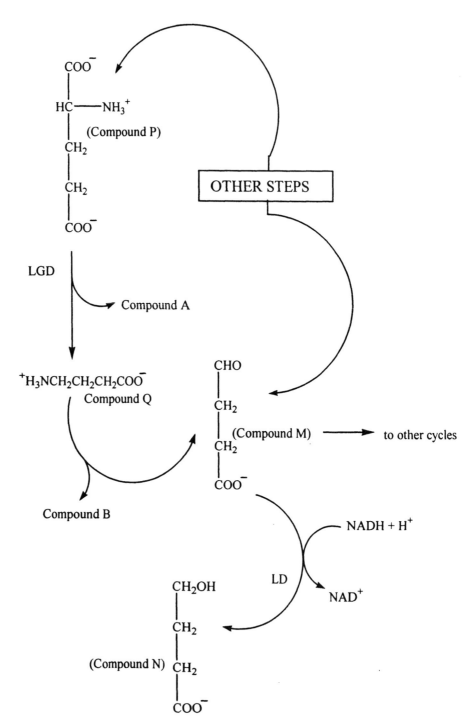

Compound P - L-Glutamate

Compound Q - γ-Aminobutyrate

5. Which of the following is the most acidic?

   A. CH_3NH_2
   B. $CH_3CH_2NH_2$
   C. $(CH_3)_2NH$
   D. CH_3OH

6. All the following can undergo hydrogen bonding themselves, EXCEPT:

   A. aniline.
   B. triethylamine.
   C. ammonia.
   D. methylamine.

7. The conjugate acid of which of the following is the most acidic?

   A. Methylamine.
   B. Ammonia.
   C. *tert*-Butylamine.
   D. Aniline.

8. The conversion of glutamate to aminobutyrate is best described as:

   A. a neutralization reaction.
   B. a decarboxylation reaction.
   C. a deamination reaction.
   D. an amination reaction.

9. The conversion of Compound M to Compound N is done by the process of:

   A. oxidation.
   B. transamination.
   C. inversion of configuration.
   D. reduction.

10. γ-Aminobutyrate can be best described as a:

    A. primary amine.
    B. secondary amine.
    C. tertiary amine.
    D. peptide.

28

Amino Acids and Proteins

A. INTRODUCTION

Proteins are polymers of amino acids. Proteins are extremely important since they have a wide range of biological significance. They serve as nutrients, enzymes, cellular products of genes by translation (reflects the hereditary information), building material of muscles and other biologically important structures.

B. AMINO ACIDS

Amino acids are the monomeric units of proteins. The general structure of an amino acid is as follows:

carboxyl group

$$^+NH_3\!\!-\!\!CH\!\!-\!\!COO^-$$

with R attached to CH

amino group

In the above diagram representing an amino acid, the characteristic amino and carboxyl groups are indicated by the arrows. Amino acids combine with other amino acids to form **peptides**.

Peptide Bond

An *amido* linkage formed between two amino acids is called **peptide bond**. Figure 28-1 shows the peptide bond between the amino acids, alanine and serine.

The peptide bond

Figure 28-1

The peptide bond is resonance stabilized.

Peptide linkage

Based on stereochemical analysis, it has been proved that in a typical peptide linkage such as shown in the figure, the atoms indicated in bold-type occupy the same plane

Figure 28-2

C. PEPTIDES

Dipeptide	– contains two amino acids.
Tripeptide	– contains three amino acids.
Tetrapeptide	– contains four amino acids.
Pentapeptide	– contains five amino acids.
Polypeptides	– contain many amino acids.
Proteins	– contain fifty or more amino acids.
	(classifications slightly vary)

D. ALPHA AND BETA AMINO ACIDS

Amino acids can be classified as α, β, γ, and so on. If the amino group is attached to the carbon next to the carboxylic carbon, the amino acid is an α–amino acid. If it is attached to carbon next to the α-carbon, the amino acid is a β-amino acid.

$$^+NH_3-\underset{\alpha}{CH}-COO^-\qquad \alpha\text{–amino acid}$$

with R substituent on the CH

$$^+NH_3\,\underset{\beta}{CH_2}\underset{\alpha}{CH}-COO^-\qquad \beta\text{–amino acid}$$

with R substituent on the CH

E. DIPOLAR NATURE OF AMINO ACIDS

Amino acids possess a dipolar nature. They are **amphoteric**, since they have both acidic and basic functional groups. Dipolar ions are often referred as **zwitterions**. In certain pH ranges, the amino acids exist predominantly as zwitterions, with a net charge of zero.

**PREDOMINANT AMINO ACID SPECIES
AT ISOELECTRIC POINT (ZWITTERIONIC)**

**PREDOMINANT AMINO ACID SPECIES
AT VERY ACIDIC ENVIRONMENT**
[acidic pH]

**PREDOMINANT AMINO ACID SPECIES
AT VERY BASIC ENVIRONMENT**
[alkaline pH]

F. CLASSIFICATION OF AMINO ACIDS

On the basis of the R groups present in the amino acids, they can be classified into various groups. There are about 20 important amino acids that are found in proteins.

HYDROPHOBIC AMINO ACIDS

1. Nonpolar amino acids with aliphatic R groups

Glycine

Alanine

Valine

Leucine

Isoleucine

Proline

2. Nonpolar amino acids with aromatic R groups

Phenylalanine

Tryptophan

Tyrosine

351

HYDROPHILIC AMINO ACIDS

1. Polar amino acids

Serine, Threonine, Cysteine, Glutamine, Methionine, Asparagine

2. Acidic amino acids

Aspartate, Glutamate

HYDROPHILIC AMINO ACIDS

3. Basic amino acids

Lysine   Arginine   Histidine

G. PROPERTIES OF AMINO ACIDS

Amino acids have ionizable groups. Each ionizable group has its own pKa value, which is the pH at which half of that particular ionizable group is in the dissociated state and the other half in the undissociated state. For the MCAT you should be familiar with the concept of isoelectric point. **Isoelectric point** of an amino acid is the pH at which the net charge of the amino acid is zero. Amino acids can sometimes act as acids or bases. This nature (property) of amino acids is called **amphoteric** property.

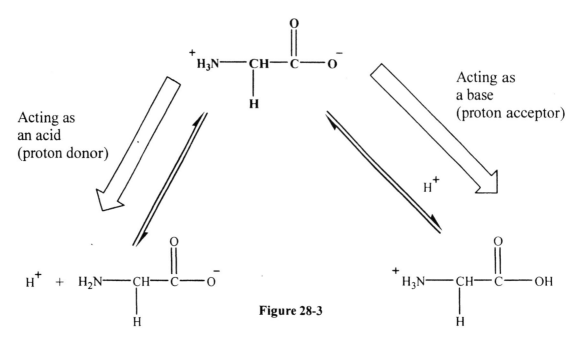

Figure 28-3

The amino acid shown in the above example is glycine. The amphoteric species is shown on top (bold faced).

H. PROTEINS

The structure of proteins can be classified into primary, secondary, tertiary, and quaternary structures, according to the level of complexity of the proteins.

Primary Structure of Proteins

The simple **sequence of amino acids** in a protein is called the **primary structure** of the protein. These sequences of amino acid chains can bend, fold, and bond to form more complex structures of proteins, which can be described in terms of secondary, tertiary, and quaternary structures. Figure 28-4 shows a tetrapeptide with amino acids: alanine, lysine, glycine, and phenylalanine.

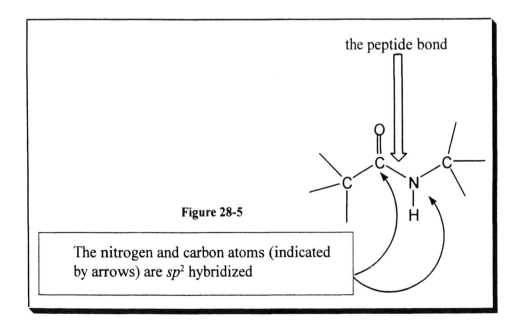

$$\overset{+}{NH_3} \underline{\quad\quad}\text{alanine-lysine-glycine-phenylalanine}\underline{\quad\quad} COO^-$$

N-terminal end   C-terminal end

Figure 28-4

peptide bonds

A peptide chain has an amino acid with the free (without a peptide bond) amino group on one end (the **N-terminal end**), and an amino acid with free (without a peptide bond) carboxylic group on the other end (the **C-terminal end**).

the peptide bond

Figure 28-5

The nitrogen and carbon atoms (indicated by arrows) are *sp²* hybridized

Secondary Structure of Proteins

The two main types of secondary structural arrangements are the α-helix and the β-pleated sheet. Generally, these conformations generate the secondary structure of proteins.

1. α-Helix

The α-helical structure or conformation is one of most important aspects of the secondary structure of proteins. This conformation of peptide chain has interactions within its chains by hydrogen bonding. A simple arrangement can be described as a helical structure in which the long polypeptide chain is wound around the long axis. The side chains (R groups) of the amino acids extend out of the helical backbone. Figure 28-6 shows right- and left-handed α-helical structures.

2. β-Pleated sheet

These represent the sheetlike arrangement of the polypeptide chains. The hydrogen bonds are found between the adjacent polypeptide chains. The polypeptide chains involved in the pleated sheet structure can be either parallel or antiparallel. Hydrogen bonds stabilize the β-pleated sheet (see Figure 28-7).

Tertiary Structure of Proteins

The tertiary structure of proteins is the three dimensional arrangement of the polypeptide chain. Tertiary structure depicts the way in which the secondary structure folds to form the three dimensional form. Different kinds of bonds or interactions are responsible for the maintenance of the tertiary structure. They include hydrophobic forces, hydrogen bonds, disulfide bonds, salt bridges, and Van der Waal forces.

Disulfide bonds: These are bonds formed by two cysteines.

Hydrophobic bonding: Hydrophobic bonding or forces are weak interactions between hydrophobic side chains of the hydrophobic amino acids in a protein.

Quaternary Structure of Proteins

Some proteins can be complex, when they contain multiple subunits of polypeptide structural entities. The way in which three-dimensional subunits interact to form the complete functional protein is called the quaternary structure of a protein. This level of hierarchy is possible only if the protein has multiple units. An example is hemoglobin.

Disulfide bond formatiom

Left handed helix   Right handed helix

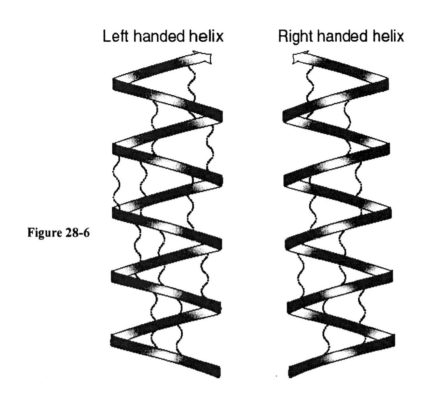

Figure 28-6

Pleated sheet (parallei)

n-terminal

n-terminal

C-terminal

C-terminal

Figure 28-7

n-terminal

C-terminal

C-terminal

n-terminal

Pleated sheet (antiparallei)

I. DENATURATION OF PROTEINS

Proteins can be denatured in many ways. A common example that we all have seen is the denaturation of egg albumin when we cook them. In this case, the denaturing agent is the temperature. Most biologically significant proteins are extremely heat sensitive. An increase in temperature can disrupt hydrogen bonds as well as hydrophobic interactions in proteins. This is one reason why we cannot survive in extreme (hot or cold) temperatures because at extreme temperatures, the proteins and other sensitive chemicals in our body denature and cease to function. Besides temperature changes, pH changes can also affect proteins. Other denaturing agents include detergents, oxidizing agents, reducing agents, UV light, and pressure.

Generally, protein denaturation includes the complete or partial unfolding of the polypeptide chain, cleavage of disulfide linkages, and breakage of noncovalent interactions. Denaturation is sometimes reversible. The reversing process is called **renaturation**.

CHAPTER 28 PRACTICE QUESTIONS

1. Which of the following is a basic amino acid?

   A. Valine
   B. Tryptophan
   C. Arginine
   D. Threonine

2. All the following amino acids are optically active, EXCEPT:

   A. Valine
   B. Proline
   C. Glutamic acid
   D. Glycine

3. At a particular pH, the amino acid glutamic acid has a net charge of zero. When this pH is achieved, it is said to be at glutamic acid's:

   A. isobaric point.
   B. isomeric point.
   C. isotonic point .
   D. isoelectric point.

4. Which of following groups are not present in any of the common amino acids?

   A. Amino group
   B. Carbonyl group
   C. Aldehyde group
   D. All the above groups are present.

5. Amino acids can be bonded to each other covalently by means of:

   A. hydrogen bonds.
   B. dipole-dipole interactions.
   C. phosphodiester linkages.
   D. peptide linkages.

6. Proteins are made of:

   A. monosaccharides.
   B. sugars.
   C. lipids.
   D. amino acids.

7. Which of the following will certainly NOT affect the structure of a protein?

   A. Proteases
   B. Strong bases
   C. Strong acids
   D. All the above can have some effect on the structure of proteins.

8. Which amino acid is responsible for the formation of disulfide bonds?

   A. lysine
   B. phenylalanine
   C. tryptophan
   D. cysteine

Questions 9-14 are based on the following passage.

Passage 1

Amino acids play an essential role in the physiological processes in our body. They are the main building blocks of the principal structures in our body. Amino acids themselves or in combination with carbohydrates, lipids, etc., form an intricate system of physiologically important structures and functional domains without which life as we know it cannot exist.

From a biological point of view with respect to life forms, only 20 amino acids are important, even though many more are found in nature. Most amino acids are optically active. With the functional groups and their chemical behavior, we can predict certain properties of amino acids such as ionization properties. Amino acids join together to form peptides. Table-1 shows the pKa values of some amino acids.

Table-1

	-COOH	NH₃⁺	Side chain
Alanine	2.3	9.7	
Arginine	2.2	9.0	12.5
Cysteine	2.0	10.3	8.2
Glutamate	2.2	9.7	4.3
Glycine	2.3	9.6	
Serine	2.2	9.2	
Threonine	2.1	9.1	
Tryptophan	2.8	9.4	
Tyrosine	2.2	9.1	10.1
Lysine	2.2	9.0	10.5

$$H_2N-CH-\overset{\overset{\displaystyle O}{\|}}{C}-OH$$

Aspartic acid

9. Which of the following are true regarding amino acids?

I. Amino acids have carboxyl group.
II. Amino acids have high melting points.
III. Some amino acids can have a net positive charge.
IV. Some amino acids can have a net negative charge.

A. I, III & IV only
B. I, II & III only
C. I, III & IV only
D. I, II, III & IV

10. Which of the following represents the pH at which there is no net movement of the amino acid when subjected to an electric field?

A. pH at pKa
B. pH at pKb
C. pH at isoelectric point
D. There is no such pH for amino acids because some amino acids are acidic, some are basic, and some are neutral.

11. Which of the following represents a peptide bond?

A. a
B. b
C. c
D. d

12. In our body, some amino acids are changed into metabolic intermediates which can enter metabolic cycles. One such example is given below. The example shows the conversion of serine into pyruvate which can be converted to acetyl CoA and enter the Krebs cycle. Compound Y can be best described as:

A. an amide.
B. an imine.
C. a phenol.
D. an imidazol.

13. Which of the following amino acids will migrate toward the positive electrode when subjected to an electric field at a pH of 7.0?

A. Alanine
B. Arginine
C. Lysine
D. Glutamic acid

14. All the following are NOT basic amino acids, EXCEPT:

A. Glutamate.
B. Aspartate.
C. Alanine.
D. Lysine.

29

Carbohydrates

A. INTRODUCTION

Carbohydrates, commonly known as sugars, are the most abundant group of biomolecules in nature. Our daily regimen of foods includes different forms of carbohydrates. Potatoes, rice, bread, pasta are carbohydrate-rich sources of food. There are different types of carbohydrates. The simplest units are called **monosaccharides**. A **disaccharide** contains two monosaccharides. A **polysaccharide** contains many monosaccharide subunits.

B. MONOSACCHARIDES

Based on the number of carbons, monosaccharides can be called trioses (three carbons), tetroses (four carbons), pentoses (five carbons), hexoses (six carbons), heptoses (seven carbons), octoses (eight carbons), and so on.

Monosaccharides contain many hydroxyl groups and a carbonyl group. If a monosaccharide contains an aldehyde group, it is called an **aldose** sugar. If a monosaccharide contains an keto group, it is called an **ketose** sugar.

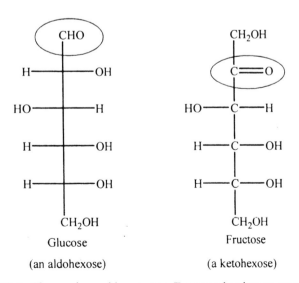

Figure 29-1 Glucose is an aldose sugar. Fructose is a ketose sugar.

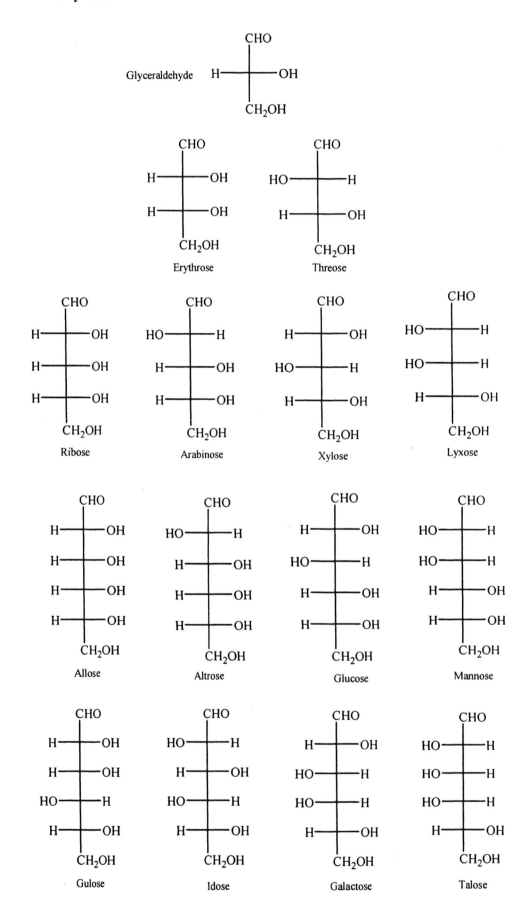

Figure 29-2 D-aldose sugars

C. CONFIGURATIONS OF MONOSACCHARIDES

Monosaccharides have chiral centers and thus exhibit optical activity. Let's explore the structure of glyceraldehyde. In the three-dimensional representation, the dotted wedges indicate the bonds that extent backwards from the chiral carbon (away from you or into the plane of the page); and the solid wedges indicate the bonds that are projected toward you (out of the plane of the page). In stereochemistry, Fischer projection is an important way to represent the spatial orientation of molecules. In Fischer projection representation, the bonds that are pointed backward (away from you or into the page) are indicated by vertical lines, and the bonds that extend toward you (out of the page) are represented by horizontal lines. For a more detailed approach, refer to Chapter 19 (Stereochemistry).

D glyceraldehyde

L glyceraldehyde

Figure 29-3

By convention, the carbonyl group is always drawn on top. With that as the standard, we can describe the structure of D-glyceraldehyde as follows:

D-glyceraldehyde has a hydroxyl group represented on the right side of the chiral carbon. L-Glyceraldehyde has a hydroxyl group represented on the left side of the chiral carbon. To determine whether a sugar structure shown is L or D, we have to locate the chiral carbon that is farthest from the carbonyl group, and see whether the hydroxyl group is on the right or on the left of the chiral carbon.

D. CYCLIC STRUCTURE OF HEXOSES

Glucose

Glucose is a six-carbon aldohexose. The straight chain hexose structures can become cyclic. When aldehydes and ketones undergo reactions with alcohols, hemiacetals or hemiketals are formed. In aldohexoses, the cyclic structure is formed when the hydroxyl group in the fifth carbon reacts (nucleophilic addition) with the carbonyl carbon of the aldehyde group. The product formed is a hemiacetal. The cyclization is represented in Figure 29-4.

A few facts worth remembering

1) The six-membered (hemiacetal) ring formed is called the **pyranose** ring.
2) The oxygen in the ring is from the hydroxyl group involved in the ring closure.
3) The carbon which is denoted as "carbon one" in the cyclic structure is the carbonyl carbon of the straight chain (the aldehyde group).
4) Notice that the cyclic structure can go either way in the sense that the resulting cyclic structure can either be an α- or a β-anomer.
5) The carbon number 'one' shown in the cyclic structure is called the anomeric carbon.
6) In aqueous solutions, the α- and β-anomers can interconvert, and the process is termed mutarotation.

Figure 29-4 The formation of cyclic structures of glucose

Fructose

Fructose is a ketohexose sugar. The cyclic structure formed is called a hemiketal, and the five membered ring that is formed is called **furanose** ring. The straight chain structure and the cyclic structures of fructose are shown in Figure 29-5.

CYCLIC STRUCTURES OF FRUCTOSE

Figure 29-5

Epimers are any two isomeric sugars which differ in their configurations only at one of the chiral carbon atoms. Glucose and mannose are epimers. Glucose and galactose are also epimers.

E. OXIDATION OF MONOSACCHARIDES

Monosaccharides can be oxidized. Benedict's reagent (oxidizing agent) can accomplish this by reacting with the aldehyde group of the open-chain form. Thus aldose and ketose sugars are reducing sugars. In fact, all monosaccharides are reducing sugars. Some disaccharides can be oxidized by Benedict's reagent.

BENEDICT'S TEST FOR REDUCING SUGARS

[red precipitate]

Copper(I) oxide

$$RCHO + 2Cu^{2+} \xrightarrow{\overline{O}H} RCOOH + Cu_2O + H_2O$$

OXIDATION

Benedict's reagent is reduced in the process to cuprous oxide.

F. DISACCHARIDES

Disaccharides are sugar units containing two monosaccharides linked by a covalent bond called **glycosidic bond**. Maltose, sucrose, and lactose are examples of disaccharides. Maltose is formed by the linkage of two glucose molecules by a glycosidic bond. Sucrose is a combination of glucose and fructose. Lactose is composed of glucose and galactose. The hydrolysis of disaccharides gives their corresponding monosaccharide subunits.

HYDROLYSIS OF DISACCHARIDES

Figure 29-6 The structure of maltose

Figure 29-7 The structure of sucrose

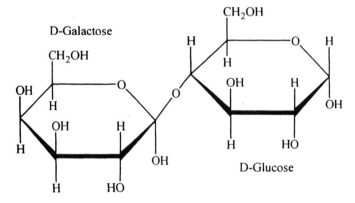

Figure 29-8 The structure of lactose

G. POLYSACCHARIDES

Polysaccharides are polymers of monosaccharides. Starch, glycogen, and cellulose are examples of polysaccharides. Polysaccharides can be homogeneous in terms of its fundamental unit (monosaccharide). If more than one type of monosaccharide is present in a polysaccharide, then it is called a heteropolysaccharide.

Starch

Starch is composed of two types of polymer structures derived from α-glucose – a linear polymer form called **amylose**, and a branched polymer form called **amylopectin**. Figure 29-9 shows the two types of glucose polymers involved in the formation of starch. The amylose has $\alpha(1\rightarrow4)$ linkages of glucose subunits, and the amylopectin has $\alpha(1\rightarrow6)$ and $\alpha(1\rightarrow4)$ linkages.

Glycogen

Glycogen is a polysaccharide found in most animals as a storage medium of carbohydrate. It is stored mainly in the skeletal muscles and the liver. We can say that starch is to plants as glycogen is to animals. In other words, the animal carbohydrate storage medium is glycogen, and the plant carbohydrate storage medium is starch. The structure of glycogen is mostly like that of the amylopectin structures found in starch, only with more branching.

Cellulose

Cellulose is a polysaccharide found in plants. But unlike starch and glycogen, the monosaccharide units that build up the cellulose are β-glucose units. Also the polysaccharide chains found in the cellulose structure are unbranched. In addition, the linkages in cellulose units are β-linkages instead of α-linkages. This type of β-linkage is the reason why humans cannot digest cellulose. To be more precise, the enzymes that we have do not work on such linkages. Some herbivores such as cattle have cellulose digesting bacteria in their stomachs which digest the foods containing cellulose. Once the bacterial enzymes break the cellulose structures into simple sugars, then the animal can use them for its metabolic needs.

Figure 29-9 The glucose polymers that are involved in the formation of starch

CHAPTER 29 PRACTICE QUESTIONS

1. All the following are monosaccharides, EXCEPT:

   A. galactose
   B. glucose
   C. ribose
   D. maltose

2. What is the name of the structure drawn below?

   A. D-glucose
   B. L-mannose
   C. D-galactose
   D. L-ribose

3. A lab technician making a fresh sugar solution noticed that the optical activity of the sugar solution changed after the solution had been standing for several hours. This change in optical activity is best explained by the phenomenon called:

   A. Tyndall effect.
   B. Brownian movement.
   C. optical anomaly.
   D. mutarotation.

4. Which of the following is NOT a disaccharide?

   A. Maltose
   B. Sucrose
   C. Glycogen
   D. Lactose

5. The structure shown below is that of a monosaccharide. How many optical isomers are possible for this structure?

$$
\begin{array}{c}
\text{CHO} \\
\text{H}\!-\!\!-\!\!-\!\text{OH} \\
\text{H}\!-\!\!-\!\!-\!\text{OH} \\
\text{CH}_2\text{OH}
\end{array}
$$

   A. 2
   B. 4
   C. 6
   D. 9

Questions 6-11 are based on the following passage.

Passage 1
The structures of some monosaccharides are drawn below.

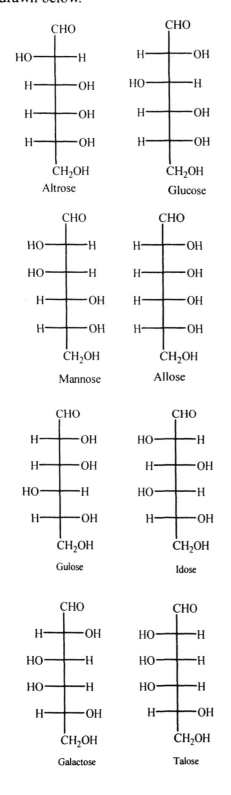

6. All the following are monosaccharides, EXCEPT:

    A. sucrose.
    B. fructose.
    C. glucose.
    D. galactose.

7. The structure given below is:

    A. glucose.
    B. ribose.
    C. fructose.
    D. maltose.

8. Which of the following statements are true regarding the two structures (Compounds I & II) drawn below?

Compound I

Compound II

Statement (1) - Compound I is glucose.
Statement (2) - Compound II is glucose.
Statement (3) - Compound II is fructose.
Statement (4) - Compound II is fructose.

A. Statements 1 & 2
B. Statements 2 & 3
C. Statements 3 & 4
D. Statements 2 & 3

9. Glucose and mannose are:

A. anomers.
B. epimers.
C. enantiomers.
D. non superimposable mirror images.

10. The structure of a disaccharide is shown below. The bond indicated by the arrow is called:

A. a glycosidic linkage.
B. a peptide linkage.
C. a glucose linkage.
D. an ester linkage.

11. The two stereogenic structures shown below are best related by the term:

A. enantiomers.
B. resonance structures.
C. anomers.
D. mesomers.

30

Lipids

A. INTRODUCTION

Lipids are a group of compounds which are hydrophobic, and have nonpolar groups predominantly. They can also contain polar groups. Lipids are important to living beings. Fats, a form of lipid, are used to store energy in organisms. Lipids are found in a wide variety of capacities; as hormones, as part of membranes, and as cofactors. Lipids are water insoluble. This makes them different and unique for their roles as biomolecules. Examples of lipids include waxes, steroids, and prostaglandins.

B. FATTY ACIDS

Fatty acids are carboxylic acids with long hydrocarbon chains. If the hydrocarbon chain in a fatty acid is saturated (no carbon-carbon double bonds), then it is called a **saturated fatty acid**. If there are (one or more) carbon-carbon double bonds in the hydrocarbon chain of a fatty acid, then it is called an **unsaturated fatty acid**. As the length of the hydrocarbon chain increases, the lipid solubility of fatty acids increases, and the water solubility decreases. Fats and oils are derivatives of fatty acids.

Table 30-1

Saturated Fatty Acids	
$CH_3(CH_2)_{12}COOH$	Myristic acid
$CH_3(CH_2)_{14}COOH$	Palmitic acid
$CH_3(CH_2)_{16}COOH$	Stearic acid

Table 30-2

Unsaturated Fatty Acids	
$H_3C(H_2C)_7HC{=}CH(CH_2)_7COOH$	Oleic acid
$H_3C(H_2C)_4HC{=}CHCH_2CH{=}CH(CH_2)_7COOH$	Linoleic acid
$H_3CH_2CHC{=}CHCH_2CH{=}CHCH_2CH{=}CH(CH_2)_7COOH$	Linolenic acid

C. TRIACYLGLYCEROLS

Triacylglycerols are esters of fatty acids. **Fats** or **triglycerides** are triacylglycerols. In a triacylglycerol, a glycerol molecule is linked with three fatty acids by ester linkages. The structure of glycerol is shown below:

GLYCEROL

$$
\begin{array}{l}
H_2C{-}OH \\
\quad | \\
HC{-}OH \\
\quad | \\
H_2C{-}OH
\end{array}
$$

The fatty acids that are present in fats are mostly straight-chain fatty acids (saturated and unsaturated), with even number of carbon atoms. According to the number of fatty acids esterifying the glycerol's hydroxyl groups, the glyceride formed could be a monoglyceride, a diglyceride or a triglyceride. Glycerides with long chain fatty acids are insoluble in water.

TRIACYLGLYCEROL

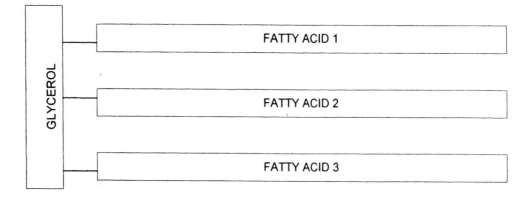

Figure 30-1

A diagrammatic representation of a triglyceride (triacylglycerol) is shown in Figure 30-1. In the figure, the vertical bar represents glycerol and the horizontal bars represent the fatty acids. The fatty acids (1, 2, & 3) present in a triacylglycerol molecule can be the same three fatty acids, or can be different fatty acids.

Fats can be solid or liquid. This physical property is a direct effect of the fatty acid substituents that are present in them. When fats are in their liquid state they are commonly called oils. Broadly we can generalize that solid fats mainly contain saturated fatty acids, and liquid fats mainly contain unsaturated fatty acids. We should not confuse this generalization with the fact that the naturally occurring fats and oils contain many different types of fatty acids, both saturated and unsaturated. The physical properties of fats are mostly a function of the fatty acids that are present in them. For example, human stored fat contains predominantly oleic acid (a saturated fatty acid) which constitutes about 47 % of the total fatty acid content. It also contains palmitic acid, linoleic acid, stearic acid, myristic acid, and other fatty acids in decreasing amounts respectively.

D. STEROIDS

A steroid has a drastically different structure from that of fats. **Steroids** are lipids having a particular fused-ring structure; a ring structure which has three six-carbon rings and a five-carbon ring. All steroids have this basic unit in their structures. Steroids include a wide variety of molecules, including cholesterol and its derivatives such as steroid hormones, and have tremendous biological significance. The steroid hormones include adrenocorticoid hormones and sex hormones.

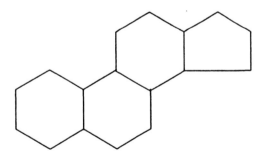

The fused ring of steroids

Cholesterol

Adrenocorticoid hormones

Cortisone

Aldosterone

Sex hormones

Testosterone   Estradiol

Notice that all these compounds have the fused-ring structure that we mentioned earlier. In fact, cholesterol acts as the starting material for the synthesis of steroid hormones. The steroid hormones play a very important role in the proper development and functioning of our body. The structures given above are just for reference and understanding the general structural integrity of steroids. You don't have to memorize them.

CHAPTER 30 PRACTICE QUESTIONS

1. If 1 mol of triglyceride is subjected to complete hydrolysis by using a lipase enzyme, the products formed are:

   A. 3 moles of glycerol and 1 mol of fatty acid.
   B. 1 mol of glycerol and 3 moles of fatty acid.
   C. 1 mol of glycerol and 1 mol of fatty acid.
   D. 2 moles of cholesterol.

2. Which of the following is not a steroid?

   A. Vitamin D
   B. Testosterone
   C. Estradiol
   D. All the above are steroids.

31

Phosphoric Acid Chemistry

A. INTRODUCTION

Phosphoric acid is H_3PO_4. It is an important molecule with respect to its part in a wide variety of biomolecules in our body such as adenosine triphosphate (ATP), deoxyribonucleic acid (DNA), and ribonucleic acid (RNA).

Phosphoric acid

B. DISSOCIATION OF PHOSPHORIC ACID

Phosphoric acid is a triprotic acid. That means it has three pKa values.

C. ESTERS AND ANHYDRIDES

Phosphoric acid can form esters with alcohols. It can form monoesters, diesters, and triesters. A general representation of the formation of phosphoesters is given below. R represents the alkyl group.

Figure 31-1

Besides esters, phosphoric acid forms anhydrides such as phosphoric anhydrides by reacting with themselves. One such combination is shown in Figure 31-2.

High energy P—O—P linkage

Figure 31-2

These anhydrides are biologically useful since the —P—O—P— linkages found in them are high energy linkages, and are used by the body to store energy. When energy is required, the linkage is hydrolyzed to give off the stored energy which is in turn used for the metabolic processes in the body.

D. BIOLOGICAL SIGNIFICANCE OF PHOSPHORIC ACID

We cannot completely fathom the importance of phosphoric acid in biological processes. It is a part of our genetic make up in the sense that phosphoric acid is a part of the deoxyribonucleic acid (DNA) and the ribonucleic acid (RNA). The deoxyribose sugars in the DNA are connected using phosphoric acid entities by forming linkages called **phosphodiester bonds**. These phosphodiester bonds connect the 3' hydroxyl group of one sugar to the 5' hydroxyl group of the next sugar forming the back bone of the nucleic acids. See Figure 31-3.

Figure 31-3 Part of a DNA backbone showing the phosphodiester bonds. The deoxyribose sugars are linked by the phosphate groups (indicated by the circles).

At normal biological pH range (7.35-7.45), the phosphate esters usually show a double negative charge. This property of the phosphate esters makes them generally water soluble, and thus perfect for the physiological environment in our body.

Another noteworthy biomolecule that contains the phosphate groups is the ATP (adenosine triphosphate). The ATP molecules act as one of the major energy currencies of living beings. It is a triphosphate ester. The formation of ATP from AMP (adenosine monophosphate) is shown in Figure 31-4.

Figure 31-4 The formation of ATP from AMP

CHAPTER 31 PRACTICE QUESTIONS

Questions 1-7 are based on the following passage.

Passage 1

Phosphoric acid is an integral part of some of the most important biomolecules in our body.

Reaction 1

Compound X

Compound Y

Reaction 1 depicts the conversion of phospho-enol pyruvate to pyruvate.

Phosphate is a part of many high-energy compounds in biological systems. Examples include ATP (adenosine triphosphate)) and GTP (guanosine triphosphate).

The structure of ATP

$$ATP \xrightarrow{H_2O} ADP + Pi$$

$$\Delta G = -31 \text{ kJ/mol}$$

1. The bond indicated by the arrow is a:

A. phosphate ketone bond.
B. phosphate anhydride bond.
C. phosphate ester bond.
D. *N*-glycosidic bond.

2. Reaction 1 can be best described as a:

   A. reduction reaction.
   B. dehydration reaction.
   C. dehydrohalogenation reaction.
   D. hydrolysis reaction.

3. The interconversion of Compounds X and Y is called:

   A. resolution.
   B. tautomerism.
   C. Tyndall effect.
   D. Brownian movement.

4. The bond indicated by the arrow is a:

   A. phosphate ketone bond.
   B. phosphate anhydride bond.
   C. phosphate ester bond.
   D. N-glycosidic bond.

5. The phosphate anhydride bonds present in the ATP molecules are high-energy bonds. Which of the following is true regarding the hydrolysis of these bonds?

   A. The products of hydrolysis have less energy than that of the reactants.
   B. The products of hydrolysis have the same energy as that of the reactants.
   C. The reactants of hydrolysis have less energy than that of the products.
   D. None of the above

6. Choose the correct change in free energy in the following conversion. (The products have higher free energy than the reactants)

   Adenosine + Phosphate → AMP

   A. −14 kJ/mol
   B. −34 kJ/mol
   C. +14 kJ/mol
   D. −40 kJ/mol

7. Phosphoric acid is a:

   A. monoprotic acid.
   B. diprotic acid.
   C. triprotic acid.
   D. strong acid.

32

Separation, Purification, and Structural Analysis of Organic Compounds

A. INTRODUCTION

For the MCAT, we should be familiar with the basic features of separation and purification of organic compounds. In this chapter, we will review some of the techniques that are commonly used by organic chemists.

B. EXTRACTION

Simple extraction involves the mixing of the organic solution with water in a separating funnel. Thorough mixing of the two phases (organic and aqueous) is done, and then the mixture is allowed to settle for sometime until the two phases separate. Then the lower layer can be poured into another flask. This procedure can separate water soluble impurities such as inorganic salts, low molecular weight carboxylic acids, and alcohols. Similarly, extraction can be done with dilute aqueous acids to remove organic bases, and with dilute aqueous bases to remove organic acids.

C. CRYSTALLIZATION

Organic compounds (solids) can be purified by a method called crystallization. **Crystallization** works by dissolving the material to be purified in a solvent (under hot conditions), followed by slow cooling of the solution. If the impurities are also soluble just like the substance we are purifying, obviously the purification will not be that effective. After the crystallization by slow cooling is completed, the crystals are collected by vacuum filtration. Then the crystals are dried.

Qualities of the Solvent Used for Crystallization

(i) The compound that is purified should be soluble in the selected solvent, only at high temperatures. At low temperatures, the compound should be insoluble.

(ii) The solvent used should have a relatively low boiling point. The boiling point of the selected solvent should not be higher than the melting point of the compound to be purified.

Solubility depends on the polarities of the solute and the solvent. According to the principle "like dissolves like," if the solute is polar, the solvent required should be polar too. On the other hand, if the solute is nonpolar, a nonpolar solvent should be used.

Some of the solvents commonly used for crystallization include acetone, chloroform, methanol, benzene, diethyl ether, carbon tetrachloride, and water.

D. DISTILLATION

Distillation is a technique that can be employed if the compounds to be separated have reasonably different boiling points. Distillation involves boiling of the mixture to vaporize it. This is followed by condensation to get the distillate. The distillates are eventually collected in the order of their condensation. There are different types of distillations.

Simple distillation is used to separate compounds, which have boiling points that sufficiently differ (difference of about >50^{0}C).

Vacuum distillation is used for the separation of compounds that have very high boiling points.

Fractional distillation is used for the separation of compounds that have very close boiling points.

E. CHROMATOGRAPHY

Chromatography is a popular and widely used method of purification. **Chromatography** is based on the differences in the adsorption and the solubility of the compounds to be separated. It involves two phases — a stationary phase and a moving (mobile) phase. The moving phase actually carries the compounds along the stationary phase. Depending on the interactions between the compounds and the stationary phase, the compounds get held up or slowed down by the stationary phase.

Thin-layer Chromatography (TLC)

Thin-layer chromatography is used for the separation of small quantities of the desired compound, especially for qualitative analysis. It is a widely used technique. In TLC, the liquid (mobile) phase is allowed to run along a layer of adsorbent. This thin layer of adsorbent (usually alumina or silica gel) is usually coated on a plate. After the sample (mixture dissolved in a solvent) is put onto the plate (usually a spot of sample is placed at the bottom of the plate), the plate is held vertical with a small amount of the solvent just touching the bottom of the plate. Due to capillary action, the solvent will ascend up the plate.

The sample will be separated between the various phases. The separation occurs as a result of differences in the rate of mobilities of the individual components of the sample. This is because of the difference in the affinities of the solute with respect to the two phases. **As a rule of thumb, the higher the polarity of the compound (component) is, the lesser the rate of upward mobility of that compound**. This generalization is based on the fact that the stationary phase used is highly polar. Polar substances bind strongly to the stationary phase. Also, the moving phase generally used is less polar with respect to the adsorbent. The separated and migrated components will appear as a series of spots on the plate. If the components are colorless, certain reagents are used to make the spots visible. Choosing the correct solvent is extremely important, and is best achieved by experience. Sometimes the best choice of solvent can be attained only by trial and error.

> R_f value is the ratio of the distance traveled by a compound to the distance traveled by the solvent.

Using known R_f values of compounds under the same conditions, we can make sure that the desired compound is present in the mixture and can be separated. R_f value is a constant (under specific conditions) for a given compound, and if the TLC is done exactly under the same conditions specified, we can be reasonably sure about the identity of the compound. Keep in mind that it is always safe to make sure of the identity of a compound with other qualitative analysis as well.

In addition to the function of identifying compounds, TLC is also used to monitor the progression of reactions, and to test the authenticity or the effectiveness of other separation techniques.

Gas-liquid Chromatography (GLC)

As the name implies, a gas phase (moving phase) and a liquid phase (stationary phase) are involved in gas-liquid chromatography. **Gas-liquid chromatography** is usually employed for the separation of volatile compounds. The device used for this is called a gas chromatograph. Usually a syringe is used to inject the sample into the device, and the sample injected is readily turned into vapor form. This vaporized form of the sample is carried along the flow of an inert gas. The sample is passed through a column containing the adsorbent (liquid-stationary phase). The column is the site where the separation of the components occurs. The separated samples as they emerge from the column are detected using a detection device.

The maintenance of the correct temperature of the column is extremely important for an efficient separation of the components. The choice of the stationary liquid phase is also important, and so is the maintenance of an optimum rate of flow of the sample through the column. The latter can be maintained by controlling the flow of the carrier gas. This technique is highly sensitive. Hence, it can be used to detect compounds even if very little of the compound is present (as low as in the order of micrograms).

Technological developments in the field of identification of compounds using infra red and NMR techniques have revolutionized the ease with which we can analyze and identify even the most complex structures in organic chemistry. For the MCAT, we should be familiar with the techniques and the basic principles that are used in this field.

F. INFRARED (IR) SPECTROSCOPY

Infrared spectroscopy is a widely used tool to identify and analyze compounds. As you know, the infrared radiation is part of the electromagnetic spectrum. The IR has wavelengths between those of the visible light and the microwaves. From the analytical point of view, only a portion of the entire infrared range is actually useful for the spectroscopic analysis.

In order to analyze organic compounds, certain properties at the molecular level are put to use in the infrared spectroscopy. In this technique, the infrared light is passed through organic compound samples. By doing this, some of the frequencies are absorbed by the sample and the other frequencies simply pass through. The percentage absorbance or transmittance is plotted against the frequency or, to be more precise, the wave number. The wave number (cm^{-1}) is the reciprocal of wavelength expressed in centimeters. The plot can be used to analyze the structure of a compound by identifying the peaks that are characteristic to the groups present in the compound.

For example, the carbonyl group ($>C=O$) shows absorbance close to 1700 cm^{-1} in the IR spectrum. The peaks around this value indicate the presence of carbonyl group in the compound that is analyzed. By knowing the IR values, we can predict the structure of a compound. Our discussion from the MCAT point of view will be limited to some of the common and important IR peaks.

Other very complex IR diagrams can only be interpreted by skilled and experienced professionals.

Vibrational Modes

Chemical bonds have characteristic natural frequencies with which they vibrate (bending and stretching) in certain specific energy levels. The special range of frequencies used in IR spectrometry is within the range of the natural vibrational frequencies of the bonds in organic compounds. By looking at the peaks, we can tell whether a particular functional group is present or absent in the compound that we are analyzing. The bonds present in the molecules of the sample vibrate when they absorb characteristic frequencies.

Molecules are always in a state of vibration. The bonds present in molecules have their own unique stretching and bending modes. Let's consider a hypothetical molecule A which has n atoms per molecule. Then, theoretically molecule A will have $3n - 6$ modes of vibration. But this does not mean that the vibrational modes strictly follow this rule. Some of the vibrational modes have frequencies that do not coincide with the frequencies of the IR that we use. We will consider the vibrational modes of the methylene group.

STRETCHING VIBRATIONS

Figure 32- 1
The stretching vibrational modes of methylene group. The two drawings show stretching vibrations — symmetric (on the left) and asymmetric on the right.

393

The MCAT Chemistry Book

BENDING VIBRATIONS

Figure 32-2
The bending vibrational modes of methylene group
The top two diagrams from the left are scissoring and rocking modes. The bottom two diagrams show wagging and twisting modes.

Besides the fundamental vibrational frequencies, overtones and combination tones can appear in the IR spectrum. For example, the overtone of a carbonyl group can appear close to $3400 cm^{-1}$ (the carbonyl peak is close to $1700 cm^{-1}$). Combination frequencies are peaks that appear when two frequencies intermingle, resulting in two weak frequencies.

Table 32-1

SOME IR ABSORBANCES

TYPE OF BOND	ABSORBANCE (cm^{-1})
—OH (Alcohol)	3200-3600
—OH (Carboxylic acid)	2500-3300
—Aromatic ring	~1500, ~1600
—CH (Aromatic)	3000-3100
—CH (sp^3)	2850-3000
=CH (sp^2)	3000-3100
≡CH (sp)	~3300
Aldehyde	~2720, ~2820
-C≡N	2210-2260
Ethers	~1000, ~1300
Amines -NH	3300-3500
-C=O (Carbonyl)	~1715 (1640-1750)
-C=O (Ketone)	~1715 (1665-1725)
-C=O (Aldehyde)	~1715 (1660-1740)
-C=O (Amide)	~1690 (1630-1690)
-C=O (Ester)	~1735 (1735-1750)
-C=O (Acid)	~1710 (1700-1730)
-C=O (Acid)	~1710 (1700-1730)
C=C (Alkene)	1620-1680

Example 32-1

Analyze the IR diagram shown below.

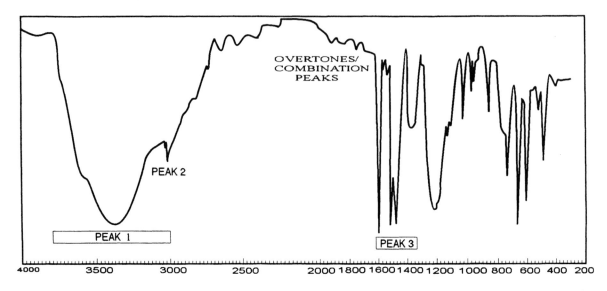

The given IR spectrum is that of phenol. Look at some of the important peaks that are present in this IR spectrum of phenol.

Analysis:

1) The peak 1 around 3400 cm^{-1} represents the peak caused by the -OH group.
2) The peak 2 at 3050 cm^{-1} represents the aromatic -CH.
3) The peak 3 denotes the benzene ring stretch.

Problem 32-1

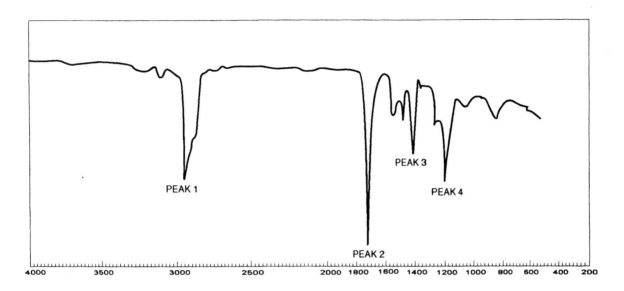

In the IR spectrum shown above, identify the most likely peak which represents the carbonyl group.

Solution:

The carbonyl peak is roughly around $1700 \ cm^{-1}$. So Peak 2 indicated in the IR diagram is the correct answer.

G. NUCLEAR MAGNETIC RESONANCE (NMR) SPECTROSCOPY

Nuclear magnetic resonance spectroscopy (NMR) is a type of analysis with which we can identify the positions of certain atoms in a compound. Only those atoms which possess nuclear spinning properties can exhibit NMR behavior. NMR spectroscopy is based on the magnetic properties exhibited by the nuclei of certain atoms. We will limit our discussion to the resonance spectroscopy (proton NMR) involving the nuclei of hydrogen atoms. With proton NMR, we can find or recognize the characteristic groups in the unknown compound, to which the specific protons are attached. In addition, we can also identify the number of different types of equivalent protons in a compound that we are analyzing.

The Basics of Proton NMR

The nucleus of an atom has an electric charge. Nuclear spin properties lead to nuclear magnetic moments. When hydrogen nuclei are exposed to a magnetic field, the nuclei will align themselves in coherence with the applied magnetic field as if they were tiny magnets. The alignment can be either along or opposite to the direction of the applied magnetic field. Among these two orientations, the one with the lower energy occurs when the alignment is along the direction of the field compared to the other orientation.

When sufficient energy (in the form of radio-frequency of the electromagnetic spectrum) is applied, the nuclei that are aligned along the magnetic field can reverse their orientation to align opposite to that of the applied magnetic field. The extent to which the nucleus is shielded from the magnetic field dictates the amount of energy required to change the orientation to a higher energy level. Based on this principle, we have to understand that depending on the extent of shielding they will absorb different frequencies. The energy that is absorbed is monitored and is recorded in the form of NMR spectrum. Thus protons in different regions of a molecule have different shifts (**chemical shifts**).

For the standard applied magnetic field, the absorption of frequencies differ only in terms of a few parts per million (ppm). In NMR spectroscopy, the relative standard molecule used is tetramethyl silane (TMS), and thus chemical shift (δ) is measured in ppm relative to the proton signal of TMS. Note that all the protons of TMS are equivalent, and thus have the same frequency of absorption, and it is considered to have a standard arbitrary value of "0 ppm" — the reference standard.

$$H_3C-\underset{\underset{CH_3}{|}}{\overset{\overset{CH_3}{|}}{Si}}-CH_3$$

The reference compound used – Tetra-methyl silane

Spin-Spin Coupling

Spin-spin coupling results from the possibility of the coupling of the neighboring protons. Signals often appear as groups of peaks as a result of spin-spin coupling. This results in what is called **signal multiplicity**. The number of peaks in a signal is dictated by the following means. Consider this hypothetical situation. Let's say there are N_1 equivalent protons in set 1, and N_2 equivalent protons in the adjacent carbon (set 2). (Note: Equivalent protons do not split themselves.) If this is the case, signal 1 will have ($N_2 + 1$) peaks, and signal 2 will have ($N_1 + 1$) peaks. The intensities of a split pattern are symmetrical (bilaterally symmetrical). The relative intensities of the peaks in a signal follow a pattern. A singlet has only one peak. There is no splitting in singlets. So there is no relative ratio to compare with. A doublet has a 1 : 1 proportion of relative intensities. A triplet has 1 : 2 : 1 proportion of relative intensities. A quartet has 1 : 3 : 3 : 1 proportion of relative intensities, and so on.

The different types of equivalent protons reflect the total number of signals. In the NMR spectrum of a compound, the levels of intensities of the signals denote the proportion of equivalent protons present in the compound. For example, the intensity of a signal resulting from six equivalent protons will be greater than the intensity of a signal resulting from two equivalent protons. The intensity is equivalent to the areas under the signals, and is proportional to the number of protons creating that particular signal.

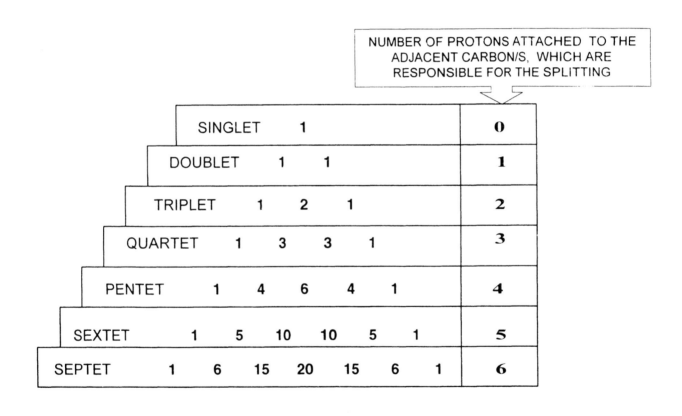

Figure 32-3 Relative intensities of the peaks

Proton Chemical Shifts

Table 32-2

Type of Proton	Chemical shift, δ (ppm)*
R-CH_3 (Primary)	0.9
R_2-CH_2 (Secondary)	1.3
R_2-CH (Tertiary)	1.5
-HC=CH (Vinyl)	4.5 - 6
$-$C≡CH (Acetylenic)	2 - 3
Ar-**H** (Aromatic)	6 - 8.5
Ar-CH (Benzylic)	2 - 3
C=CHCH_3 (Allylic)	1.6
-CHX (Halides)	2 - 4.5
-CHOH (Alcohol)	3.4 - 4
-CHOR (Ether)	3.4 - 4
-CHCOOH (Carboxylic)	2 - 2.6
-CHCOOR (Ester)	2 - 2.2
RC**H**=O (Aldehyde)	9 - 10
-CHO**H** (Hydroxyl)	1 - 5.6
-Ar-O**H** (Phenolic hydroxyl)	4 - 12
-CHCOO**H** (Carboxylic acid)	10 - 12
R-NH_2 (Amino)	1 - 5

*Approximate values with respect to TMS

Figure 32-4 The NMR spectrum of methyl propionate

Look at the NMR spectrum of methyl propionate given in Figure 32-4.

$$CH_3-O-\overset{\overset{\displaystyle O}{\|}}{C}-\overset{\overset{\displaystyle H_2}{}}{C}-CH_3 \qquad \text{Methyl propionate}$$

In the NMR spectrum, the signal at 0 ppm represents tetra methyl silane (standard). There are three distinct signals (sets of peaks). Altogether, there are 8 peaks — a set of three just after 1 ppm, a set of four just after 2 ppm, and a single peak around 3.5 ppm, totaling eight peaks. The set X is a triplet. The set Y is a quartet, and the set Z is a singlet. Sometimes it is hard to recognize the peaks distinctly because of interference between the nuclei, especially when there are multiple number of peaks.

In methyl propionate, there are three different types of protons denoted by X, Y, and Z. In the NMR spectrum, the set X is represented by the triplet in the NMR spectrum, the set Y is denoted by the quartet, and the set Z is denoted by the singlet.

401

CHAPTER 32 PRACTICE QUESTIONS

1. All the following are true regarding the process of crystallization, EXCEPT:

   A. The solvent used should easily dissolve the compound when cold.
   B. Minimum amount of solvent should be used.
   C. Crystallization process is generally used when there aren't many impurities in the material purified.
   D. Hexane is a good solvent that can be used to purify hydrocarbons.

2. Distillation is a very widely used technique for purifying compounds. Which of the following processes is involved?

   A. Vaporization is involved.
   B. Boiling is involved.
   C. Condensation is involved.
   D. All the above

Questions 3-8 are based on the following passage.

Passage 1

   A set of qualitative experiments were conducted in an organic chemistry lab.

Experiment 1

Chemist 1 treated cyclohexene with 1% aq. $KMnO_4$. One of the products was a *cis*-glycol.

Experiment 2

Chemist 2 conducted qualitative tests for some carbonyl compounds. Aldehydes and ketones gave a positive test for the reagent 2,4-dinitro-phenyl hydrazine. The compound tested for the confirmation was propanone. The product formed as a result of this test involving propanone is shown below.

Experiment 3

In Experiment 3, three compounds were tested. These three compounds were treated with concentrated hydrochloric acid in the presence of zinc chloride ($ZnCl_2$). Compound A was ethyl alcohol, Compound B was *tert*-butyl alcohol, and Compound C was 2-propanol. The reactions were based on unimolecular substitution mechanism.

Experiment 4

In Experiment 4, the chemists synthesized the following compound.

3. Based on Experiment 3, choose the true statement from the following choices.

    A. Compound A had the fastest reaction rate among the compounds tested.
    B. Compound B had the slowest reaction rate among the compounds tested.
    C. Compound C did not undergo the reaction.
    D. Compound A did not undergo the reaction.

4. In Experiment 2, which of the following IR peaks must have disappeared after the treatment of the compound with the reagent?

    A. A broad IR band at 3400 cm^{-1}
    B. A peak at 1700 cm^{-1}
    C. A peak at 800 cm^{-1}
    D. All the above peaks will be present for the product formed as a result of the reaction with the reagent.

5. Which of the following best describes the process involved in Experiment 1?

    A. Reduction
    B. Esterification
    C. Oxidation
    D. Dehydrohalogenation

6. Which of the following is true regarding Compounds A, B and C?

    A. They all have carboxyl groups.
    B. They all have double bonds.
    C. They all have IR peaks close to 3400 cm^{-1}.
    D. They all have the same reaction rate in terms of substitution reactions.

7. How many sets of peaks (signals) are expected for the Compound B?

    A. 2
    B. 3
    C. 4
    D. 10

8. Which of the following are true for the compound synthesized in Experiment 4?

    I.   The compound is insoluble in H_2O.
    II. The compound is soluble in 5% aqueous solution of NaOH.
    III. The compound is an aromatic compound.
    IV. The compound is a strong base.

    A. I & II only
    B. I & III only
    C. II & IV only
    D. II & III only

SOLUTIONS

Chapter 1 Solutions

1. The answer is D. This question tests your understanding of the concept of mole. The student is preparing a solution using calcium hydroxide. The formula of calcium hydroxide is $Ca(OH)_2$. The formula weight of calcium hydroxide is 74.1 grams/mol. Here, the student added two moles of it. So the answer is $74.1 \times 2 = 148.2$ g.

2. The answer is D. The sample weighs 56 g. The formula weight of O_2 is 32 g/mol. So the number of moles of oxygen present is roughly 1.75. Remember that 1 mol contains Avogadro number of particles. Since 1.75 moles of oxygen is present, there are $1.75 \times 6.0 \times 10^{23}$ molecules of oxygen. Are we done at this point? No! The question asks for the total number of atoms present in the sample. Since each oxygen molecule is composed of two oxygen atoms, the total number of atoms present in this sample equals $2 \times 1.75 \times 6.0 \times 10^{23} = 21 \times 10^{23}$.

3. The answer is B. Gas discharge tubes are vacuum tubes with electrodes connected to very high voltages. Cathode rays are emitted from the cathode of the tube. A cathode ray consists of a beam of electrons. Since electrons are negatively charged, cathode rays will bend away from a negatively charged plate.

4. The answer is D. This question asks for a true statement from the choices. Let's look at each of those choices. Choice A is incorrect, because neutrons and electrons do not have the same mass. Choice B claims that the mass of a neutron is less than that of an electron. That is not true either. Protons are positive and neutrons are neutral. They cannot together make the nucleus neutral. In fact, the nucleus is positively charged, not electrically neutral. So Choice C is wrong. The last choice makes perfect sense. A proton is more massive than an electron.

5. The answer is B. The actual formula of butane is C_4H_{10}. But the question is not about butane's actual formula. The question asks for the empirical formula of butane. Empirical formula is the most simplified ratio of the actual formula. So the correct answer is C_2H_5.

6. The answer is C. Let's look at the question carefully. If you did not get the right answer, carefully think about it again. The question is simply testing your understanding of a definition. The mass of a substance in one mole of it is numerically equal to its molecular weight.

7. The answer is A. Density is equal to mass per volume. Further more, the mass is equal to the product of number moles and molar mass. Equating these two equations we can get the answer. Using the letter notations given in the question, the expression of volume is given by Choice A.

8. The answer is D. The formula of sulfur dioxide is SO_2. The formula weight of SO_2 is 64 g/mol. This sample of SO_2 contains 1.5 moles of it. If we calculate the percentage mass of the oxygen, we can see that the oxygen's mass contribution is 50% in SO_2. So regardless of the amount of SO_2 present, half of its mass is due to the presence of oxygen and the other half is due to the presence of sulfur. Here we have 96 g of SO_2. Now, one half of 96 g gives 48 g.

9. The answer is A. The formula of carbon tetrachloride is CCl_4. The formula weight of CCl_4 is 154 g/mol. The percentage composition of Cl can be calculated as follows:

$$\% \text{ chlorine} = \frac{\text{mass of chlorine}}{\text{mass of } CCl_4} \times 100\% = \frac{142}{154} \times 100\% \approx 92\%$$

10. The answer is C. In the question, the percentage compositions of nitrogen and oxygen are given. With that information, we have to find the formula of that compound. Just as discussed in our review, assume that we have 100 grams of this compound. If there are 100 grams, logically it should contain 63.6 grams of nitrogen and 36.4 grams of oxygen.

Step 1

$$\# \text{ of moles of nitrogen} = \frac{63.6}{14} \approx 4.5 \text{ moles of nitrogen}$$

$$\# \text{ of moles of oxygen} = \frac{36.4}{16} \approx 2.275 \text{ moles of oxygen}$$

Step 2

Divide every number of moles with the smallest number of moles calculated in Step 1. Here the smaller one is 2.275. Divide both mole numbers by 2.275. This will give you the simplest ratio between them.

$$\text{Nitrogen} \quad \frac{4.5}{2.275} \approx 2 \qquad\qquad \text{Oxygen} \quad \frac{2.275}{2.275} \approx 1$$

Since the ratio of nitrogen to oxygen is 2:1, the compound is N_2O.

11. The answer is B. Reaction 2 is a typical example of a combustion reaction.

12. The answer is C.

$$2C_2H_6 \quad + \quad 7O_2 \quad \longrightarrow \quad 4CO_2 \quad + \quad 6H_2O$$

Reaction 2

According to Reaction 2, two moles of ethane will react with 7 moles of oxygen to form 4 moles of carbon dioxide and 6 moles of water. In the question, it is given that 54 g of water was formed. This corresponds to 3 moles of water. From the equation, we can say that 1 mol of ethane must have reacted to form 3 moles of water. We can also say that 3.5 moles of oxygen must have reacted in the formation of 3 moles of water. The last step is the conversion of moles to grams. The corresponding quantities in grams are 30 g of ethane and 112 g of oxygen.

13. The answer is B. From the question, we can say that the empirical formula of dextrose is CH_2O. The molecular weight of dextrose is also given. Let's first calculate the weight of the empirical

formula. Maybe the empirical formula represents the actual formula. The weight of the empirical formula is 30 g/mol. But the question says it is 180 g/mol. In this case, the molecular formula is not the same as the empirical formula. By dividing the actual weight by the empirical weight, we will get the coefficient with which we have to multiply the empirical formula to get the actual formula. The coefficient is 180/30 = 6. So the molecular formula is $C_6H_{12}O_6$. Have you heard of glucose? Well, dextrose is the same thing. If you knew that, you could have picked the answer right away. But more importantly, it is the process that you have to learn from this question.

14. The answer is C. The formula of methane is CH_4. The molecular weight is 16 g/mol. We have 40 g of methane. That means we have 2.5 moles of methane. So the number of hydrogen atoms can be calculated.

$$6.0 \times 10^{23} \times 2.5 \text{ moles} \times 4 \text{ hydrogen atoms/mol} = 6.0 \times 10^{24} \text{ atoms}$$

Chapter 2 Solutions

1. The answer is D. This question tests your understanding of the general classification of reactions. The reaction is clearly not a combustion reaction. Combustion reactions occur in the presence of oxygen and involve release of heat. There is no indication of that in the given reaction. You might be tempted to select Choice C since the given reaction is a replacement reaction, but double-replacement reaction best describes the given reaction. In the reaction, the iodine is replaced with the chlorine, and the chlorine is replaced with the iodine.

2. The answer is C. Choices A, B, and D are all acid-base reactions, which are neutralization reactions. Choice C is actually the formation of a base ($AlOH_3$), and it is not a neutralization reaction.

3. The answer is B. Let's start balancing the equation from the sulfate point of view. You have 3 sulfate groups in aluminum sulfate. It has to come from the sulfuric acid. So the coefficient is 3 for the sulfuric acid. Since there are 2 aluminums in aluminum sulfate, we can assign a coefficient of 2 to the aluminum hydroxide. The rest of the hydrogens and oxygens can be balanced with water.

The balanced equation should look like this:

$$3 H_2SO_4 + 2 Al(OH)_3 \longrightarrow 6 H_2O + Al_2(SO_4)_3$$

4. The answer is B. First, we have to check whether the given reaction is balanced. Without the balanced equation, the calculations will be incorrect. As a matter of fact, the given reaction is not balanced. The balanced equation is this:

$$2 NaCl + H_2SO_4 \longrightarrow Na_2SO_4 + 2 HCl$$

Now we can work out our magic calculations. The question specifies the grams of HCl synthesized. The 73 grams converted to moles should give 2 moles. According to the equation, 2 moles of NaCl are required to synthesize two moles of HCl. All you have to do now is to convert moles to grams. The correct value is 117 grams of NaCl.

5. The answer is D. This is a straightforward definition-type question. The ions that are present in the solution sometimes do not actually participate in the reaction. By writing the complete ionic equation of such a reaction, we can see that the spectator ions on both sides of the equation are in the same state or form. We can cancel them out and get the net equation of the reaction. Spectator ions are not usually depicted in the net ionic equation.

6. The answer is D. This is also a definition-type question. Amphoteric substances can exhibit both acidic and basic properties depending on the environment that they are subjected to.

7. The answer is D. The reaction mentioned in this question is the rusting of iron. The balanced reaction should look like this:

$$4\,Fe + 3\,O_2 \longrightarrow 2\,Fe_2O_3$$

8. The answer is D. The question tests your understanding of the concept of mole. In Choice A, we have 32 g of O_2 which corresponds to 1 mol of oxygen, and 32 g of SO_2 which corresponds to half a mol. Choice A is not correct. In Choice B, we have 49 g of NO_2 which corresponds to a little more than 1 mol, and 40 g of NaOH which corresponds to 1 mol. So this may be our answer. Choice C is not correct, because we have 20 g of HF which is 1 mol, and 36 g of water which is 2 moles. So Choice C is incorrect. Choice D has 60 g of C_2H_6 which is 2 moles, and 156 g of C_6H_6 is also 2 moles. So D is a better choice than B.

9. The answer is B. To answer this question, you have to use your intuition. The reaction occurs by means of the heat supplied to the aluminum hydroxide, and it is a dehydration reaction. So the most plausible answer is water.

10. The answer is D. The reactant coefficients in a balanced equation cannot be used to determine the identity of the limiting reagent. Without comparing the amounts of reactants that are actually present, we cannot determine the identity of the limiting reagent. CO being a gas has nothing to do with being the limiting reagent for the given reaction. Choice C is not logical, because it is a product. The best answer is that we cannot determine the identity of the limiting reagent, if any, without any data regarding the amount of reactants used.

11. The answer is C. Look at the items one by one. Item I says that the second student had the highest yield of products. In Experiment 1, the first student used 40.5 g of Al and 80 g of Fe_2O_3. This translates to 1.5 moles of Al and roughly 0.5 moles of Fe_2O_3. Here Fe_2O_3 is the limiting reagent. What was the second student doing? Well, the second student increased the amount of Fe_2O_3 used, keeping the same amount of Al. Since Fe_2O_3 is the limiting reagent, an increase of Fe_2O_3 will increase the product yield. So the second student must have had more yield than the first student. The first and the third students have the same yield for aluminum oxide, because the amount of limiting reagent present is the same in both cases. So items I and II are true.

12. The answer is C. By increasing the amount of aluminum used by the first student, there will not be an increase in the yield because Fe_2O_3 is the limiting reagent. Hence, Choice A is not correct. The same reasoning rules out Choice B. Increasing the amount of Fe_2O_3 by the second student will increase the yield further, because we actually have unreacted Al left according to the amounts used in the experiment. Hence, if we further increase the amount of Fe_2O_3 used, it will increase the yield until the Al runs out. Choice D is wrong.

13. The answer is A. In the question, we are given that 80 g of Fe_2O_3 is used in the reaction mixture. How much of this actually reacted is another story. That is to be found out from the yield data. The amount of CO_2 produced is 22 g. Based on the balanced equation, we can infer that for every 3 moles of CO reacted, 3 moles of CO_2 are produced. So CO and CO_2 have a 1:1 ratio. If 22 g or 0.5 moles of CO_2 is produced, 0.5 moles of CO must have reacted.

14. The answer is B. Based on the question, we can say that about 0.5 mol of Fe_2O_3 and 0.5 mol CO was present in the reacting mixture. Since the Fe_2O_3 to CO reacting ratio is 1:3, CO will completely react, and there will be some leftover unreacted Fe_2O_3 after the reaction is complete. So the limiting reagent is CO.

15. The answer is B. This question tests your understanding of the mole concept. Since we have excess amounts of Fe_2O_3, we do not have to worry about it. But, what you should consider is that the amount of CO present dictates the reaction. One mol of CO_2 contains Avogadro number (6.02×10^{23}) of molecules. The reaction results in 0.1 mol of CO_2. So 0.1 mol of CO_2 contains 6.02×10^{22} molecules.

Chapter 3 Solutions

1. The answer is A. The correct order of filling from $3s$ onward is $3s$, $3p$, $4s$, $3d$, and $4p$. For the MCAT, you must know the order of filling of subshells.

2. The answer is D. Inert gases (noble gases) have the completed outermost s and p subshells. Helium is an exception to this.

3. The answer is D. The atomic number of Kr (krypton) is 36. After the representation of Kr, how many electrons do we have? There are 14 more electrons. That adds up to an atomic number of 50. The atomic number 50 corresponds to the element Sn.

4. The correct answer is B. This is a straightforward question. The maximum number of electrons that can occupy the principal energy level is calculated using the formula $2n^2$.

5. The answer is C. The statement "no two electrons of an atom can have the same set of four quantum numbers" is Pauli exclusion principle.

6. The answer is C. The only correct statement in the set of choices is "the $5d$ subshell has higher energy than the $6s$ subshell." All other choices are wrong.

7. The answer is D. The question asks us to pick the species that is not isoelectronic (same number of electrons) with the noble gases. In order to solve this problem, you have to find the number of electrons present in them, and if it matches with the number of electrons in any of the noble gases, you can eliminate that choice. All the ions match with one or the other noble gas in terms of the number of electrons, except Mg^+.

8. The answer is D. The nitrogen atom has a total of 7 electrons. The principal quantum number could be 1 or 2. With that alone, we cannot rule out any of the choices. The next quantum number given is the azimuthal quantum number, also known as the angular momentum quantum number. The angular momentum quantum number can have values from 0 to $n-1$, where n represents the principal quantum number. Since 2 denotes the maximum n value, we cannot rule out any of the choices yet. Look at the next quantum number, which is the magnetic quantum number. The magnetic quantum number can have values from $-l$ to $+l$, where l represents angular momentum quantum number. So the magnetic quantum number cannot be +2 for nitrogen.

9. The answer is A. This question tests your ability to recognize a given electronic configuration. The fastest way to approach this type of question is to look at the root element given. The atomic number of argon is 18. We can count 14 more electrons in the given configuration to get a total of 32 electrons. The atomic number 32 is that of germanium (Ge).

10. The answer is B. Osmium, silver, and radium can have the $4d$ subshell. Copper belongs to the 4th period and therefore cannot have a $4d$ subshell. All the other elements listed belong to the periods 5, 6 and 7.

Chapter 4 Solutions

1. The answer is B. Sulfur belongs to Group VIA (the representative elements). The inner transition elements are the group of elements that are in the two rows below the main section of the periodic table. The transition elements range from IB through VIIB including the collective group of elements under Group VIII (not the zero group). Choices A and B are ruled out. Sulfur is not classified as a metal. This rules out Choice D.

2. The answer is C. The Group IA metals are collectively called the alkaline metals. The Group IIA metals are the alkaline earth metals. Among the choices, only strontium belongs to this group.

3. The answer is D. Electronegativity increases from left to right along the rows. For this question let's rephrase this trend. Electronegativity decreases from right to left along the columns, and from top to bottom.

4. The answer is B. The f block contains the inner-transition elements. The only element that is listed among the choices that is an inner-transition element is uranium.

5. The answer is C. This question can be answered on the basis of trivial knowledge. Oxygen, nitrogen, and chlorine are diatomic gases. Neon is a noble gas (zero group element) which is stable on its own.

6. The answer is D. This question tests your knowledge of a periodic trend. Here, the trend of atomic radius is asked. Along a period as the atomic number increases, the atomic radius decreases. Down a group, the atomic radius increases.

7. The answer is A. This question is similar to the previous one. It is again just a matter of comparing the size of the atoms according to the periodic trend of the atomic radius.

8. The answer is D. All the trends listed as choices are wrong. Along a period from left to right, the atomic radius decreases. So Choice A is incorrect. Along a period from left to right, the ionization energy increases. This rules out Choice B. The electronegativity of elements decreases from right to left along a period. Since Choice C contradicts this, it is incorrect.

9. The answer is D. HF is a weak acid and all the other choices are strong acids. This rules out Choice A. Among the other choices, HI is the strongest acid because it can give off the protons more easily than any of the other acids listed. The order of acidity is HI > HBr > HCl.

10. The answer is B. The given configuration is that of Group IVA (carbon family).

Chapter 5 Solutions

1. The answer is A. The central atom of the structure is sulfur. So draw the skeletal (structural) framework. In this structure, sulfur doesn't have the octet. So the next move is to introduce a double bond.

2. The answer is D. Let us look at the choices one by one. The water molecule is a bent molecule. So there is good reason to believe that it has a net nonzero dipole moment. In HCl, the hydrogen-chlorine bond is a polar bond, and thus there is clearly a separation of charge. This means it has a dipole moment. Oxygen is more electronegative than carbon. This creates a charge separation in the CO molecule. Thus the oxygen has a partial negative charge. So CO is a good candidate, having a net nonzero dipole moment. The CH_4 molecule has a tetrahedral structure and the small individual dipoles cancel out. So the net dipole of methane is zero.

3. The answer is B. The electronegativity difference between the nitrogen and the oxygen in NO_2 is not enough to cause an ionic interaction. Hence, it is not an ionic bond. The correct answer is covalent bond, because the bond is formed by the sharing of electrons between the nitrogen and the oxygen.

4. The answer is A. Ammonia (NH_3) and boron trifluoride (BF_3) can undergo a special type of covalent bonding – coordinate covalent bond. Even though this is a covalent bond, the electrons for the bond formation are supplied by one of the partners involved in the bonding. Boron has only three electrons in its outermost shell and they are already involved in the formation of the BF_3 molecule itself. There are no more electrons available from boron. But that is not the case with the nitrogen atom in NH_3. Two lone electrons are available from the nitrogen in NH_3 which make this bond formation possible.

5. The answer is A. To answer this question, we have to use our intuition. We do not have any specific data on any of the compounds listed as choices. But we can do an intelligent elimination. Choices B and D have the same zero dipole moment. Now it is just a matter of deciding which one of the remaining choices (A and C) is the answer. The electronegativity of fluorine is higher than that of bromine. So HF has the highest dipole moment.

6. The answer is B. BCl_3 can be drawn as shown below. The geometry is trigonal planar.

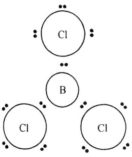

7. The answer is D. If you draw the electron-dot structure of the CCl_4 molecule, you can see that there are four electron pairs around the central carbon atom. All these electrons form four carbon-chlorine bonds which make the molecular geometry – tetrahedral.

8. The answer is A. The Lewis structure of the nitrate ion is shown. By analyzing the Lewis structure, the best prediction is that the nitrate ion is trigonal planar.

9. The answer is C.

10. The answer is D. All the statements (I, II, III, and IV) are correct. Let's see why this is the case. All the individual bonds in both compounds are dipoles. This makes items I and II correct. The question says that both molecules are tetrahedral. Hence, these individual bond dipoles cancel out to give a net zero dipole.

11. The answer is C. An ionic bond is formed mainly when there is a noticeable electronegativity difference between the atoms. Usually ionic bonds have the highest electronegativity difference. Choice A is incorrect. Covalently bonded atoms have lesser electronegativity difference. Among Choices B and C, nonpolar covalent bonds obviously have the least electronegativity difference. So our answer is C. Choice D is not true in this case. We do not need any more data to predict this general trend.

12. The answer is C. For Compound A, we should compare the atoms involved in the bond in question. Chlorine is more electronegative than boron. This rules out Choices B and D. For Compound B, the bond dipole should be directed toward the carbon atom. This rules out Choices A and D. So the only choice which has not been ruled out is C.

13. The answer is D. This question is a bit tricky. Many students will quickly select angular as the answer. But you have to be careful. The question is not asking for the molecular geometry of water. It is actually asking for the electronic orientation or electronic geometry of water which is tetrahedral. The four electron pairs (two bonded pairs and two lone pairs) of the water molecule result in a tetrahedral geometry. Moreover, Choices A and B are essentially the same. If one is not correct, the other cannot be correct either.

Chapter 6 Solutions

1. The answer is C. First, we should write the balanced equation. Without the balanced equation there is a good chance we might choose the incorrect answer.

$$2\,NO\ (g)\ +\ O_2\,(g)\ \longrightarrow\ 2\,NO_2\,(g)$$

According to the balanced equation, 2 liters of NO react with 1 liter of O_2 to give 2 liters of NO_2. According to the question, 4 liters of NO_2 were formed. By taking proportionality, we can say that 4 liters of NO and 2 liters of O_2 must have reacted so far.

2. The answer is B. Density is mass per unit volume. Since we know the density and the volume, we can find the weight of the gas. Since this represents 1 mol of the gas, that itself is its molecular weight.

$$\text{Molecular weight of the gas } = 1.8\ \frac{g}{L}\ \times\ 45\ \frac{L}{mol}\ =\ 81\ g\,/\,mol$$

3. The answer is C. One mol of an ideal gas occupies 22.5 L at STP. From the density-volume-mass relationship, we can find the mass of 1 mol of this gas. We know both the density and the volume of the gas.

$$\text{Weight of the gas} = 1.4\ \text{g}/\text{L} \times 22.5\ \text{L}/\text{mol} = 31.5\ \text{g}/\text{mol}$$

This molecular weight is closest to that of oxygen.

4. The answer is B. The objective of this question is to convert the given pressure value (in mmHg) to Pascal units. In order to do this, we should first convert the given value into atmospheres. Since one atm equals 760 mmHg, 1330 mmHg equals 1.75 atm. The conversion of atmospheres to Pascal units is given in the question. The conversion is:

$$1.75\ \text{atm} = 1.75\,\text{atm}\ \times\ 101.3\ \text{kPa}\ =\ 1.8 \times 10^2\ \text{kPa}\ =\ 1.8 \times 10^5\ \text{Pa}$$

5. The answer is B. This is a simple conversion problem that every MCAT student should know and do without any reference. This conversion should come automatically

$$273 - 27 = 246\ \text{K}$$

6. The answer is A. The given quantity of CO_2 corresponds to 0.26 mol. This quantity of CO_2 will occupy $0.26 \times 22.5 \approx 5.9$ L. If you still don't understand this type of calculation, review the chapter again.

7. The answer is B. Gases best behave the most ideally under conditions such as high temperature and low pressure. Choice D is wrong. The passage makes the behavior of gases very clear: They depend on the prevailing temperature and pressure.

8. The answer is C. By rearranging the ideal gas equation, we can find the correct unit of the gas constant.

9. The answer is A. The question is asking for effusion rates of SO_2 and O_2. The rate of effusion of a molecule is inversely proportional to the square root of its molecular weight. The problem should be solved as follows:

$$\frac{\text{Rate of } SO_2 \text{ effusion}}{\text{Rate of } O_2 \text{ effusion}} = \sqrt{\frac{\text{Mol. wt of } O_2}{\text{Mol. wt of } SO_2}} = \sqrt{\frac{32}{64}} \approx 0.7$$

10. The answer is A. A value of zero alone will not ensure ideal behavior. So gas A does not behave ideally. Hence item I is correct. Item II contradicts what we just said. We cannot say whether gas A is xenon. So item III is not a valid statement.

11. The answer is D. The clues to answer this question have to be taken from the given data. What can we infer from the data given about halogens? The correction factor of fluorine is 1.170 L^2.atm/mol^2. The correction factor of chlorine is 6.340 L^2.atm/mol^2. By analyzing the trend, we can deduce that bromine must have a correction factor that is higher than that of chlorine. The only value that is higher than that of chlorine is 9.80 L^2.atm/mol^2. Hence, the best choice is D. If you were looking at the values of b, you probably did not notice the units represented in the answers. All units correspond to that of constant a and not of b.

12. The answer is D.

13. The answer is D. According to the kinetic-molecular theory, all the items are true.

Chapter 7 Solutions

1. The answer is D. The conversion of a gas to a solid is called deposition. Sublimation is the conversion of a solid to a gas. Condensation is the conversion of a gas to a liquid. Freezing is the conversion of a liquid to a solid.

2. The answer is B. Vaporization, sublimation, and melting require heat (consume heat). The only process listed which releases heat is condensation.

3. The answer is D. Potassium fluoride is an ionic compound. See the chapter for descriptions of all types of solids.

4. The answer is C. In order to answer this question we have to think in terms of ionic bonding. What enables the formation of an ionic bond in the first place? The electronegativity differences between the bonded atoms make ionic bonds possible. It is in fact the electrostatic forces that hold the atoms involved in an ionic bond.

5. The answer is B. To answer this question, we need to recall some basic aspects regarding phase diagrams. Just by knowing those, we can eliminate some of the choices right away. In Choices A and D, the phases are wrongly labeled. The phases are correctly labeled only in Choices B and C. This rules out Choices A and D. Water has some anomalous properties. Such properties make water unique. In fact, the solid-liquid segment in the phase diagram of water has a negative slope.

6. The answer is B. See the explanation for Question 5.

7. The answer is B. The question describes a phase change scenario based on the diagram given in the passage. Substance M will be a liquid at point A. If the pressure is decreased, the most likely phase change will be from liquid (the phase before the change) to gas.

8. The answer is C. This is a definition-type question. The point indicated by the X mark is called "triple point." At the triple point of a substance, the three phases coexist at equilibrium. Below this point, the solid to gas conversion or vice versa is direct without the intermediate liquid phase.

9. The answer is C. The critical temperature is defined to be the temperature above which a gas cannot be changed into a liquid. The choice that best reflects this idea is C.

10. The answer is A. In the phase diagram given in the passage, locate the segment XZ. This segment separates the liquid and the gas phases.

Chapter 8 Solutions

1. The answer is C. Normality of a solution is the number of equivalents of solute per liter of solution.

2. The answer is A.

$$\text{The number of moles of glucose} = \frac{270 \text{ g}}{180 \text{ } g/mol} = 1.5 \text{ moles}$$

$$\text{Molarity} = \frac{\text{moles of solute}}{\text{liters of solution}} = \frac{1.5 \text{ moles}}{1 \text{ liter}} = 1.5 \text{ M.}$$

3. The answer is D. First, we should calculate the molar mass of HCl which is 36.5 g/mol. We have a 2.5 molar solution of HCl. That means every liter of the solution will have 2.5 moles of HCl. Here we have 1.25 L of the solution, and a total of 3.125 moles of HCl. That comes closest to $3.125 \times 36.5 = 114$ g.

4. The answer is B. We can equate the diluted solution with the stock solution as follows: (Molarity of solution made × Volume of solution made) is equal to (Molarity of the stock solution × Volume of the stock solution required). With this in mind, let's plug in the values that we know.

$$2\,M \times 30 \text{ ml} = 10\,M \times \text{Volume of the stock solution required}$$

We need not convert the milliliters into liters for this problem, because the molar units will cancel out.

$$\text{Volume of stock solution required} = \frac{2\,M \times 30\,ml}{10\,M} = 6\,ml$$

5. The answer is C. The quickest way to solve this problem is to calculate how many moles of NaCl are present in this solution. Then convert the number of moles to grams of NaCl. The correct answer is 5.1 g.

6. The answer is D. All the solubilities shown in the graph are endothermic. In fact most compounds (solids) dissolve endothermically. The graph shows that as the temperature increases, the solubility of the salts increases. In other words, as the temperature increases, more and more of the salt present is dissociated into ions. This is exactly how an endothermic process works.

7. The answer is D. The first step in answering this question is to find the molality of the solution. Then plug that number into the boiling-point-change equation given in the passage.

$$\text{Molality of the glucose solution} = \frac{315\,g\,C_6H_{12}O_6}{0.750\,kg\,H_2O} \times \frac{1\,mol\,C_6H_{12}O_6}{180\,g\,C_6H_{12}O_6} = 2.33\,m$$

$$\Delta T_b = K_b\,m = (0.512^0\,C/m)(2.33\,m) = 1.2^0\,C.$$

The answer is $100^0\,C + 1.2^0\,C = 101.2^0\,C.$

8. The answer is B. The observed changes in colligative properties are less than what was theoretically predicted. This is because the ionization of salts in water is not as complete as we expect. Some of the oppositely charged ions stick together and function as a unit. So the number of particles (units) is lower than what we expect. As the concentration increases, the possibility of the oppositely charged ions sticking together is greater than that in dilute solutions.

9. The answer is D. This question is a bit tricky. You may have selected Choice A. But you have to understand what exactly is asked in the question. The question is not asking about the change in boiling point (ΔT). Instead, it asks what happens to the boiling point. It will not double; it will only increase slightly.

10. The answer is C. Choice C is the only true statement given. Looking closely at Choices A and B, you should realize that they represent the same relationship. Since you cannot have two correct answers, this rules out Choices A and B. Thus, such logical elimination-techniques can be used to solve many MCAT problems and save valuable time.

Chapter 9 Solutions

1. The answer is B. This question tests your understanding of the concept of pH. You also have to use some mathematical skill to answer this question, since you are not allowed to use a calculator.

$$pH = -\log[H^+]$$

To get the hydrogen ion (hydronium or H_3O^+) concentration, we have to take the antilog. If the pH were 2, the molar concentration would have been 10^{-2}. If the pH were 3, the molar concentration would have been 10^{-3}. Since the pH is 2.5, the best choice is 3.2×10^{-3}.

2. The answer is C. NaCl is a salt. Think about its source. NaCl is a salt of sodium hydroxide and hydrogen chloride. NaOH is a strong base and HCl is a strong acid. A salt solution of a strong acid and a strong base is neutral.

3. The answer is D. An acid which can furnish more than one proton per molecule of the acid is called a "polyprotic acid." Choices A, B and C are all polyprotic acids. So the reasonable choice is 'none of the above.' Note that the question asked for an acid which is NOT a polyprotic acid. You should make a habit of underlining or circling key words in the question, especially when the question stem contains words such as "not, except, increasing, decreasing."

4. The answer is C. To answer this question, you have to manipulate the given equation.

The given equation is:

$$pOH = pK_b + \log \frac{[\text{conjugate acid}]}{[\text{base}]}$$

$$pOH = -\log [OH^-]$$

$$pK_b = -\log [K_b]$$

$$-\log [OH^-] = -\log [K_b] + \log \frac{[\text{conjugate acid}]}{[\text{base}]}$$

$$\log [K_b] = \log [OH^-] + \log \frac{[\text{conjugate acid}]}{[\text{base}]}$$

$$\log [K_b] = \log [OH^-] - \log \frac{[\text{base}]}{[\text{conjugate acid}]}$$

5. The answer is C.

$$H_3PO_4 \xrightarrow{1} H^+ + H_2PO_4^-$$
$$\downarrow 2$$
$$H^+ + PO_4^{3-} \xleftarrow{3} HPO_4^{2-} + H^+$$

The choices are phosphoric acid and its dissociation products (see above). In a polyprotic acid, such as H_3PO_4, almost invariably the first dissociation will be of the highest degree. So the highest pKa is for HPO_4^{2-}. This is Choice C. For a comparison, the Ka values are given below. But as you know, we do not need them to answer this question.

$$H_3PO_4 \text{———} Ka_1 = 7.5 \times 10^{-3}$$
$$H_2PO_4^- \text{———} Ka_2 = 6.2 \times 10^{-8}$$
$$HPO_4^{2-} \text{———} Ka_3 = 3.6 \times 10^{-11}$$

6. The answer is A. The question asks for the net ionic equation of the given acid-base equation. The given reaction is a strong acid-strong base reaction.

7. The answer is A. For this question, we are looking for a strong acid-strong base curve. Why? Well, the answer is simple. In Reaction 1, we have a strong monoprotic acid ($HClO_4$) reacting against a strong base (NaOH). The only curve that satisfies this criterion is given in Choice A.

8. The answer is D. In this question, we are asked to analyze the upper and lower limit ratios of base-to-acid at the best buffering pH. How can we answer this question? Well, there are some clues in the passage. According to the passage, the effective pH range of a buffer system is between pKa − 1 and pKa + 1. What other relevant information do we have in the passage? The passage also gives us an equation with which we can relate the pH and the pKa.

$$pH = pKa + \log \frac{[A^-]}{[HA]}$$

In order to have a pH value of pKa − 1, the second half of the equation with the log should be negative 1. For this the base-acid ratio should be 0.1; log 0.1 = −1. For the other criterion pKa + 1, the log value should be +1. For this, the ratio should be 10.

9. The answer is B. This is a straight forward question. The question asks for the pH of a solution of HCl. HCl is a strong acid, and strong acids completely ionize. So we don't have to worry about partial ionization such as in weak acids.

$$pH = -\log[H^+] = 3.2 \times 10^{-4} \approx 3.5$$

10. The answer is B. This is actually one way of defining pKa value. At the pKa value, the acid-base ratio is 1. So the best answer is Choice B. In addition, it is near the pKa value that the solution will have its best buffering capacity. So Choice D wrong.

Chapter 10 Solutions

1. The answer is A. "Bomb calorimeter" is a device used to determine the energy changes that are associated with reactions by measuring the amount of heat generated or absorbed by a reaction at constant volume. The changes (measurements) are made at constant temperature and constant volume. There is nothing true about Choice B. Keeping the volume constant is not an impossible task! This rules out Choice B. Choice C is wrong, since there is no change in volume, and theoretically there is no work done.

2. The answer is B. The figure shows the conversion of ice (*s*) to water (*l*). The process is melting. What happens when a solid is converted to its liquid form? There will be an increase in randomness. This rules out Choice D. Choice C doesn't make any sense. Since the randomness is increased, the entropy is increased.

3. The answer is C. The change in free energy (ΔG) is related to enthalpy and entropy by the following equation:

$$\Delta G = \Delta H - T \Delta S$$

In this question, the change in free energy is zero. This means that there is no <u>net</u> transfer of free energy. This in turn means that the forward and backward reactions are both favorable and thus the reacting system is in equilibrium.

4. The answer is D. This question tests your knowledge and ability to make reasonable judgements based on a limited amount of information. We are given only an equation and a description of that equation. Without further data on this reaction, we cannot be sure whether the reaction is exothermic or endothermic. We cannot say whether the reaction is spontaneous or nonspontaneous without pertinent data. Choice C is untrue.

5. The answer is C. According to the third law of thermodynamics, the entropy of a pure, crystalline substance at 0 K is zero.

Chapter 11 Solutions

1. The answer is D. The equilibrium constant is the equilibrium molar concentrations of the products raised to their corresponding coefficients, divided by concentrations of the reactants raised to their corresponding coefficients. The coefficients can be taken directly from the balanced equation of the reaction.

$$N_2 (g) + 3 H_2 (g) \rightleftharpoons 2 NH_3 (g)$$

The equilibrium expression is:

$$K = \frac{[NH_3]^2}{[N_2][H_2]^3}$$

2. The answer is C. From the given equation, we can write the general form of the rate as:

$$\text{Rate} = k [X]^m [Y]^n$$

Our next step is to find m and n using the given information. Examining the first and the second experiments shows that the concentration of X is kept constant, but the concentration of Y is doubled. When the concentration of Y is doubled, the rate also is doubled. So the order (n) with respect to Y is 1. Now compare experiments 2 and 3. In experiments 2 and 3, the concentration of Y is kept constant, but the concentration of X is doubled. This time, the rate is quadrupled. Hence, the order (m) with respect to X should be 2. So the correct expression is Rate = k [X]² [Y].

3. The answer is D. This question tests your basic understanding of the factors that affect the rate of reactions. All the listed factors can influence the rate of reactions.

4. The answer is D. This is the potential energy diagram of a reaction. For the MCAT, you should be familiar with diagrams of this type. Since the direction of the reaction-coordinate is indicated in the diagram, we can predict the potential energy level of the reactants and the products. The bump in the graph represents the activation energy of the reaction. So Choice A doesn't make any sense. According to Choice B, there is a net absorption of energy. But in contrast to this statement, there is a net release of energy. This prediction is based on the fact that the energy level of the products is below that of the reactants. This makes Choice C wrong. That leaves us with Choice D. In fact the diagram is that of an exothermic reaction.

5. The answer is A. Catalysts can change the rate of reactions, by decreasing the activation energy. Catalysts are not consumed by the reactants. If a substance is consumed in the process, it cannot be a catalyst.

6. The answer is B. According to the question, the reverse reaction of Reaction 1 is endothermic. This means the forward reaction is exothermic. For exothermic reactions, the ΔH is negative.

7. The answer is C. In the experiment, the hydrogen is removed. Such a change in concentration will upset the equilibrium. We have to approach this problem in terms of LeChatelier's principle. Changes in the concentrations of reactants or products of this reaction will turn the system into a non-equilibrium state. The result will be an adjustment of the reaction mode to restore the system to equilibrium. So if we take H_2 away, the backward reaction will be favored for restoring the equilibrium.

8. The answer is C. The pressure is decreased in the system. Such a decrease in pressure will not change the reaction mode. Let's take a look at the reacting system.

$$H_2 \; + \; I_2 \; \rightleftharpoons \; 2HI \qquad \text{(Reaction 1)}$$

Both sides of the equation have equal number of moles – two on the reactant side and two on the product side. So the pressure change will not affect the reaction in this case.

9. The answer is C.

$$N_2\,(g) \; + \; 3H_2(g) \; \rightleftharpoons \; 2NH_3\,(g) \qquad \text{(Reaction 2)}$$

In Reaction 2, a pressure change will affect the reaction. Here, the pressure is increased and that will increase the forward reaction. In other words, the reaction shifts to the right. Item I says that the reaction shifts to the right. But for the wrong reason. According to the equation, we have more moles on the reactant side. So item I is not fully correct. Item II is also ruled out because the reaction shifts to the right. Item III makes perfect sense.

10. The answer is D.

11. The answer is B. There are 2.5 moles (70 g) of nitrogen. The amount of H_2 used should also be taken into account. According to the question, 10 g of hydrogen was used, which is equivalent to 5 moles. So the hydrogen acts as the limiting reagent. By the reaction of 5 moles of hydrogen with excess of nitrogen, the number of moles of ammonia produced should equal 10/3 moles. Now, it is a matter of converting moles to grams.

$$\frac{10}{3} \text{ moles} \times \frac{17 \text{g NH}_3}{1 \text{ mol NH}_3} \approx 57 \text{ grams}$$

12. The answer is B. Entropy is a thermodynamic quantity which measures the randomness in a system. An increase in randomness means an increase in the entropy. In general, gas phase has a higher entropy than liquid phase, and liquid phase has a higher entropy than solid phase. But in this reaction, all the components are in their gas phases, and the reactant side has more of them. The production of ammonia causes the entropy to decrease because there is less randomness than before the reaction began.

13. The answer is D. We cannot predict the spontaneity of the reaction accurately based on the information given in the passage. The only fact that we know regarding the reaction is that it has a ΔH value of −92 kJ. Based on that alone, it is not possible to predict the spontaneity accurately.

Chapter 12 Solutions

1. The answer is C. A redox equation is represented in the question. The electrode potential of the reaction is also given. The question also says that the reaction occurred spontaneously. For the given direction of the reaction, the electrode potential is negative. So the reaction must have taken place in the opposite direction of what is given in the question and thus had a positive potential. A net positive potential means a negative free energy change. A negative free energy change denotes spontaneity. We can rewrite the equation:

$$\text{Zn } (s) + \text{Sn}^{2+} \longrightarrow \text{Zn}^{2+} (s) + \text{Sn } (s)$$

$$E^o = +0.62 \text{ V}$$

Now we have a positive voltage, where the zinc is oxidized and a tin ion is reduced. Oxidation of zinc means it is losing electrons. Recall that oxidation is losing electrons, and reduction is gaining electrons.

2. The answer is A. In the half-reaction, chromium is going from a +2 oxidation state to a +3 oxidation state. This is oxidation. Oxidation involves the losing of electrons. You can also predict this by simply examining the increase in oxidation number (+2 to +3), which is a result of oxidation. Oxidation occurs at the anode, whereas reduction occurs at the cathode.

3. The answer is D. Based on the given information in the question, we can say that E^o is directly related to K. The question also says that the product concentrations are greater than the reactant concentrations. So we can say that the equilibrium constant value is greater than 1. We can rule out Choice A, because there is no such thing as a negative concentration. So K cannot be negative anyway. Since we know that K is greater than 1, the natural logarithm of K will be positive. So from the equation, we can say that E^o cannot be negative, which rules out Choice B. Hence, the E^o value should be positive. The change in free energy, $\Delta G = - n \, F \, E^o$. From this equation, we can predict that if the overall potential (E^o) is positive, the change in free energy (ΔG) is negative. A negative ΔG means that the reaction is spontaneous.

4. The answer is C. Ampere is defined as the total amount of charge that flows per second.

$$\text{Ampere} \; = \; \frac{\text{Coulombs}}{\text{seconds}}$$

The charge in coulombs = 5 A × 3.5 min. × 60 s/ 1 min. = 1050 coulombs.

5. The answer is B. For a reaction to be spontaneous, the electrode potential should be positive. Oxidation of copper has a negative electrode potential. That rules out Choice A. Oxidation of fluoride ion and reduction of zinc ion have negative electrode potentials, which rules out Choices C and D respectively. The reduction of chlorine represented below has a positive potential which indicates spontaneity.

$$Cl_2 + 2\,e \longrightarrow 2\,Cl \qquad E^o \, (V) = \; +1.36$$

6. The answer is D. The two half-reactions can be written as shown below:

$$Ni \longrightarrow Ni^{2+} + 2\,e^{-} \qquad +0.25$$
$$Ag^{+} + \; \bar{e} \longrightarrow Ag \qquad +0.80$$
$$\overline{\phantom{Ag^{+} + \; \bar{e} \longrightarrow Ag \qquad }}$$
$$+1.05 \; V$$

Now, it is just a matter of adding the individual potentials to get the overall potential. A word of caution: when you add the individual half-electrode potentials, make sure that the appropriate sign has been assigned to them.

7. The answer is D. Even though a salt bridge allows an electrical connection between the two half-cells in a galvanic cell, the function of a salt bridge is not to conduct electricity. So Choice A is ruled out. Choice B makes no sense. The salt bridge does not control the voltage. The function of a salt bridge is to maintain electrical neutrality in the half-cells so that excess buildup of charge will not occur in the half-cells. If excess charge builds up in the half-cells, the reaction will slow down and quickly die out.

8. The answer is C. The question asks for the best oxidizing agent. An oxidizing agent gets reduced in the process. So the oxidizing agent (species) should be able to accept electrons with ease. The most positive reduction potential is that of chlorine (Cl_2), which makes chlorine the best oxidizing agent among the choices.

$$Cl_2 + 2\,\bar{e} \longrightarrow 2\,Cl^{-} \Longrightarrow \qquad + 1.36$$

9. The answer is B. The question asks for the species that has the highest <u>oxidation</u> potential. Oxidation is losing electrons. Thus all the half reactions should be considered in the oxidation sense. Since the table gives you reduction half-reactions, you have to reverse all the equations, and when you reverse the equations the sign of the potentials should also be reversed. The most positive value is that of the oxidation of potassium.

$$Cr \longrightarrow Cr^{3+} + 3\,\bar{e} \qquad\qquad +0.74\ V$$

$$K \longrightarrow K^{+} + \bar{e} \qquad\qquad +2.92\ V$$

$$Cr \longrightarrow Cr^{2+} + 2\,\bar{e} \qquad\qquad +0.34\ V$$

$$Ag \longrightarrow Ag^{+} + \bar{e} \qquad\qquad +0.80\ V$$

10. The answer is B. The process described in the question is Fe changing to Fe^{2+}, which is oxidation. Oxidation occurs at the anode and reduction occurs at the cathode.

Chapter 13 Solutions

1. The answer is B. We are asked to evaluate the radioactive change. The equation should look like this:

$$^{226}_{88}Ra \rightarrow\ ^{222}_{86}Rn\ +\ ^{4}_{2}He$$

Notice that the atomic and mass numbers decreased by 2 and 4 units, respectively. The helium nucleus shown in the equation is an alpha particle.

2. The answer is C. In the given radioactive decay, sodium is converted to neon. Notice that the atomic number decreased by one, but the mass number remained the same. The most likely particle that is emitted is a positron. A positron is a positively charged electron. The equation is shown below:

$$^{22}_{11}Na \rightarrow\ ^{22}_{10}Ne\ +\ ^{0}_{1}e^{+}\ +\ \gamma$$

A gamma particle is also emitted, but that information is not needed to answer this question.

3. The answer is A. This question tests your knowledge of common radioactive emissions. The only emission listed that is a high-energy electromagnetic radiation is the gamma ray. Electromagnetic rays travel at the speed of light. The only emission that travels close to the speed of light are beta particles. But the best choice is gamma ray. So the answer is A. In addition to the greater speed, gamma rays have the highest penetrating power.

4. The answer is C. See the explanation for Question 3.

5. The answer is D. This question tests your knowledge of the concept of half-life. Half-life is defined as the amount of time for a radioactive substance to decay to half its initial quantity. Since the half-life of substance X is 12 years, it takes twelve years for substance X to decay to half its initial quantity. We have 9 grams of substance X present. The amount of substance X that was originally present is 150 grams. So it must have undergone radioactive decay for at least four half-lives. Write the decay mode, starting from the original amount present.

$$150 \Rightarrow 75 \Rightarrow 37.5 \Rightarrow 18.75 \Rightarrow 9.375$$

Each arrow indicates one half-life, for a total of four half-lives. Since one half-life is 12 years, the total time elapsed is $12 \times 4 = 48$ years. The exact answer is a little above 48 years. But the approximation is correct since the choices are far apart and no values higher than 48 are given.

6. The answer is D. Half-life is the amount of time required for a radioactive substance to disintegrate to half its initial quantity. The sample described in the question has disintegrated to 3% of its original quantity. The disintegration can be analyzed as follows:

$$100\% \Rightarrow 50\% \Rightarrow 25\% \Rightarrow 12.5\% \Rightarrow 6.25\% \Rightarrow 3.125\%$$

This means, at least 5 half-lives must have elapsed.

7. The answer is A. A beta particle is an electron. By the emission of a β-particle, the nucleus must have changed into protactinium (Pa) which has atomic number 91. Remember that a β emission decreases the atomic number by one.

8. The answer is C. Since alpha particles are positively charged and beta particles are negatively charged, Choices A and B are true. Gamma rays are not deflected because they have no charge. Choice D is also true.

9. The answer is B. According to the figure given in the passage, as the number of protons increases the neutron-proton ratio increases and becomes greater than or equal to one. (Clue: Look at the slope)

10. The answer is D. The mass loss can be equated with the binding energy. In essence, mass loss can be calculated using the equation $E = mc^2$.

$$\text{Energy} = (3.1 \times 10^{-5} \text{ kg})(3 \times 10^8 \text{ m/s})^2 = 2.8 \times 10^{12} \text{ kg. m/s}^2 = 2.8 \times 10^{12} \text{ J}.$$

11. The answer is D.

$$^{232}_{90}\text{Th} \rightarrow \; ??? + \, ^{224}_{88}\text{Ra}$$

The question tests your ability to evaluate radioactive emissions by analyzing a given radioactive emission reaction. Notice that the atomic number decreased by 2 and the mass number decreased by 8. If two alpha particles were emitted, that would decrease the mass number to 224, because an alpha particle is a helium nucleus (^4_2He). It would also decrease the atomic number by 4. But apparently that is not the case here. The atomic number decrease by only 2. This can be accounted for if two β-particles were also emitted.

Chapter 14 Solutions

1. The answer is B. The carbon indicated by the arrow is an sp^2 hybridized carbon atom. Notice that the indicated carbon has a double bond and two single bonds. The double bond connects this carbon to the end-carbon. A hydrogen atom and the 3rd carbon are attached to this carbon via single bonds.

2. The answer is A. Acetylene is the first member of the alkyne group. The carbon-carbon bond is a triple bond which contains only one sigma bond.

3. The answer is B. The triple bond of 2-propyne (an alkyne) contains one sigma bond and two pi bonds.

4. The answer is C. The sp^3 hybrid orbitals such as those seen in alkanes have a tetrahedral orientation.

5. The answer is D. This question also tests your basic knowledge of hybridization in carbon compounds. A triple bond means three bonds. Since there are three bonds, six electrons are involved in the bond.

6. The answer is B. Methane has a tetrahedral geometry. So the hydrogen-carbon-hydrogen bond angle is closest to 109.5°.

7. The answer is C. The triple bond is the shortest among the bonds indicated by the arrows. The only triple bond-bearing compound given is Choice C.

8. The answer is B. The carbon-hydrogen bond is a single covalent bond.

Chapter 15 Solutions

1. The answer is B.

    To answer this question, we can use the following clues from the question:
    i) The compound is composed of only carbon and hydrogen atoms.
    ii) It is a saturated hydrocarbon.
    iii) It does not have a ring structure.
    So the compound is an alkane. Alkanes have the general formula C_nH_{2n+2}. Now this becomes a simple algebra problem. Since there are 14 hydrogens, 2n+2 = 14.

    $$So, n = \frac{14 - 2}{2} = 6.$$

2. The answer is A.

3. The answer is D. Constitution isomers are compounds with the same molecular formula, but differ in the order with which the atoms are bonded. This definition matches the relationship between n-butane and isobutane.

4. The answer is C. First, we have to number the carbon chain to get the longest possible chain in the structure. The numbering should be done in such a way that the branches will have the smallest substituent number. The numbering is done as follows:

There are 9 carbons in the parent chain. So the parent chain is clear and the complete name ends with "nonane." This rules out Choices A and B. There are 2 methyl groups on carbons 3 and 6. So the compound is 3,6-dimethyl nonane.

5. The answer is C. Butane contains 4 carbon atoms and if one mole of butane is completely combusted, at least 4 moles of carbon dioxide will be formed provided that there is enough oxygen.

6. The answer is B. A secondary carbon atom should be attached to two other carbon atoms. The carbon atoms indicated by arrows I and III are secondary carbon atoms.

7. The answer is A. A carbonium ion is the same as a carbocation. A carbocation is a positively charged species.

8. The answer is C. Gauche conformation is a form of staggered conformation. The conformation is Gauche if the relative separation of two substituents on adjacent atoms is 60°. The Newman representation of a Gauche conformation is shown:

Gauche

ANGLE OF TORSION IS 60^0

9. The answer is B. The angle closest to 109.5° is 110°. That is the most likely bond angle, having the least angle strain.

10. The answer is A. All the given choices are alkanes. Item I is an unbranched alkane. Items II, III, IV have increasing degrees of branching. Branching decreases the area of contact and thereby decreases the intermolecular interactions. So the unbranched alkane has the highest boiling point. Keep in mind that without actually measuring the properties, we can only compare compounds of comparable weights and number of carbons with reasonable accuracy.

11. The answer is D. The question asks for the type of force that is important with respect to alkanes. Alkanes cannot undergo hydrogen bonding. So Choice A is out. Choice B is generally not important in alkanes. Since there are no ionic bonds in an alkane, Choice C is wrong. The correct choice is Van der Waals forces.

12. The answer is D. To answer this question you have to do some intuitive thinking based on the information given in the passage. Butane is a four-carbon alkane with the formula C_4H_{10}. It is a bigger molecule than propane, but a smaller molecule than pentane. So the boiling point of butane should be between propane and pentane. We are talking in terms of the relative boiling points. But the question asks for the melting point. So let's translate this idea in terms of melting point. Obviously, the melting point of a substance should be below its boiling point. So the answer

cannot be either 37.5°C or 55.1°C. This rules out Choices A and B. Choice C is not a sensible answer because butane is a gas at 25°C.

13. The answer is C. Choice A is an initiation step. Choice B is a chain termination step. Choice D is also a chain termination step. The only choice which represents a chain propagation step is Choice C.

14. The answer is A. This question tests your knowledge of intermolecular forces and other interactions that give rise to some of the chemical and physical properties of compounds. Let's take a look at the compound 2,3-dimethylbutane. We do not have a clue about the precise properties of the compound asked in this question. But what we do know is the boiling point of one of its relatives. In the table given in the passage, we are told that the boiling point of 3-methylpentane is 63.3° C. If we compare these two compounds, we see that they have the same number of carbons and hydrogens – both are six-carbon alkanes. If the boiling point of 3-methylpentane is 63.3° C, then 2,3-dimethylbutane will have a boiling point lower than that. The only choice with a lower value is Choice A.

15. The answer is C. The only way to answer this question is to draw the possible isomers by trial and error. There is no choice other than drawing out the possible structures, starting from the straight chain form of heptane.

Chapter 16 Solutions

1. The answer is B. Acid-catalyzed dehydration of the alcohol shown will result in a mixture of alkenes. All the given choices are alkenes. But Choice B is different, because it has 8 carbons. The parent alcohol has only 7 carbons. So Choice B is not possible as one of the products. All the other compounds given are possible products because of the rearrangement involved in this type of reaction.

2. The answer is C. The question asks for the number of double bonds present in the unsaturated alkene that undergoes complete hydrogenation. Each double bond to be converted to a saturated bond requires 2 hydrogen atoms. If 8 moles of hydrogen (hydrogen is diatomic) is used per mole of the compound, the compound should have 8 double bonds.

3. The answer is D. Ozonolysis is a two-step reaction sequence in which carbonyl groups are generated. The double bonded carbon atoms become the carbon of the carbonyl groups that are created.

4. The answer is B. In this reaction, 2-butene is reacted with peroxyacetic acid. This reagent converts the alkene into an epoxide, which is a compound that has a three-sided ring with an oxygen atom in the ring.

5. The answer is C. This reaction (hydroboration-oxidation) involves the conversion of 1-butene into an alcohol by hydration. The hydration follows anti-Markovnikov's rule. There is no rearrangement in this reaction.

$$CH_3CH_2CH{=}CH_2 \xrightarrow[\text{2. } H_2O_2/ \, OH^-]{\text{1. } B_2H_6} CH_3CH_2CH_2CH_2OH$$

6. The answer is A. The heat of hydrogenation decreases as there are more and more substituents in the alkene group. Among the choices, the least amount of substitution is for ethylene.

7. The answer is A. The reaction between 1-propene and HBr in the presence of peroxides results in the addition of HBr into the alkene group. The addition follows anti-Markovnikov's rule. The reaction is shown below:

$$H_3CH_2C{=}CH_2 \longrightarrow H_3CH_2C\text{-}CH_2Br$$

8. The answer is B.

9. The answer is C. Since acid-catalyzed dehydration sequence may involve rearrangement depending on the alcohol involved, Choice A is wrong. Choice B is only partially correct. Even though it is true that there can be rearrangement, the process of rearrangement results in more stable intermediates rather than less stable intermediates. The major product is the most substituted product, because the most substituted product translates to higher stability.

10. The answer is B. Rearrangement is possible in acid-catalyzed dehydration of alcohols. The intermediate is a carbocation, not a carbanion. This eliminates statements I and III. Depending on the type of alcohol, the rearrangement may involve either methyl shift or hydride shift.

11. The answer is D. All the compounds listed in the choices can be synthesized by the oxidation of alkenes.

12. The answer is B.

13. The answer is B.

14. The answer is D.

These two products are *cis-trans* isomers and are commonly called *geometric isomers*.

15. The answer is B.

$$\underset{\text{HIGH}}{\text{Br}}\overset{\text{LOW}}{\underset{}{\text{H}_3\text{C}}}\text{C}=\text{C}\overset{\text{H}}{\underset{\text{NO}_2}{}}\underset{\text{HIGH}}{\text{LOW}}$$

The given structure has Z-configuration. Recall that the priorities are based on the atomic number of the atom bonded to the double bonded carbon.

Chapter 17 Solutions

1. The answer is B. The shortest bond here is the triple bond.

2. The answer is B.

> Bottle A – *cis*-2-Butene
> Bottle B – 1-Propyne
> Bottle C – Butene

Compare the carbon-carbon bonds that distinguish these compounds. *cis*-2-Butene is an alkene which has a carbon-carbon double bond. 1-Butyne is an alkyne and has a carbon-carbon triple bond and butane has carbon-carbon single bonds. The triple bonded carbon-carbon bonds have the highest bond dissociation energy. Bottle B contains 1-propyne.

3. The answer is C. Of the given choices, acetylene is the most acidic and has the lowest pKa value.

4. The answer is B. Lindlar catalyst is a combination catalyst which does selective or restrictive hydrogenation of alkynes to alkenes. Furthermore, the product is a cis-alkene.

5. The answer is C. When 1-butyne is treated with sulfuric acid in the presence of mercuric oxide as catalyst, hydration occurs. The hydration follows Markovnikov's rule and forms a ketone. The reaction is given below:

$$\text{HC}\equiv\text{CCH}_2\text{CH}_3 \xrightarrow[\substack{\text{Mercuric}\\\text{oxide}}]{\text{H}_2\text{SO}_4} \overset{\overset{\text{O}}{\|}}{\text{CH}_3\text{CCH}_2\text{CH}_3}$$
$$\text{2-Butanone}$$

6. The answer is D. When 3-hexyne undergoes ozonolysis, propanoic acid is formed.

$$\text{CH}_3\text{CH}_2\text{C}\equiv\text{CCH}_2\text{CH}_3 \xrightarrow[\text{2. H}_2\text{O}]{\text{1. O}_3} \text{CH}_3\text{CII}_2\text{COOH}$$

7. The answer is B.

The general structure of a vicinal dihalide:

$$R-\underset{\underset{X}{|}}{\overset{\overset{H}{|}}{C}}-\underset{\underset{X}{|}}{\overset{\overset{H}{|}}{C}}-R' \qquad X=\text{Halogen}$$

The double dehydrohalogenation (two dehydrohalogenations or eliminations) of vicinal dihalide results in an alkyne.

8. The answer is D. There is nothing there to dehydrate or dehydrohalogenate in an alkyne. This eliminates Choices A and B. Hydrolysis will not help the direct conversion of an alkyne to alkane. A simple hydrogenation is the best way to accomplish this conversion.

9. The answer is A. The liquid ammonia-sodium combination can be used to convert an alkyne to a *trans*-alkene. In essence, this reaction involves the restrictive hydrogenation of an alkyne to an alkene (*trans*-product).

10. The answer is D. Alkynes have higher boiling points than corresponding alkanes. So Choice A is true. Alkynes have *sp* hybridized carbons. So Choice B is true. Choice C is also true, since a terminal alkyne like acetylene can form acetylide ions when exposed to strong bases.

$$HC\equiv C\overset{-}{:} \qquad \text{(Acetylide ion)}$$

11. The answer is C. Alkynes are characterized by hybrid orbitals called *sp* orbitals. In the *sp* orbitals, there is 50% *s* character and 50% *p* character.

12. The answer is B.

Reaction 3

$$H_3CC\equiv CH \xrightarrow{\text{HBr}} H_3C\underset{}{\overset{\overset{Br}{|}}{C}}=CH_2$$

Alkynes, just like alkenes, can undergo addition reactions. Reaction 2 is a typical example of an addition reaction.

13. The answer is D.

$$HC\equiv CH \xrightarrow[\text{Liq.NH}_3]{\text{NaNH}_2} HC\equiv \overset{+}{C}\overset{-}{Na} \xrightarrow{\substack{n\text{-butyl} \\ \text{bromide}}} HC\equiv C(CH_2)_3CH_3$$

14. The answer is C. Oxidizing agents oxidize other compounds; they do not reduce! This rules out Choice D. Choice B does not make any sense either. The alkyne is not being reduced to an alkane, but is being reduced to an alkene. This is not the most reduced form. Choice A is incorrect. The function of quinoline is to moderate the activity of the catalyst so that the double bonded alkenes that are formed will not undergo further reduction to form alkanes. Moreover, quinoline is not the actual catalyst.

15. The answer is D. According to the passage, quinoline is a heterocyclic amine.

Quinoline

16. The answer is D. The product of this catalytic conversion reaction is a *trans*-alkene. The combination of reagents (group I metal with liquid ammonia) used is unique in the sense that the product formed is a *trans*-product. The intermediate involved in this reaction, called the alkenyl radical, readily forms the resulting *trans*-product.

Chapter 18 Solutions

1. The answer is B. Dimethylated benzenes are called xylenes.

CH₃

CH₃

CH₃

CH₃

CH₃

CH₃

CH₃

2. The answer is B.

The carbons in the benzene ring are *sp²* hybridized.

3. The answer is C. See explanation for Question 1.

Phenol   Benzoic acid   Toluene

4. The answer is B. For a compound to be aromatic, it should have 4n+2 number of pi electrons. So the numbers satisfying the 4n+2 condition are 2, 6, 10, 14, ... Four is not in this series and that is the answer.

5. The answer is A. This reaction is an electrophilic aromatic substitution reaction. The product formed is nitrobenzene. In the reaction, nitronium ion acts as the electrophile which attacks the benzene to form the cyclohexadienyl intermediate, followed by the elimination of the proton to form nitrobenzene. The reaction mechanism follows:

Cyclohexadienyl ion

6. The answer is D. This reaction is best described as a Friedel-Crafts alkylation reaction.

7. The answer is A. This reaction is commonly called the Clemmenson reaction.

8. The answer is D. The nitro group ($-NO_2$) is a strongly electron withdrawing group, and thus a meta deactivating group. So it favors meta substitutions the most.

9. The answer is C. The regioselectivity of halogens favor ortho/para positions. Halogens are electron withdrawing entities that are ortho/para directing and also deactivating groups.

10. The answer is B. The -CHO group present in the ring is best described as a meta-directing group. So the most likely position of substitution is the meta position.

11. The answer is D. This reaction is a Friedel-Crafts alkylation reaction. This rules out Choice A. In an alkylation reaction, there is a possibility of rearrangement. The primary alkyl halide (*n*-propyl chloride) can form secondary carbocations by rearrangement. To avoid this type of rearrangement, chemists often use Friedel-Crafts acylation reactions which do not involve rearrangement. The carbonyl group in the acylation product can be easily reduced to get the desired hydrocarbon.

12. The answer is A. An alkoxy group can be represented as -OR, where R stands for an alkyl group. It is an ortho/para-directing group and also a good activating group.

13. The answer is C. The substituent -OH is an ortho/para activator. The resulting product is a bromine substitution product. The only choice that fits the reasoning is C.

14. The answer is A. The reaction shown is neither an addition reaction, nor an elimination reaction. So the Choices B, C, and D can be ruled out. This is a typical electrophilic substitution reaction.

15. The answer is C. The inscribed circle stands for the pi-system of electrons present in the benzene ring. Let's be more precise: The circle represents the 6 pi electrons of the benzene ring. Choice D states "8 pi-electrons" which is wrong.

16. The answer is D. To answer this question, we have to think about the substituent; the nitro group. The nitro group is a meta deactivating group. So the substitution predominantly results in a meta-product (1,3 substituted). According to the passage, compound C is the major product.

Chapter 19 Solutions

1. The answer is B. Enantiomers are non-superimposable mirror images. These compounds are enantiomers.

2. The answer is A. The two compounds are stereoisomers. To be precise, they are diastereomers. Diastereomers are not mirror images. Hence, the two compounds given are not mirror images.

3. The answer is D. Since the enantiomer is what is asked for, the answer can be ascertained by visualizing the mirror image.

4. The answer is C. The given representation is called Fischer projection. The Fischer projection is a 2-dimensional way of representing structures. To manipulate the Fischer projection, we should think in terms of 3-D. This can be done by interchanging two pairs of substituents at a time. If only

one pair is interchanged, we will not get the equivalent structure. Let's say we interchanged only one pair. This will result in its enantiomer. Such an example is Choice C which is the only non-equivalent structure.

5. The answer is D. The given structure is an ethane derivative, not a methane derivative. This rules out Choices A and B. In the Fischer projection, the horizontal lines represent the bonds extending out of the plane of the paper toward you. The vertical lines represent the bonds pointing into the plane of the paper (away from you). With this in mind, we can start the switching of groups as follows:

The switching is done so that the lowest ranking substituent (here, it is H) points away (into the plane of paper). The numbering or priority is based on decreasing atomic number. That means the substituent atom with the highest atomic number gets number 1, the next highest gets number 2, and so on. Since the order is clockwise, the configuration is R.

6. The answer is B. Only statements I and II are true. All enantiomers are stereoisomers, but not all stereoisomers are enantiomers. Diastereomers are also stereoisomers.

7. The answer is B.

Chapter 20   Solutions

1. The answer is B.

$$\overset{\displaystyle Cl}{\underset{\displaystyle |}{CH_3CH_2CHCH_3}}$$

This is straightforward question, involving an important idea. The halogen is attached to a secondary carbon atom and hence it is a secondary alkyl halide.

2. The answer is C. In general, as the number of carbons increases, the boiling point increases. But in this question, all the given choices are derivatives of the same alkane. In other words, they all have the same number of carbon atoms. The compound 1-chloroethane is monochlorinated, the compound 1,1-dichloroethane is dichlorinated, and the compound 1,1,3-trichloroethane is trichlorinated. As the number of Cl atoms increases, the attractive forces also increase, which means the boiling point increases.

3. The answer is D. The reactivity-trend of alcohols with hydrogen halides:

Tertiary alcohol > Secondary alcohol > Primary alcohol

4. The answer is B. The generalization in Choice A is not correct. Alkyl halides are generally insoluble in water. Choice C is wrong. The only reasonable choice is B.

5. The answer is C. The question asks for the order of reactivity of bimolecular substitution reactions. The general order of reactivity is:

Methyl halide > Primary halide > Secondary halide > Tertiary halide.

6. The answer is D. Choice A is not true because tertiary halides usually undergo substitution by S_N1 mechanism. Choice B doesn't make any sense at all. Choice C is not correct, because S_N2 mechanism generally does not involve a carbocation intermediate, whereas S_N1 mechanism does involve a carbocation intermediate. Hence, by elimination the answer is D.

7. The answer is D. For this reaction, Choices A, B, and C are possible products. Besides substitution, elimination is also possible, resulting in three products.

8. The answer is B. The inversion of configuration (at the stereogenic carbon involved in the substitution) is a characteristic of S_N2 reactions.

9. The answer is A. Among alkyl halides, alkyl fluorides have the lowest nucleophilic substitution rate. The fastest are alkyl iodides, followed by alkyl bromides and alkyl chlorides.

Chapter 21 Solutions

1. The answer is C. One of the most important properties of alcohols is their ability to undergo hydrogen bonding. The higher boiling points exhibited by alcohols when compared to similar alkanes and ethers are caused by the ability of alcohols to undergo hydrogen bonding.

2. The answer is C.

3. The answer is D. All the listed processes are possible ways of making alcohols.

4. The answer is B. The oxymercuration-demercuration reaction converts an alkene to an alcohol. The hydration follows Markovnikov's rule and thus the hydrogen adds to the carbon atom with greater number of hydrogens.

5. The answer is A. Alcohols are much more acidic than alkanes. Among alcohols, primary alcohols are the most acidic ones. Compound A is a primary alcohol. Compound B is a secondary alcohol and Compound C is a tertiary alcohol.

6. The answer is C. Primary alcohols can be converted (oxidized) directly to carboxylic acids. Oxidation of secondary alcohols results in ketones. In some rare cases, secondary alcohols can be converted into carboxylic acids using very strong oxidizing agents, but generally that is not the case. Tertiary alcohols cannot be oxidized. So the best choice is C.

7. The answer is B. Reduction of a ketone usually results in a secondary alcohol.

8. The answer is D. When ethyl magnesium bromide is reacted with ethylene oxide, the carbon chain extends by two more carbons. The product is an alcohol with four carbon atoms.

9. The answer is B.

Reaction I sequence results in the alcohol shown above (Compound A). The alcohol formed is oxidized by pyridinium dichromate. The product formed is an aldehyde (propanal).

10. The answer is B. The given organic compound is an aldehyde. The reduction of an aldehyde results in a primary alcohol.

11. The answer is A. The numbering of carbon in the ring should be done as follows:

The substituents are *cis* to each other.

12. The answer is D. Primary alcohols are more acidic than secondary alcohols, and secondary alcohols are more acidic than tertiary alcohols. Ammonia is much weaker than any other compound in the remaining choices. In fact NH_3 has a pKa of roughly 36. All the alcohols listed have pKa values ranging from 16 through 18.

13. The answer is C. The complete reaction is shown below:

$$2\ CH_3CH_2OH \xrightarrow{2\ Na} 2\ NaOCH_2CH_3\ +\ H_2$$

14. The answer is A. Primary alcohols are the most reactive alcohols toward metals. Methanol is a primary alcohol. The other choices are tertiary and secondary alcohols.

15. The answer is D. The question asks for a compound which can be directly converted to propanol by oxidation. If an aldehyde is oxidized, it is converted to a carboxylic acid. Oxidation of compounds in Choices B and C cannot produce an alcohol directly by oxidation.

Chapter 22 Solutions

1. The answer is B. Aldehydes can undergo nucleophilic addition reaction with Grignard reagents. The major product here is 3-pentanol which is a five carbon alcohol.

$$CH_3CH_2CHO \xrightarrow[\text{(ether)}]{CH_3CH_2MgBr/\ H_3\overset{+}{O}} CH_3CH_2CHOHCH_2CH_3$$

2. The answer is B.

$$\underset{\overset{\displaystyle |}{\overset{\displaystyle OH}{}}}{CH_3CH_2CHOCH_2CH_3}$$

The product formed as a result of nucleophilic addition reaction between an alcohol and an aldehyde is called a hemiacetal. The given structure is a hemiacetal.

3. The answer is B. The reaction described in the question is an oxidation reaction.

4. The choice is A. The reaction can be written as follows:

$$2 \ CH_3CH_2CH_2CH_2CH_2CHO$$

NaOH / H_2O
△

$$CH_3CH_2CH_2CH_2CH_2CHOHCH(CHO)CH_2CH_2CH_2CH_3$$

5. The answer is B. The carbonyl group can act as an electron-withdrawing group. This greatly increases the acidity of a carbonyl compound. Proximity to the carbonyl group is of very great influence in the case of acidity. In essence, carbonyl groups increase the acidity of protons that are connected to the adjacent carbon atoms. The closest protons influenced by the carbonyl group are indicated by the arrows a and b. Among these positions, the protons indicated by b are more acidic because they are influenced by the carbonyl groups from both sides.

6. The answer is D.

7. The correct answer is D.

8. The answer is C.

9. The answer is D. Iodoform test is used to identify methyl ketones. Methyl ketones give a positive iodoform test which is indicated by a yellow precipitate.

10. The answer is B. Chromic acid test is a qualitative test that can be used to confirm whether a given unknown compound is an aldehyde or not. Even though aldehydes give a positive response to this test, ketones do not. A sample reaction is shown below:

(orange color)

$$CH_3CHO \xrightarrow{H_2Cr_2O_7 \,/\, H_2SO_4} CH_3COOH \quad + \quad Cr_2(SO_4)_3$$

(green precipitate)

A green precipitate confirms a positive test.

11. The answer is B. The product that is formed in Experiment 2 is an acetal. When one mol of the given compound reacts with two moles of the alcohol, the product formed is an acetal. A simple acetal does not have the -OH group, whereas a hemiacetal has the -OH group.

12. The answer is B. This question tests your ability to judge the type of reaction presented. The conversion is a reduction reaction.

13. The answer is D.

The compound shown in Experiment 4 can be converted to an alcohol by the addition of Grignard reagents. The proper Grignard reagent that should be used for this conversion can be found by comparing the reactant and the desired product.

14. The answer is C. In the experiment, 3-propanal is converted to 2-butanol. Direct oxidation is not an option because there aren't enough carbons in propanal to form an alcohol with four carbons. So Choice A is ruled out. Choice B is not completely true. With appropriate steps, the reaction is possible. One of the best ways to accomplish the reaction is to first treat the reactant with the appropriate Grignard reagent. Since Grignard reagents are nucleophilic, they can add to the carbonyl group. This extends the carbon chain. The product formed can be then hydrolyzed to form the alcohol.

$$CH_3CH_2CHO \xrightarrow{CH_3MgBr} \overset{\overset{\displaystyle OMgBr}{\displaystyle |}}{CH_3CH_2CHCH_3} \xrightarrow{H_3O^+} CH_3CH_2CH(OH)CH_3$$

15. The answer is D. By definition, an organometallic compound should have a bond between a carbon atom and a metal atom. The only compound listed here which does not satisfy the definition is Choice D.

16. The answer is C. The conversion is an oxidation reaction.

Chapter 23 Solutions

1. The answer is D. Alkyl magnesium halide or Grignard reagent can react with carbon dioxide to form carboxylic salts. The description of the reaction mentioned in the question also says that the reaction occured in acidic conditions. Under acidic conditions, the salt is converted to a carboxylic acid. So statement II is true. Furthermore, alkyl magnesium halide (Grignard reagent) acts as the nucleophile in the reaction. So statement III is true.

2. The answer is C. The first step results in n-butyl cyanide (Compound A). n-Butyl cyanide on hydrolysis produces pentanoic acid.

3. The answer is C. Butanoic acid reacts with methanol in the presence of an acid catalyst to form methyl butanoate.

4. The answer is A. Alkanes and ketones have lower boiling points compared to carboxylic acids and alcohols. This aspect rules out Choices C and D. Comparing Choices A and B, we can say that carboxylic acid is a better choice since it can undergo extensive hydrogen bonding. In essence, carboxylic acids have higher boiling points than comparable alcohols.

5. The answer is D. Compound A is more acidic because it is a carboxylic acid. In general, carboxylic acids are more acidic than alcohols.

6. The answer is D. Substituents, especially electronegative ones, increase the acidity of carboxylic acids. Choice D has more substituents of this type than the other choices. So the carboxylic acid represented in Choice D is the most acidic.

7. The answer is D. LiAlH$_4$ is a very good reducing agent. The product is benzyl alcohol.

8. The answer is D.

9. The answer is B.

10. The answer is B.

11. The answer is C. Choice A is true. Carboxylic acids can undergo hydrogen bonding. Choice B is also true and so is Choice D. Choice C is not true. In fact, the hydroxyl group makes its carbonyl group less electrophilic. In a ketone there is no hydroxyl group and that makes its carbonyl group more electrophilic than that of a carboxylic acid.

12. The answer is C. The conversion is an oxidation reaction. This rules out Choices B and D. $LiAlH_4$ is a reducing agent. So Choice A is wrong. $KMnO_4$ is a good oxidizing agent which can accomplish this conversion.

13. The answer is B.

14. The answer is D.

Formic acid is HCOOH.

sp^2 hybridization

15. The answer is C. The question asks for the compound that has the highest pKa value. Highest pKa value means the weakest acid. The inductive effects become less and less pronounced as the electronegative substituents are farther away from the carboxylic group.

16. The answer is C. $NaOCH_3$ is basic. Carboxylic acids are much more acidic than alkynes. Choices B and D are ruled out. It is a tough call between Choices A and C. The carboxylic group of acetic acid is attached to an alkyl group. The carboxylic group of benzoic acid is attached to an aryl group. The sp^2 carbons in the benzoic acid ring are more electron withdrawing than the sp^3 carbon in the acetic acid. This makes benzoic acid more acidic than acetic acid.

Chapter 24 Solutions

1. The answer is B. Among the acid derivatives, the acyl chloride is the least stable and the most reactive compound toward hydrolysis.

2. The answer is A.

3. The answer is C. Esters can react with Grignard reagents to form tertiary alcohols. The intermediary compound formed is a ketone which reacts with the second Grignard reagent molecule to form the tertiary alcohol. A representative reaction is shown below:

$$CH_3\overset{\overset{\textstyle O}{\|}}{C}OCH_3 \xrightarrow{\ CH_3MgBr\ } CH_3\overset{\overset{\textstyle O}{\|}}{C}CH_3$$

$$CH_3MgBr\ /\ H_3O^+$$

$$(CH_3)_3OH$$

4. The answer is B.

5. The answer is C.

6. The answer is B.

$$CH_3\overset{\overset{\textstyle O}{\|}}{C}Cl \xrightarrow{\ NH_3\ } CH_3\overset{\overset{\textstyle O}{\|}}{C}NH_2$$
$$\text{Amide}$$

7. The answer is D. Choices A, B, and C describe possible ways of preparing carboxylic acids. Oxidation of an aldehyde can result in a carboxylic acid.

Chapter 25 Solutions

1. The answer is A.

2. The answer is D. Alcohols, water, and carboxylic acids can undergo intermolecular hydrogen bonding. Ethers cannot undergo intermolecular hydrogen bonding. Alkanes cannot form intermolecular hydrogen bonding either. So the best conclusion is that ethers have boiling points similar to that of alkanes.

3. The answer is D. Ethers are polar. Hence, Choice A is true. Ethers are relatively less reactive and are widely used as solvents. Hence, Choices B and C are true.

4. The answer is A. It is true that ethers are not very reactive. Hence, statement I is true and statement II is false. Ethers are flammable. Hence, statement III is true. Ethers have very low boiling points compared to that of alcohols. Hence, statement IV is false.

5. The answer is A. The reaction given in the passage is called Williamson ether synthesis. By looking at the reaction we cannot answer this question. But a clue is given in the question. According

to the question the reaction is most effective if it undergoes by S$_N$2 mechanism. Now we have something to hang on to. Since the reaction is mostly effective when undergoing by S$_N$2 mechanism, the alkyl halide most appropriately used must be a primary alkyl halide. The only primary halide among the choices is methyl chloride.

6. The answer is D. In the Williamson ether synthesis, if the alkyl halide is either tertiary or secondary, there is a good chance that elimination reaction can prevail. However, this is not desired in this reaction. In fact, the compounds given in Choices A, B, and C can undergo elimination reaction. Only the compound in Choice D is exempt from undergoing elimination.

7. The answer is A. Ethers are usually not so reactive, but they will react with concentrated acids. This is exactly the type of reaction given in the question. Methyl bromide is the product formed, and the reaction is a nucleophilic substitution reaction.

8. The answer is B. All the compounds given are ethers except in Choice B. Choice B is an ester.

Chapter 26 Solutions

1. The answer is B.

Reaction 1 results in bromobenzene (Compound A). In Reaction 2, the bromobenzene formed is hydrolyzed to phenol.

2. The answer is B. Phenol has the hydroxyl group which is an ortho/para activator. So the substitutions are more likely to be in the ortho and para positions of the ring.

3. The answer is A.

As you can see in the diagram, the intramolecular hydrogen bonding is most pronounced in ortho-nitrophenol because of the proximity of the -NO$_2$ group to the hydroxyl group.

Chapter 27 Solutions

1. The answer is B. The lowest boiling point is likely to be exhibited by Compound B which is an alkane. The highest boiling point is attributed to Compound A which can undergo extensive inter-molecular hydrogen bonding, followed by the alcohol, and trailed by Compound D.

2. The answer is D. In general, aryl amines are less basic than ammonia. Alkyl amines are more basic than ammonia. Among alkyl amines, secondary amines are generally more basic than primary amines.

3. The answer is D.

4. The answer is D. This is a straightforward question. The given reaction is a reduction reaction.

5. The answer is D. In general, alcohols (comparable) are more acidic than amines. In the choices, the only alcohol given is ethanol.

6. The answer is B. Tertiary amines cannot have hydrogen bonds themselves, because they have no nitrogen-hydrogen bond connections unlike the other compounds listed.

7. The answer is D. From the values in Table 1, we can compare the basicity of the compounds. It appears that the weakest base is the conjugate base of aniline, which also makes it the most acidic.

8. The answer is B. The conversion that is asked for in the question is accompanied by the loss of carbon dioxide (CO_2). This is a typical example of a decarboxylation reaction.

(L-Glutamate)

9. The answer is D. The conversion is best described as a reduction reaction.

10. The answer is A.

Chapter 28 Solutions

1. The answer is C.

2. The answer is D. All amino acids are optically active except glycine. Glycine has a simple structure and is achiral.

The structure of glycine.

3. The answer is D. At a certain pH (unique for each amino acid), the net charge of an amino acid equals zero. When this pH is achieved, it is said to be at the amino acid's isoelectric point. At the

isoelectric pH of an amino acid, the net movement of that particular amino acid will be zero when the amino acid is subjected to an electric field.

4. The answer is C. The general structure of an amino acid is shown below:

$$R—\underset{\underset{H}{|}}{\overset{\overset{NH_3^+}{|}}{C}}—COO^-$$

5. The answer is D.

6. The answer is D.

7. The answer is D. Proteases are enzymes that can affect the structural integrity of proteins. Strong bases and acids can also affect the structural mode of proteins.

8. The answer is D.

9. The answer is D. All amino acids have at least one carboxyl group. Hence, statement I is true. Amino acids have high melting points since they can have multiple charges. This results in strong ionic interactions and hence much energy is required to break the ionic interactions between them. Thus it is hard to break the crystal lattice, and they have high boiling points. Hence, statement II is true. Depending on the pH and the particular amino acid's nature, amino acids can have either a net positive charge, a net negative charge, or a net zero charge. Hence, statements III and IV are true.

10. The answer is C. See the explanation for Question 3.

11. The answer is C. Peptide bond is a covalent bond which connects amino acids in the formation of a peptide or the primary structure of a protein. The peptide link is formed between the amino group of one amino acid and the carboxyl group of the adjacent amino acid.

12. The answer is B.

13. The answer is D. From the table, we can assess the behavior of amino acids by comparing the pKa values of the amino acids. At pH 7 only glutamate will have a net negative charge.

14. The answer is D.

Chapter 29 Solutions

1. The answer is D. Galactose, glucose, and ribose are monosaccharides. Maltose is a disaccharide made of glucose units.

2. The answer is B. We can rule out Choices A and C, because the given sugar is not a D-sugar. Ribose is a 5-carbon sugar. So Choice D is also ruled out.

3. The answer is D. The synthesis of sugar probably resulted in mostly one form of the sugar. According to the question, there was a change in optical activity. This is due to a phenomenon called mutarotation. The sugar solution that was made mutarotated to form its corresponding anomer, which changed the observed optical activity. The mutarotation will continue until an equilibrium is established.

4. The answer is C. Glycogen is the only non-disaccharide listed. All the other molecules are disaccharides. In animals, carbohydrates are stored mainly in the form of glycogen. It is mostly stored in the liver and the skeletal muscles.

5. The answer is B.

$$
\begin{array}{c}
\text{CHO} \\
\text{H} \!-\!\!-\!\!-\! \text{OH} \\
\text{H} \!-\!\!-\!\!-\! \text{OH} \\
\text{CH}_2\text{OH}
\end{array}
$$

There are two chiral carbons in the given structure. So the number of possible optical isomers is $2^2 = 4$.

6. The answer is A. Fructose, glucose, and galactose are monosaccharides. The only choice that is not a monosaccharide is sucrose. Sucrose is a disaccharide formed by glucose and fructose.

The structure of sucrose

7. The correct answer C. The given structure is not glucose. Ribose is a five-carbon sugar. The given structure is a six-carbon sugar. Maltose is a disaccharide. Further, the given structure is a ketose sugar, and the only ketohexose sugar listed is fructose.

8. The answer is A.

Beta-D-Glucofuranose   Beta-D-Glucapyranose

Statements 1 and 2 are true. Both given structures are glucose; one is in the furanose ring form, and the other is in the pyranose ring form. The five-membered ring of glucose is called glucofuranose. The six-membered ring of glucose is called glucopyranose.

9. The answer is B. Glucose and mannose are not anomers, nor are they are mirror images. So Choices A and C are ruled out. Choice D is not true. In fact, they are epimers. Epimers are isomeric sugars that differ in their configurations only at one of their stereogenic centers.

10. The answer is A. Disaccharides are formed by the combination or bonding of two monosaccharides by a linkage called the glycosidic linkage.

11. The answer is C. Anomers differ only in stereogenicity at the anomeric carbon. The structures of α-D-glucose and β-D-glucose are drawn below. They are anomers.

α-D-glucose   β-D-glucose

Chapter 30 Solutions

1. The answer is B. Triglycerides are triesters of glycerol. A triglyceride can be represented as follows:

As a result of hydrolysis, each mole of a triglyceride can give 1 mol of glycerol and 3 moles of fatty acids.

2. The answer is D.

Chapter 31 Solutions

1. The answer is B. The indicated bond is best described as a phosphate anhydride bond.

2. The answer is D. The given reaction is a hydrolysis reaction.

3. The answer is B. The interconversion between the compounds X and Y is a typical example of tautomerism. Compound X is the enol form of pyruvate. Compound Y is the keto form of pyruvate. The interconversion of such forms is called tautomerism.

4. The answer is D. The bond indicated by the arrow is an example of N-glycosidic bond.

5. The answer is A. According to the passage, the hydrolysis of ATP has a negative change in free energy (ΔG). So it is sensible to say that the products have less energy than that of the reactants.

6. The answer is C. ATP is a higher energy-currency than AMP. So the hydrolysis of AMP will have a ΔG that is less negative than -31 kJ/mol (given in the passage). Moreover, the conversion represented in the question is the formation of AMP rather than the hydrolysis of AMP. This eliminates Choices B and D. According to the clue given in the question, the products have higher free energy than the reactants. This can give only a positive ΔG.

7. The answer is C.

Chapter 32 Solutions

1. The answer is A.

2. The answer is D.

3. The answer is D. According to the passage, the reactions in Experiment 3 are based on unimolecular substitution mechanism. Based on this information, we can say that compound B has the fastest reaction rate. The second fastest is Compound C. These observations rule out Choices A, B, and C. Compound A is a primary alcohol and is not likely to undergo S_N1 reaction.

4. The answer is B. According to the passage, propanone is reacted with the reagent to form a product that lacks the carbonyl group. Note that the compound propanone is a ketone and contains a carbonyl group. But after the reaction, the carbonyl group is not present in the product formed. So the peak that disappeared is the carbonyl peak.

5. The answer is C. The conversion results in the formation of a glycol (an alcohol). Such a conversion is best described as an oxidation reaction.

6. The answer is C. The compounds A, B and C are alcohols. They do not have carboxyl groups. They have different reaction rates in terms of substitution reactions. Since they are alcohols, they all will exhibit broad IR peaks around 3400 cm^{-1}.

7. The answer is A.

   The compound B is *tert*-butyl alcohol.

$$H_3C - \underset{\underset{CH_3}{|}}{\overset{\overset{CH_3}{|}}{C}} - OH$$

Even though there are three methyl groups, all the methyl groups are equivalent and so are their protons. So the methyl protons give rise to one peak. The hydroxylic proton will give rise to another peak, totaling two sets of NMR peaks.

8. The answer is B. Since the compound is insoluble in water, statement I is true. Since the compound is insoluble in 5% aqueous sodium hydroxide, statement II is false. Since the compound is an aromatic compound, statement III is true. The compound is not a strong base. Hence, statement IV is false.

APPENDIX

Table-1 Common Physical Constants

Avogadro's number (N_A)	$= 6.02 \times 10^{23}$ /mol
Electronic charge (e)	$= 1.60 \times 10^{-19}$ C
Electron's mass (m_e)	$= 9.11 \times 10^{-31}$ kg
Neutron's mass (m_n)	$= 1.675 \times 10^{-27}$ kg
Proton's mass (m_p)	$= 1.673 \times 10^{-27}$ kg
Faraday constant (F)	$= 96500$ C/mol
Molar gas constant (R)	$= 0.082$ L . atm/K . mol) $= 8.31$ J/(K . mol)
Standard Temperature & Pressure, STP	$\rightarrow$ 273K & 1atm
Standard State (temperature & pressure)	$\rightarrow$ 298K (25 $^{\circ}$C) & 1atm
Ideal molar gas volume at STP	$= 22.4$ L/mol
Planck's constant (h)	$= 6.63 \times 10^{-34}$ J . s
Speed of light in vacuum (C)	$= 3.0 \times 10^{8}$ m/s
Rydberg constant for H atom (R_H)	$= 2.18 \times 10^{-18}$ J

Table-2 Conversion Factors

$1 \text{ amu} = 1.66 \times 10^{-27} \text{ kg}$

$1 \text{ cal} = 4.184 \text{ J}$

$1 \text{ J} = 1 \text{ kg} \cdot \text{m}^2/\text{s}^2$

$1 \text{ atm} = 760 \text{ mmHg} = 760 \text{ torr} = 1.01325 \times 10^5 \text{ Pa}$

$1 \text{ Pa} = 1 \text{ kg}/(\text{m} \cdot \text{s})^2 = 1 \text{ N}/\text{m}^2$

$^{\circ}\text{C} = 5/9 \ (^{\circ}\text{F} - 32)$

$^{\circ}\text{F} = 9/5 \ ^{\circ}\text{C} + 32$

$\text{K} = ^{\circ}\text{C} + 273$

$1 \text{ L} = 1 \text{ dm}^3 = 10^{-3} \text{ m}^3$

Table-3 SI prefixes
(most important ones are starred)

10^{12}	tera (T)
10^{9}	giga (G)*
10^{6}	mega (M)*
10^{3}	kilo (k)*
10^{2}	hecto (h)
10^{1}	deka (da)
10^{-1}	deci (d)*
10^{-2}	centi (c)*
10^{-3}	milli (m)*
10^{-6}	micro (μ)*
10^{-9}	nano (n)*
10^{-12}	pico (p)

Table-4
Some Common Groups

CH_3—   methyl

CH_3CH_2—   ethyl

$CH_3CH_2CH_2$—   propyl

isopropyl

$CH_3CH_2CH_2CH_2$—   *n*-butyl

isobutyl

sec-butyl

tert-butyl (*t*-butyl)

acetyl

allyl

vinyl

phenyl

benzyl

benzoyl

Table-5 Some Common Functional Groups

Name	General Formula	Example
alkane	R—H	$CH_3CH_2CH_3$ (butane)
alkene	RCH=CHR'	$CH_3CH=CHCH_3$ (2-butene)
alkyne	R—C≡C—R'	$H_3C—C≡C—CH_3$ (2-butyne)
Arene	Ar—H	(benzene)
alkyl halide	R—X	$CH_3CH_2CH_2Br$ (butyl bromide)
alcohol	R—OH	$CH_3CH_2CH_2OH$ (propanol)
thiol	R—SH	CH_3CH_2SH (ethanethiol)
phenol	Ar—OH	(phenol)
ether	R—O—R'	$CH_3CH_2OCH_2CH_3$ (diethyl ether)
aldehyde	$R-\overset{O}{\overset{\|}{C}}-H$	$CH_3CH_2CH_2-\overset{O}{\overset{\|}{C}}-H$ (butanal)
ketone	$R-\overset{O}{\overset{\|}{C}}-R'$	$CH_3-\overset{O}{\overset{\|}{C}}-CH_2CH_3$ (2-butanone)
carboxylic acid	$R-\overset{O}{\overset{\|}{C}}-OH$	$CH_3-\overset{O}{\overset{\|}{C}}-OH$ (acetic acid or ethanoic acid))
ester	$R-\overset{O}{\overset{\|}{C}}-OR'$	$CH_3-\overset{O}{\overset{\|}{C}}-OCH_2CH_3$ (ethyl acetate)
amide	$R-\overset{O}{\overset{\|}{C}}-NH_2$	$H_3C-\overset{O}{\overset{\|}{C}}-NH_2$ (ethanamide)
anhydride	$R-\overset{O}{\overset{\|}{C}}-O-\overset{O}{\overset{\|}{C}}-R'$	$CH_3-\overset{O}{\overset{\|}{C}}-O-\overset{O}{\overset{\|}{C}}-CH_3$ (acetic anhydride)
acyl halide	$R-\overset{O}{\overset{\|}{C}}-X$	$CH_3-\overset{O}{\overset{\|}{C}}-Cl$ (ethanoyl chloride)
amine	R—NH$_2$	H_3C-NH_2 (methylamine)
nitrile	R—C≡N	$CH_3-C≡N$ (ethanenitrile or acetonitrile)

NOTES

CPSIA information can be obtained at www.ICGtesting.com
Printed in the USA
BVOW052030250312

285967BV00002B/1/P